A Name for Herself

SELECTED WRITINGS, 1891–1917

Years before she published her internationally celebrated first novel, *Anne of Green Gables*, L.M. Montgomery (1874–1942) started contributing short works to periodicals across North America. While these works consisted primarily of poems and short stories, she also experimented with a wider range of forms, particularly during the early years of her career, at which point she tested out several authorial identities before settling on the professional moniker "L.M. Montgomery."

A Name for Herself: Selected Writings, 1891–1917 is the first in a series of volumes collecting Montgomery's extensive contributions to periodicals. Leading Montgomery scholar Benjamin Lefebvre discusses these so-called miscellaneous pieces in relation to the works of English-speaking women writers who preceded her and the strategies they used to succeed, including the decision to publish under gender-neutral signatures. Among the highlights of the volume are Montgomery's contributions to student periodicals, a weekly newspaper column entitled "Around the Table," a long-lost story narrated first by a woman trapped in an unhappy marriage and then by the man she wishes she had married instead, and a new edition of her 1917 celebrity memoir, "The Alpine Path." Drawing fascinating links to Montgomery's life writing, career, and fiction, this volume will offer scholars and readers alike an intriguing new look at the work of Canada's most enduringly popular author.

(THE L.M. MONTGOMERY LIBRARY)

BENJAMIN LEFEBVRE, editor of The L.M. Montgomery Library, is director of L.M. Montgomery Online. His publications include an edition of Montgomery's rediscovered final book, *The Blythes Are Quoted*, and the three-volume critical anthology *The L.M. Montgomery Reader*, which won the 2016 PROSE Award for Literature from the Association of American Publishers. He lives in Kitchener, Ontario.

THE L.M. MONTGOMERY LIBRARY

Edited by Benjamin Lefebvre

A Name for Herself: Selected Writings, 1891–1917

A World of Songs: Selected Poems, 1894–1921

L.M. MONTGOMERY

A Name for Herself

SELECTED WRITINGS, 1891–1917

Edited by BENJAMIN LEFEBVRE

UNIVERSITY OF TORONTO PRESS
Toronto Buffalo London

Toronto Buffalo London
www.utorontopress.com
Printed in Canada

ISBN 978-1-4875-0403-8 (cloth) ISBN 978-1-4875-2308-4 (paper)

Printed on acid-free, 100% post-consumer recycled paper
with vegetable-based inks.

LIBRARY AND ARCHIVES CANADA CATALOGUING IN PUBLICATION

Montgomery, L.M. (Lucy Maud), 1874–1942
[Works. Selections]
A name for herself : selected writings, 1891–1917 / L.M. Montgomery;
edited by Benjamin Lefebvre.

(The L.M. Montgomery library ; 1)

Includes bibliographical references and index.
ISBN 978-1-4875-0403-8 (cloth) ISBN 978-1-4875-2308-4 (paper)

I. Lefebvre, Benjamin, 1977–, editor. II. Title.
III. Series: L.M. Montgomery Library; 1

PS8526.O55A6 2018 C813'.52 C2018-902580-8

This book has been published with the help of a grant from the Federation for the Humanities and Social Sciences, through the Awards to Scholarly Publications Program, using funds provided by the Social Sciences and Humanities Research Council of Canada.

University of Toronto Press acknowledges the financial assistance to its publishing program of the Canada Council for the Arts and the Ontario Arts Council, an agency of the Government of Ontario.

Canada Council for the Arts
Conseil des Arts du Canada

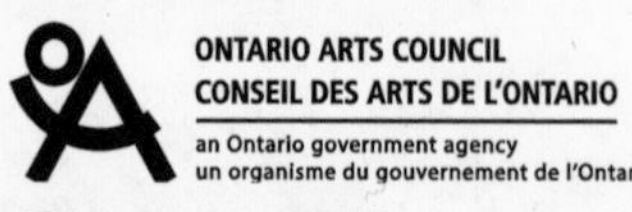

Funded by the Government of Canada
Financé par le gouvernement du Canada

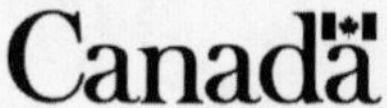

Contents

List of Illustrations

FIGURES

TABLES

Acknowledgments

As with all large-scale editorial projects, this one has incurred many debts. I am grateful to Vanessa Brown, Cecily Devereux, Jason Dickson, Kelly Norah Drukker, Elizabeth Rollins Epperly, Melanie J. Fishbane, Irene Gammel, Carole Gerson, Caroline E. Jones, Katja Lee, Jennifer H. Litster, Andrea McKenzie, Laura M. Robinson, Mary Henley Rubio, Kate Sutherland, Elizabeth Hillman Waterston, Emily Woster, and Lorraine York for their encouragement and conversation over several years of research. I am equally grateful to E. Holly Pike, who generously provided me with digital files containing the majority of Montgomery's "Around the Table" columns from the pages of the *Halifax Daily Echo*. This volume builds on the pioneering research of the late Francis W.P. Bolger and the late Rea Wilmshurst, which I also gratefully acknowledge.

For research and editorial help, I am grateful to Donna J. Campbell, Mary Beth Cavert, Carolyn Strom Collins, Katharine MacDonald, Carrie Martens, Rachel McMillan, Melissa Myers, Tamara Shantz, Naava Smolash, Meg Taylor, and Janice Weaver. I am also grateful to colleagues at several institutions: Kathryn Harvey, Heather Callaghan, Ashley Shifflett McBrayne, and Darlene Wiltsie, Archival and Special Collections, University of Guelph Library; Simon Lloyd, University of Prince Edward Island Library; Kathleen Mackinnon and Paige Matthie, Confederation Centre Art Gallery; Karen Smith, Dalhousie University Library; the interlibrary loan staff at Wilfrid Laurier University Library; and the staff at Library and Archives Canada, where I did research on some of the items in this book in 2008,

2014, and 2015. I would also like to thank Mark Thompson, Frances Mundy, Ani Deyirmenjian, Sandra Friesen, Val Cooke, and their colleagues at University of Toronto Press for their expertise and sound advice at all stages of this book's development and production, as well as two anonymous assessors who read this book in manuscript and provided generous and astute feedback. I gratefully acknowledge travel funding in the form of the Marie Tremaine Fellowship, awarded by the Bibliographical Society of Canada / La Société bibliographique du Canada in 2013. Once again, special thanks are to members of my family, particularly my mother, Claire Pelland Lefebvre, and my partner, Jacob Letkemann.

Finally, I would like to acknowledge my debt to the late Christy Woster (1955–2016), to whose memory I dedicate this book. Christy was an indefatigable researcher whose generosity with her knowledge and her materials has enriched the study of Montgomery's works immeasurably. She is missed by so many.

B.L.

A Note on the Author

L.M. Montgomery is now widely recognized as a major twentieth-century author, one whose bestselling books remain hugely popular and influential all over the world more than three-quarters of a century after her death. Born in Clifton (now New London), Prince Edward Island, in 1874, into a family whose ancestors had immigrated to Canada from Scotland and England, she was raised in nearby Cavendish by her maternal grandparents following the death of her mother and spent a year during her adolescence with her father and his new family in Saskatchewan. Raised in a household that distrusted novels but prized poetry and oral storytelling, she began to write during childhood, although few examples of her juvenilia survive. She received a teaching certificate from Prince of Wales College (Charlottetown) and, after one year of teaching school, took undergraduate courses in English literature for a year at Dalhousie University (Halifax), but she did not have the financial resources to complete her degree. During this time, she began publishing essays, short fiction, and poems in North American periodicals. In 1898, after two more years of teaching school, she returned to Cavendish to take care of her widowed grandmother and to write full-time, soon earning more from her pen than she had teaching school. With the exception of a nine-month stint on the staff of the *Halifax Daily Echo*, where her duties included writing a weekly column entitled "Around the Table," Montgomery remained in Cavendish until 1911, when the death of her grandmother freed her to marry a Presbyterian minister. After a honeymoon in England and Scotland, she and her husband moved to southern Ontario, where she divided her time between writing, motherhood, and the responsibilities that came with her position as a minister's wife.

Her first novel, *Anne of Green Gables* (1908), the benchmark against which her remaining body of work is measured, was followed by twenty-three additional books, including ten featuring Anne Shirley: *Anne of Avonlea* (1909), *Chronicles of Avonlea* (1912), *Anne of the Island* (1915), *Anne's House of Dreams* (1917), *Rainbow Valley* (1919), *Further Chronicles of Avonlea* (1920), *Rilla of Ingleside* (1921), *Anne of Windy Poplars* (1936), *Anne of Ingleside* (1939), and *The Blythes Are Quoted*, completed shortly before her death but not published in its entirety until 2009. During her distinguished career, she was made a Fellow of the British Royal Society of Arts, was named one of the twelve greatest women in Canada by the *Toronto Star*, and became an Officer of the Order of the British Empire. When she died in 1942, apparently by her own hand, her obituary in the *Globe and Mail* declared that her body of work "showed no lessening of that freshness and simplicity of style that characterized *Anne of Green Gables*." Since her death, several collections of her periodical pieces have been published, as have more than a dozen volumes of her journals, letters, essays, and scrapbooks. Ontario and Prince Edward Island are home to many tourist sites and archival collections devoted to her, and her books continue to be adapted for stage and screen.

Abbreviations

PUBLISHED WORK BY L.M. MONTGOMERY

AA	*Anne of Avonlea*
AGG	*Anne of Green Gables*
AHD	*Anne's House of Dreams*
AIn	*Anne of Ingleside*
AIs	*Anne of the Island*
AP	*The Alpine Path: The Story of My Career*
CJLMM, 1	*The Complete Journals of L.M. Montgomery: The PEI Years, 1889–1900*
CJLMM, 2	*The Complete Journals of L.M. Montgomery: The PEI Years, 1901–1911*
DCMF	*The Diary of Charles Macneill, Farmer, 1892–1896* (jointly with Charles Macneill)
EC	*Emily Climbs*
ENM	*Emily of New Moon*
EQ	*Emily's Quest*
GGL	*The Green Gables Letters from L.M. Montgomery to Ephraim Weber, 1905–1909*

GR	*The Golden Road*
JLH	*Jane of Lantern Hill*
LMMCJ, 1	*L.M. Montgomery's Complete Journals: The Ontario Years, 1911–1917*
LMMCJ, 2	*L.M. Montgomery's Complete Journals: The Ontario Years, 1918–1921*
LMMCJ, 3	*L.M. Montgomery's Complete Journals: The Ontario Years, 1922–1925*
LMMCJ, 4	*L.M. Montgomery's Complete Journals: The Ontario Years, 1926–1929*
MDMM	*My Dear Mr. M: Letters to G.B. MacMillan from L.M. Montgomery*
MP	*Mistress Pat: A Novel of Silver Bush*
RI	*Rilla of Ingleside*
RV	*Rainbow Valley*
SG	*The Story Girl*
SJLMM	*The Selected Journals of L.M. Montgomery*, Volume 1: *1889–1910*; Volume 2: *1910–1921*; Volume 3: *1921–1929*; Volume 4: *1929–1935*; Volume 5: *1935–1942*
TW	*A Tangled Web*
WOP	*The Watchman and Other Poems*

SECONDARY SOURCES

KJV	*The Bible: Authorized King James Version*
OED	*Oxford English Dictionary*

Preface

IN MARCH 2018, HISTORICA CANADA RELEASED A Heritage Minute film on L.M. Montgomery (1874–1942), who, according to Adrienne Clarkson's voiceover, "battled depression, rejection, and sexism, to become known around the world for *Anne of Green Gables* and nineteen other novels."[1] The fact that this first novel is the only one of Montgomery's works mentioned in the film is not surprising, since it remains, more than a century after its publication in 1908, the standard against which all of her remaining work is measured. Still, while the continued popularity of this novel has led to the publication of numerous editions across the children's, adult trade, and scholarly markets, the attention given to it and to her book-length fiction more broadly obscures the more than one thousand items that Montgomery published in periodicals over a period of half a century, from 1890 to her death in 1942: these include five hundred short stories, five hundred poems, and a range of texts that the compilers of *Lucy Maud Montgomery: A Preliminary Bibliography* (1986) refer to as "Miscellaneous Pieces."[2] And so, while the Heritage Minute rightly claims Montgomery as "a part of our heritage," a significant proportion of her literary output remains largely unknown.

The L.M. Montgomery Library is a set of volumes that collects this periodical work for Montgomery's sizeable readership around the world. As a complement to her twenty-two book-length works of fiction,[3] which have been translated into at least three dozen languages, her periodical work is important because of her unique position as an author whose writing is the subject of an ever-growing body of scholarship while still being read by the general public more than seven decades after her death.[4] More crucially still, this work offers us today the opportunity to see what editors of a wide range of periodicals from the late nineteenth to the mid-twentieth centuries believed would connect with large readerships, and it also gives us the chance to trace shifting attitudes about gender, race, class, childhood, marriage, and nationhood that circulated in the mainstream print media during a period of significant cultural and social change. As she started to make a living as a freelance writer, Montgomery taught herself to shape her work for the demands of periodical editors, many of whom prioritized sales potential over literary innovation, whether these periodicals targeted women, children, rural readers, faith-based readers, or the public at large. Moreover, this extensive training would give her the ability to write a first novel that would appeal to readers of all ages, genders, backgrounds, and locations and that remains today as popular as ever.

Whereas my three-volume critical anthology, *The L.M. Montgomery Reader* (2013–2015), collected non-fiction texts by a slew of authors (many of them unidentified) and traced the evolution of Montgomery's career and legacy beginning with the publication of *Anne of Green Gables*, this first volume in The L.M. Montgomery Library, *A Name for Herself*, gathers a selection of materials that she published between 1891 and 1917, first of all, to demonstrate a facet of her development as an author, and second of all, to take a new look at her major retrospective account of that development.[5] Although her career as a published author would solidify around the poem (starting in 1890), the short story (starting in 1895), and the novel (starting in 1908), supplemented by occasional essays and multi-chapter fiction serials, her earliest publications show a greater experimentation with form and genre: the playlet, the travel narrative, the animal story, the personal essay, the newspaper column, and even the advertisement. Moreover, while she began signing her work "L.M. Montgomery" as early as 1891, she also tested out a wide range of authorial identities in the early years of her career. So, rather than call this first book *Not Short Stories and Not Poems*, I have organized these materials around Montgomery's creation of a name for herself as an author who earned a living selling work to mainstream periodicals across North America.

Once again, Montgomery's scrapbooks have been enormously invaluable to my research, in that they offer a comprehensive – although not quite complete – record of her periodical work. In a set of scrapbooks housed at the Confederation Centre Art Gallery in Charlottetown and displayed during the summer months at the Lucy Maud Montgomery Birthplace in New London,[6] Montgomery placed and arranged clippings of most of her periodical publications as well as miscellaneous clippings about her career, frequently with annotations and corrections in ink. In Scrapbook 7, which covers the years 1890 to 1898, Montgomery included most of her earliest publications, including many of the pieces in this volume as well as her first published poems and short stories. In Scrapbook 3, which includes clippings from items published between 1901 and 1904, Montgomery arranged all but one instalment of her newspaper column, "Around the Table" (included in full in this volume), as a continuous text, omitting dates of individual columns and obscuring the point at which some instalments end and others begin. These twelve scrapbooks are joined by a five-hundred-page scrapbook of review clippings for most of her books and by several personal scrapbooks that she kept from late adolescence onward.[7] But while Montgomery's scrapbooks have been a major repository of her published work, she evidently did not see the value of hanging on to manuscripts or typescripts of her periodical pieces at any point in her career as she did with those of most of her book-length works.[8]

Part 1, "Early and Student Publications," consists of items that originally appeared between 1891 and 1899, including her first prose publications and several items published during her student days at Prince of Wales College and Dalhousie University. These pieces can be claimed as juvenilia only with some difficulty – if we follow Neville Braybrooke's cut-off age of sixteen in his volume *Seeds in the Wind: Juvenilia from W.B. Yeats to Ted Hughes* (1989), only her poem "On Cape Le Force," published in late November 1890, would make the cut by a matter of days[9] – but they still serve a concrete function when it comes to understanding Montgomery's development as an author. As

Gillian Beer notes in her introduction to *The Juvenilia of Jane Austen and Charlotte Brontë* (1986), such texts, although "crude and sometimes childish,"

> serve to demonstrate their authors' originality and freedom of spirit, their delight in the very process of creation, their changing attitudes towards character and style. The youthful work of [Austen and Brontë], taken as a whole, can in fact be seen to reveal a certain winnowing process: some experiments are tried and modified or abandoned, others are pursued and developed, to recur in their later novels. Over time we can see decisions, whether conscious or otherwise, taking form that will lead with astonishing steadiness from the pure fun of their first outpourings towards their artistically and morally mature work. Both sets of juvenilia provide us with an extraordinary opportunity to watch the growth and coalescence of the creative consciousness.[10]

Granted, in the case of the work collected here, a certain amount of "winnowing" has already occurred, given that these are hardly Montgomery's earliest attempts at writing and given that they were published (which is not necessarily to say they were professionally edited prior to publication). Still, the level of experimentation here – particularly with form – informs our understanding of her books, particularly her final book, *The Blythes Are Quoted* (2009), which likewise experiments with form by marrying prose, poetry, and dialogue.

Part 2, "Maud Montgomery, Newspaper Woman," collects for the first time the complete run of Montgomery's newspaper column, "Around the Table," which she published in the *Halifax Daily Echo* under the signature "Cynthia" over a nine-month period between September 1901 and May 1902, along with several rediscovered non-fiction pieces from that period. As Montgomery noted in her journals (excerpts of which appear in "The Alpine Path"), when she was hired as "proof-reader and general handyman" at the *Echo* in September 1901,[11] she soon discovered that her weekly salary of five dollars covered only her basic living expenses. To supplement this income, Carole Gerson explains, Montgomery "returned to the practice of her school-teaching years, doing her own writing early in the mornings and in the limited spare minutes squeezed between other tasks. Not only did she thrive ... but she also gained practice in writing under pressure, a skill that would serve her well after she married."[12] Given that she had been hired as a proofreader, it is unclear how her weekly column came about or whether the responsibility of writing it allowed for a supplement to that weekly salary. Having published the first instalment under the title "Over the Tea-Cups" on 28 September 1901 – a week after the appearance of the first instalment of Laurie Lansfeldt's serial "Her Bid for Love," whose first chapter is also entitled "Over the Tea-Cups" – she would go on to write thirty-four additional instalments under the header "Around the Table." Although the appearance of that column for the entire duration of Montgomery's time at the *Halifax Daily Echo* is proof enough of its success with readers, I have not been able to find any mention of it in the paper outside the column itself. In other words, I cannot say whether the column was unambiguously presented to readers as fiction, especially given that the characters in the column occasionally break the fourth wall, so to speak, and draw attention to their awareness that Cynthia is writing about their lives in a public forum.[13] And although the newspaper did not include a masthead and most of its contributions were unsigned, when Montgomery published the poem "Harbor Sunset" in *Ainslee's Magazine* in January 1902, the *Echo* republished the poem – under the title "Sunset on Halifax Harbor" – and claimed its author, L.M. Montgomery, as "one of the staff of this paper."[14]

"Around the Table" is a bit of an anomaly, since it is not journalism per se (in the sense that "Cynthia" rarely reports on local or world events) and does not appear as part of a separate "women's page" common to so many newspapers. In a monograph focusing on the work of Irish Canadian journalist Kathleen "Kit" Coleman (1856–1915), whose work included overseeing the "Woman's Kingdom" page of the Saturday edition of Toronto's *Daily Mail*, Barbara M. Freeman notes that, appearing by the last decade of the nineteenth century, "women's pages" in newspapers "were not invented to improve the status of women, but to draw advertisers and readers. Despite the advances of the time, women were still seen as being primarily concerned with hearth and home and newspaper editors hired female journalists, who were a decided minority in their field, to write 'light' articles on domestic issues, fashion notes and household items." Promoting a dominant ideology in the nineteenth century that "women's most crucial role was mothering the nation," many newspaper editors "refused to believe that their female audiences were interested in weightier matters and discouraged coverage of political and social issues, unless they had a bearing on women's domestic roles."[15] Montgomery escaped these constraints to an extent simply due to the fact that the *Halifax Daily Echo*, which printed eight to twelve pages daily except for Sundays, did not have a "women's page." And while much of the "action" of the "Around the Table" columns takes place within the home, it is only occasionally concerned with domestic issues of any kind, focusing instead on the idiosyncrasies of the characters who live in the home.

Part 3, "The Upward Climb to Heights Sublime," charts Montgomery's "arrival" as bestselling author L.M. Montgomery. It consists of the undated short piece "Two Sides of a Life Story," published under the signature "J.C. Neville," and a new edition of her 25,000-word celebrity memoir, "The Alpine Path: The Story of My Career," which appeared in six instalments in the Toronto magazine *Everywoman's World* between June and November 1917. First appearing in book form in 1974, more than a decade prior to the publication of the first volume of *The Selected Journals of L.M. Montgomery*, this memoir has since been taken up either as a piece of life writing that contrasts sharply with the text and tone of Montgomery's journals or as her most sustained articulation in print of her personal brand.

This new edition of "The Alpine Path" returns to the original magazine text and restores the twenty photographs and first-person captions that Montgomery included in that text but were dropped from the 1974 book version; these "change how we read the text and how we understand its role in affirming and crafting Montgomery's public image," according to Katja Lee.[16] Moreover, although William V. Thompson notes that some of the anecdotes in "The Alpine Path" are lifted out of a journal entry dated January 1910,[17] my research has revealed that her borrowings are far more extensive than that, drawing from numerous entries dated 1892 to 1912.[18] In my notes, I identify both overlaps with and departures from the journal text as a way to showcase the choices Montgomery made in transforming a private record into a highly controlled public one. In fact, although much has been made of Montgomery's stated decision, in the winter of 1919, to transcribe the text of her journals into uniform ledgers for eventual posthumous publication,[19] it seems more likely now, given how much of her journal text was woven into "The Alpine Path," that she realized the value of her journals as a public record of her life earlier than she claimed.

Returning to this work now, after the publication so far of eleven volumes of Montgomery's journals and three volumes of her letters,[20] allows us to consider two versions of her evolution as an author: one that we can see through the pieces in this volume and a more intentional one she offered the readers of *Everywoman's World* a century ago. In the items appearing in both this volume and in the collections of poems and stories that will follow, we can appreciate fully for the first time the wide reach of Montgomery's pen as she engaged with audiences of readers – sometimes local, in the case of student publications and work published in newspapers of a single city, and sometimes national, in the case of items published in wide-reaching magazines. For while her work in many ways seems timeless now, in reality she was never writing in a vacuum. In a sense, and as the volumes in this series will show, Montgomery's awareness of her audience shaped the narratives she wanted to tell.

BENJAMIN LEFEBVRE

NOTES

1 The Heritage Minute film, directed by Stephen Dunn, features Meghan Greeley as Montgomery and Nadia Tonen as Anne.

2 See Russell, Russell, and Wilmshurst, *Lucy Maud Montgomery*, 125–27.

3 Montgomery published twenty-four books over her career. *Anne of Green Gables* was followed by *Anne of Avonlea* (1909), *Chronicles of Avonlea* (1912), *Anne of the Island* (1915), *Anne's House of Dreams* (1917), *Rainbow Valley* (1919), *Further Chronicles of Avonlea* (1920), *Rilla of Ingleside* (1921), *Anne of Windy Poplars* (1936, in the UK and Australia as *Anne of Windy Willows*), and *Anne of Ingleside* (1939); *The Blythes Are Quoted*,

which I edited, was published in its entirety in 2009. Montgomery also published *The Story Girl* (1911), followed by *The Golden Road* (1913); *Emily of New Moon* (1923), followed by *Emily Climbs* (1925) and *Emily's Quest* (1927); *Pat of Silver Bush* (1933), followed by *Mistress Pat: A Novel of Silver Bush* (1935); and the standalone novels *Kilmeny of the Orchard* (1910), *The Blue Castle* (1926), *Magic for Marigold* (1929), *A Tangled Web* (1931, in the UK as *Aunt Becky Began It*), and *Jane of Lantern Hill* (1937). She also published *The Watchman and Other Poems* (1916) and collaborated with Marian Keith and Mabel Burns McKinley on the volume of biographical essays *Courageous Women* (1934), but neither of these two books remained in print for long; her contributions to the latter volume appear in Volume 1 of *The L.M. Montgomery Reader*.

4 Previous posthumous collections of Montgomery's short stories and poems, organized mostly by theme rather than chronology, include *The Road to Yesterday* (1974), a truncated version of *The Blythes Are Quoted*; *The Doctor's Sweetheart and Other Stories* (1979), selected by Catherine McLay; *The Poetry of Lucy Maud Montgomery* (1987), selected by John Ferns and Kevin McCabe; *Akin to Anne: Tales of Other Orphans* (1988), *Along the Shore: Tales by the Sea* (1989), *Among the Shadows: Tales from the Darker Side* (1990), *After Many Days: Tales of Time Passed* (1991), *Against the Odds: Tales of Achievement* (1993), *At the Altar: Matrimonial Tales* (1994), *Across the Miles: Tales of Correspondence* (1995), and *Christmas with Anne and Other Holiday Stories* (1995), all edited by Rea Wilmshurst; and *After Many Years* (2017), edited by Carolyn Strom Collins and Christy Woster.

5 Although this volume consists mainly of non-fiction, it does not reproduce any of the more than two dozen essays by Montgomery that originally appeared between 1911 and 1939 and that were collected in Volume 1 of *The L.M. Montgomery Reader*.

6 Bound photocopies are available to researchers at the University of Prince Edward Island and University of Guelph libraries. These copies were numbered Scrapbooks 1 to 12 without respect to chronology.

7 The locations of Montgomery's scrapbooks are listed in the bibliography. For more on Montgomery's scrapbooks, see the work of Carolyn Strom Collins and Elizabeth Rollins Epperly.

8 The Confederation Centre Art Gallery in Charlottetown holds partial or complete manuscripts for the following novels by Montgomery: *Anne of Green Gables*, *The Golden Road*, *Anne of the Island* ("Anne of Redmond"), *Anne's House of Dreams*, *Rainbow Valley*, *Emily of New Moon*, *Emily Climbs*, *The Blue Castle*, *Emily's Quest*, *Magic for Marigold*, *A Tangled Web*, *Pat of Silver Bush*, *Mistress Pat* ("The Girls of Silver Bush"), *Anne of Windy Poplars*, *Jane of Lantern Hill*, and *Anne of Ingleside*. The L.M. Montgomery Collection, part of Archival and Special Collections at the University of Guelph Library, holds the manuscript for *Rilla of Ingleside*, a transcript of which was prepared by Elizabeth Waterston and Kate Waterston and published as *Readying Rilla* (2016), as well as three typescripts for *The Blythes Are Quoted*, the last of which formed the basis of the published edition.

9 Braybrooke, Introduction, 14. It is also worth noting that only fifteen of the sixty authors whose early work is included in Braybrooke's volume were women.

10 Beer, Introduction, 8–9. See also the chapters in Christine Alexander and Juliet McMaster's collection of essays *The Child Writer from Austen to Woolf* (2005).

11 Montgomery, 13 November 1901, in *CJLMM*, 2: 22.

12 Gerson, "L.M. Montgomery," 69.

13 This is not to say that no other item ever mentioned the "Around the Table" column. The only known copy of the *Halifax Daily Echo* is on a microfilm housed at Library and Archives Canada, so my search through the newspaper for additional mentions of the column was limited by time constraints during short trips in 2015 and 2016. Perhaps, if or when that newspaper is digitized and made text searchable, future researchers will be able to uncover additional materials pertaining to Montgomery.

14 *Halifax Daily Echo*, "The Beachcomber," 4.

15 Freeman, *Kit's Kingdom*, 2, 8. For comprehensive coverage of journalism by Canadian women between 1880 and 1945, see Lang, *Women Who Made the News*.

16 Lee, "Protecting Her Brand," 195.

17 Thompson, "The Shadow on the House of Dreams," 116.

18 While these borrowings from Montgomery's journals are extensive, they do not mark the last time she mined her journals for her published non-fiction. Her commentary on the diary of her neighbour

and distant relative Charles Macneill, recorded in her journal in 1925 along with a transcription of Macneill's diary, formed the basis of her 1936 article "Come Back with Me to Prince Edward Island," whereas her 1924 journal entry on her family trip to Mammoth Cave in Kentucky became a starting point for an article entitled "A Trip to Mammoth Cave," whose publication details are not confirmed but whose manuscript is now housed at the University of Prince Edward Island Library. See Montgomery, 17 August 1924, in *LMMCJ*, 3: 274–80; Montgomery, 1 March 1925, in *LMMCJ*, 3: 326, 329–50; Montgomery, in *DCMF*, 83–104; Montgomery, 16 February 1936, in *SJLMM*, 5: 58; Montgomery, 9 April 1936, in *SJLMM*, 5: 60. For a recent study of Montgomery's creative engagement with the Macneill diary, see Litster, "The Scotsman."

19 See Brown and Lefebvre, "Archival Adventures with L.M. Montgomery," 375–76, 381–83.

20 *The Selected Journals of L.M. Montgomery*, edited by Mary Rubio and Elizabeth Waterston, appeared in five volumes between 1985 and 2004. In 2012, Rubio and Waterston published *The Complete Journals of L.M. Montgomery: The PEI Years, 1889–1900*, with a second volume covering the years 1901 to 1911 appearing in 2013. Since 2016, Jen Rubio has continued this project, publishing *L.M. Montgomery's Complete Journals: The Ontario Years, 1911–1917*, followed by three additional volumes covering the years 1918 to 1929 and further volumes in preparation. Francis W.P. Bolger and Elizabeth R. Epperly's *My Dear Mr. M: Letters to G.B. MacMillan from L.M. Montgomery* (1980) and Hildi Froese Tiessen and Paul Gerard Tiessen's *After Green Gables: L.M. Montgomery's Letters to Ephraim Weber, 1916–1941* (2006) were likewise published after the book version of "The Alpine Path," which was preceded by *The Green Gables Letters from L.M. Montgomery to Ephraim Weber, 1905–1909* (1960), edited by Wilfrid Eggleston.

A Note on the Text

The items included in this volume were first published in a wide range of North American periodicals across a span of more than twenty-five years. They supplement the non-fiction pieces that Montgomery published after the publication of *Anne of Green Gables* and that are included in Volume 1 of my three-volume critical anthology, *The L.M. Montgomery Reader*. Some of these items have been collected in book form before; these include some of Montgomery's first publications in Francis W.P. Bolger's *The Years Before "Anne"* in 1974, the same year that "The Alpine Path" was published as a stand-alone book, as well as a handful of extracts from Montgomery's "Around the Table" column in Kevin McCabe's collection of essays *The Lucy Maud Montgomery Album* (1999) and one in Elizabeth Rollins Epperly's *Through Lover's Lane: L.M. Montgomery's Photography and Visual Imagination* (2007). In all cases, I have relied on the original publications as my copy-texts, collating them against the copies found in Montgomery's scrapbooks. I have treated her handwritten corrections as authoritative and mention them in the notes.

In the case of the thirty-five instalments of Montgomery's "Around the Table" column, I have provided a courtesy title for each instalment and placed it within brackets, except for the first instalment, published as "Over the Tea-Cups," whose title I retain. When it appeared in *Everywoman's World* in 1917, "The Alpine Path: The Story of My Career" was divided randomly into six instalments, sometimes in the middle of a journal entry or an anecdote; for this reason, I have opted to run the entire text continually, but I note where each instalment from the magazine edition (as well as each chapter in the 1974 edition) begins. Photos appear rather randomly in the original publication, sometimes in clusters – photos of Montgomery's sons appear alongside text that likens the publication of *Anne of Green Gables* to a form of creation, for instance – so whenever possible, for ease of reading, I have placed these images where their contents are mentioned in the text. I also include, for ease of reference, the signatures Montgomery used for the items in this volume, except those signed "L.M. Montgomery" or unsigned.

I have not attempted to regularize spelling, punctuation, or hyphenation, although for ease of reading I have made some silent amendments, including italicizing periodical and book titles, names of ships, and non-English phrases (such as *sotto voce*), as well as normalizing quotation marks, particularly for quotations that extend beyond one paragraph, and correcting obvious typographical errors. More substantive corrections are explained in the notes, as are errors or misquotations that I did not correct.

The notes also identify allusions to texts, people, and events, draw parallels to Montgomery's fiction and life writing, and provide bibliographical details about the items included in this volume. When bibliographical details could not be confirmed because the original periodicals could not be located, these details appear within brackets and the copy-text is from one of Montgomery's scrapbooks, which do not have page numbers. Many of these items in her scrapbooks appear with minor annotations in Montgomery's hand (including dates of composition and publication), all of which are noted.

B.L.

A Name for Herself

SELECTED WRITINGS, 1891–1917

FICTION

L. M. Montgomery—a face of balance and refinement. The smooth high forehead shows love of stories and sympathetic perception, the height and squareness above the temples and the arched eyebrows suggest poetic feeling and artistic taste, while the full eyes show facility of expression.

FIGURE 1 A photograph and description of L.M. Montgomery appearing in *Everywoman's World* in August 1917 alongside an instalment of her celebrity memoir, "The Alpine Path: The Story of My Career."

PART I

Early and Student Publications

THE WRECK OF THE "MARCO POLO."

In writing an essay for the *Witness* it is not my intention to relate any hairbreadth escapes of my ancestors, for, though they endured all the hardships incidental to the opening up of a new country, I do not think they ever had any hair-raising adventures with bears or Indians. It is my purpose, instead, to relate the incidents connected with the wreck of the celebrated "Marco Polo" off Cavendish, in the summer of 1883.

Cavendish is a pretty little village, bordering on the Gulf of St. Lawrence and possessing a beautiful sea-coast, part of which is a stretch of rugged rocks and the rest of broad level beach of white sand. On a fine summer day a scene more beautiful could not be found than the sparkling blue waters of the Gulf, dotted over with white sails and stately fish-ing vessels. But it is not always so calm and bright; very often furious storms arise, which sometimes last for several days, and it was in one of these that the "Marco Polo" came ashore.

MISS L. M. MONTGOMERY.

FIGURE 2 L.M. Montgomery's first prose publication (detail), appearing in the *Montreal Daily Witness*, 5 March 1891.

The Wreck of the "Marco Polo"

LUCY MAUD MONTGOMERY

After L.M. Montgomery died on 24 April 1942, her obituary in the *Globe and Mail* stated that "at the age of 12 she won a story-writing contest sponsored by the *Montreal Star*."[1] Such an assertion requires several corrections and clarifications: Montgomery was fifteen, not twelve, when she won the prize;[2] the competition was for sketches and compositions, not for fiction; it was sponsored by the *Montreal Daily Witness*, not the *Montreal Star*; and Montgomery won third prize for Queens County in Prince Edward Island, as opposed to a national prize. Written as a school assignment in February 1890 and submitted as part of a nationwide competition referred to interchangeably as "Canadian Stories Competition," "Canada Competition Prize," and "Dominion Competition Prize" (to which she had submitted an essay on the legend of Cape Leforce the year before),[3] the essay narrates a shipwreck that occurred on Cavendish beach in 1883, the summer after Montgomery's eighth birthday.[4] Montgomery mentioned in passing the results of that year's competition in a journal entry dated 31 May 1890, but while she included in her scrapbook a clipping of the comments made by the judge for her award of third prize for her county, which described her piece as "a very chaste description of a sad event of coast life,"[5] she omitted those comments from her journal entry. And although the publication of her first poem in November 1890, mere days before her sixteenth birthday, received its own journal entry,[6] the publication of this school essay in the winter of 1891 – while she was living in Prince Albert, Saskatchewan, with her father and his new family – was not mentioned at all in her journal for that year; her scrapbook even states that the piece was published in February 1891, when in fact it appeared on 5 March 1891 in the *Montreal Daily*

Witness and on 11 March 1891 in the Charlottetown *Daily Patriot*. The piece is signed "Lucy Maud Montgomery / Cavendish, Queen's County, P.E.I." but is accompanied by a sketch drawing of the young author that is captioned "Miss L.M. Montgomery" (see figure 2).

Forty years after this piece appeared in the *Montreal Daily Witness* as a submission to a national essay contest, Montgomery herself donned the judge's hat for two contests: the Canadian portion of the International Kodak Company Competition in 1931[7] and the Nancy Durham Memorial Contest held by the Circle of Young Canada column of the Toronto *Globe*.[8] Montgomery's published report for the fiction portion of the latter contest offers some practical advice to young writers about what constitutes good writing, including – somewhat surprisingly given her propensity as an adolescent to draw on some of the oral stories of her community – the recommendation that beginning writers resist attempting to rework old plots.[9]

IN WRITING AN ESSAY FOR THE *WITNESS* IT IS NOT MY INtention to relate any hairbreadth escapes of my ancestors, for, though they endured all the hardships incidental to the opening up of a new country, I do not think they ever had any hair-raising adventures with bears or Indians. It is my purpose, instead, to relate the incidents connected with the wreck of the celebrated "Marco Polo" off Cavendish,[10] in the summer of 1883.

Cavendish is a pretty little village, bordering on the Gulf of St. Lawrence and possessing a beautiful sea coast, part of which is a stretch of rugged rocks and the rest of broad level beach of white sand. On a fine summer day a scene more beautiful could not be found than the sparkling blue waters of the Gulf, dotted over with white sails and stately fishing vessels. But it is not always so calm and bright; very often furious storms arise, which sometimes last for several days, and it was in one of these that the "Marco Polo" came ashore.

The "Marco Polo" was a barque of the "Black Ball" line of packets and was the fastest sailing vessel ever built, her record never having been beaten.[11] She was, at the time of her shipwreck, owned by a firm in Norway and was chartered by an English firm to bring a cargo of deal planks[12] from Canada. The enterprise was risky, for she was almost too rotten to hold together, but she made the outward trip in safety and obtained her cargo; but, on her return, she was caught in a furious storm and became so water-logged that the captain, P.A. Bull of Christiania,[13] resolved to run her ashore as the only way to save crew and cargo.

What a day that 25th of July was in Cavendish! The wind blew a hurricane and the waves ran mountains high; the storm had begun two days before and had now reached its highest pitch of fury. When at its worst, the report was spread that a large vessel was coming ashore off a little fishing station called Cawnpore,[14] and soon an excited crowd was assembled on the beach. The wind was nor'-nor'-east, as sailors say,[15] and the vessel, coming in before the gale, with every stitch of canvas set, was a sight never to be forgotten! She grounded about 300 yards from the shore, and, just as she struck, the crew cut the rigging, and the foremast and the huge iron mainmast, carrying the mizzen-topmast with it, went over with a crash that could be heard for miles above the roaring of the storm![16] Then the ship broached to and lay there with the waves breaking over her.

By this time, half the people in Cavendish were assembled on the beach and the excitement was intense. As long as the crew remained on the vessel they were safe, but, if ignorant of the danger of such a proceeding, they attempted to land, death was certain. When it was seen that they were evidently preparing to hazard a landing all sorts of devices to warn them back were tried, but none were successful until a large board was put up, with the words, "Stick to the ship at all hazards" painted on it. When they saw this they made no further attempt to land and thus night fell.

The storm continued all night but by morning was sufficiently abated to permit a boat to go out to the ship and bring the crew ashore. They were a hard looking lot – tired, wet and hungry, but in high spirits over their rescue, and, while they were refreshing the inner man, the jokes flew thick and fast. One little fellow, on being asked, "if it wasn't pretty windy out there," responded, with a shrug of his shoulders, "Oh, no, der vas not too mooch vind but der vas too mooch vater!"

Lively times for Cavendish followed. The crew, consisting of about twenty men, found boarding places around the settlement and contrived to keep the neighborhood in perpetual uproar, while the fussy good-natured captain came to our place. He was a corpulent, bustling little man, bluff and hearty – the typical sea-captain; he was idolized by his crew, who would have gone through fire and water for him any day. And such a crew! Almost every nationality was represented. There were Norwegians, Swedes, Dutchmen, Englishmen, Irishmen, Spaniards, two Tahitians, and one quarrelsome, obstinate little German who refused to work his passage home and demanded to be sent back to his fatherland by steamer. It was amusing to hear them trying to master the pronunciation of our English names. We had a dog called "Gyp" whose name was a constant source of vexation to them. The Norwegians called him "Yip," the irritable little German termed him "Schnip" and one old tar twisted it into "Ship."[17]

But the time passed all too quickly by. The "Marco Polo" and her cargo were sold to parties in St. John, N.B.,[18] and the captain and his motley crew took their departure. A company of men were at once hired to assist in taking out her cargo and eighteen schooner loads of deal were taken from her. The planks had so swelled from the wet that it was found necessary to cut her beams through in order to get them out and consequently she was soon nothing but a mere shell with about half of her cargo still in her.

One night in August, about a month after she had come ashore, the men who were engaged in the work of unloading resolved to remain on the vessel until the following morning. It was a wild thing to think of remaining on her over night, but, seeing no indication of a storm, they decided to do so. It was a rarely beautiful evening; too fine, indeed – what old weather-prophets call a "pet" day.[19] The sun set amid clouds of crimson, tinging the dusky wavelets with fire and lingering on the beautiful vessel as she lay at rest on the shining sea, while the fresh evening breeze danced over the purple waters. Who could have thought that, before morning, that lovely, tranquil scene would have given place to one of tempestuous fury! But it was so. By dawn a storm was raging, compared to which, that in which the "Marco Polo" came ashore was nothing.

The tidings spread quickly and soon the shore was lined with people gazing with horror stricken eyes at the vessel, which, cut up as she was, must inevitably go to pieces in a short time. One can only imagine the agony of the relatives and friends of the poor men at seeing their dear ones in such danger and knowing that they were powerless to aid them. As for the men themselves, they were fully alive to their danger, for they knew that the vessel could not hold together much longer. Their only boat was stove in[20] by the fury of the waves so that their sole hope of rescue lay in some boat being able to reach them from the shore which, in the then state of the sea, was impossible. In spite of the fact that the boat was full of water three of the men insanely got into it and tried to reach land. Of course the boat was instantly swamped and the men left struggling in the water. Two of them managed to regain the wreck in safety, but the third, a poor Frenchman called Peter Buote, was drowned instantly and, several days after the storm, his body was picked up some distance away.[21]

The horror-stricken onlookers still kept their eyes fixed on the fated vessel, in horrible expectation of the inevitable catastrophe; suddenly a cry of horror burst from every lip as the ship was seen to part at the forecastle head and at once go down. The next minute, however, it was seen that the windlass and a small piece of the bow still remained held by the anchors, and that the men were clinging to this. With the courage of desperation, several attempts were now made to reach the wreck, but all the boats filled with water and were compelled to return. Nothing could now be done till the storm would abate and it was only one chance in a hundred that the fragment would hold so long.

Meanwhile the beach was a sight to behold; the vessel having broken up, the planks in her washed ashore and for miles the shore was piled with deals and all sorts of wreckage till it was absolutely impassable!

At last, towards evening, the sea grew a little smoother and, though the attempt was still fraught with much danger, a seine-boat[22] was procured and a party of brave men went to the rescue. They reached the wreck in safety and hauled the men on board the boat by means of ropes. Thus they were all brought safely to land, exhausted with cold, wet, and hunger, but still alive. What rejoicing there was when they were safely landed, and, as the kindly neighbors crowded around with that "touch of nature that makes the whole world kin,"[23] there was joy indeed except among the poor Frenchman's relatives, who were mourning the loss of their friend.

About a week afterward, in another gale, the last vestige of the vessel disappeared and that was the end of the famous "Marco Polo," celebrated in song and story. Her copper bottom, chains, anchors, etc., in all, it was said, about $10,000, are still there, and, though almost buried in the sands, on a clear calm day the little fishing boats sailing over the spot can discern, far beneath, the remnants that mark the spot where the "Marco Polo" went down.

(1891)

A Western Eden

LUCY MAUD MONTGOMERY

This article, signed Lucy Maud Montgomery, appeared in the *Prince Albert Times and Saskatchewan Review* in June 1891, five months before Montgomery's seventeenth birthday. In her journal, she called the article "a description of the prairies and scenery and the characteristics of the Indians," adding that it would "finish up with a flowery peroration on the possibilities of the country as a whole." A later journal entry indicates that the article had made "quite a bit of sensation" in her community.[1] The article was reprinted with minor variations a few weeks later in the *Manitoba Daily Free Press* (Winnipeg), signed Lucy Ward Montgomery and including a descriptive phrase that called the piece "an article on the great Saskatchewan district": "Beauty of the Noblest of All Northwestern Rivers – Prince Albert's Pride – Words from the Pen of a Lady Writer."

"Let others raise the song of praise
Of lands renowned in story;
The land for me of the maple tree
And the pine in all its glory!
Hurrah, for the grand old forest land
Where Freedom spreads her pinion!
Hurrah, with me for the maple tree!
Hurrah for the new Dominion."

McLAUCHLIN[2]

AN UNLIMITED EXPANSE OF GENTLE SLOPES AND VELVET meadows, dotted with groves and clumps of poplar, a pretty little town nestling at the foot of the terraced hills, a noble river flowing past, and beyond it the vast sweep of the "forest primeval"[3] – that is Saskatchewan and Prince Albert. To be fully appreciated, Saskatchewan must be seen, for no pen, however gifted or graphic, can describe, with anything like justice, the splendid natural resources, the unequalled fertility, and the rare beauty of the prairies of this Western Eden. Nature has here seemed to shower down with most unstinted generosity her choicest gifts; and certainly, if richness of soil and mineral wealth, beautiful scenery, and unsurpassed climate have anything to do with the advancement of a country, then Saskatchewan is bound to speedily come to the front as one of the finest and wealthiest portions of this, our fair Dominion.

To any lover of nature, a ride over the prairies of Saskatchewan is filled with the keenest pleasure. Never does one feel such a deep sense of the beauty of the universe as when, pausing on some breezy hill-top, spread out beneath is seen this magnificent wilderness where a century ago the buffalo and deer roamed undisturbed and where, even as yet, civilization has obtained little more than a footing. Pause with me here, reader, and let us from this point of vantage take a look over this country which some timid people have, in days of yore, asserted to possess a winter nine months long and a remaining three of very doubtful character. On every hand, as far as eye can reach, extend the prairies adorned with groves of willow and poplar, clear and distinct near by, but in the distance mingling into a seeming forest clothed, over the outline of the distant hills, in hazy purple mists. Here the prairies extend in level, grassy meadows, sweet with the breath of the dainty prairie bluebells and wild roses; there they swell in ranges of picturesque bluff which curve around, every few yards, to enclose a tiny blue lake in its encircling of frost-yellowed grasses, like a sapphire set in gold. All is quiet – sound there is none save when some happy bird trills out a gush of warbling among the willows, or when the cool breeze rustles the poplar leaves in silvery music, and sweeps airily over the hills, bringing with it delicious whiffs of sweet clover and meadow grasses. The drowsy summer sunshine sleeps lazily on the slopes, the air is full of fragrance, and above, the peerless Canadian sky – dark azure in the tranquil deeps o'erhead, paling to silvery blue and pearl towards the horizon, with here and there trails of filmy white clouds tinged golden on the sunward side – arches its glorious dome over a scene which inspires us to exclaim with enthusiastic pride, –

"This is my own, my native land!"[4]

But look! see those cloud-mountains away in the south-west horizons. Heaped on each other in soft, white masses, golden and rose in the shadows, they are beautiful indeed, but certain ominous dark vapors stealing upward from their base warn us that perhaps a thunderstorm may be near, and that we'd better leave our sunny hill if we don't want a wetting, though we must admit that wettings are rare in Saskatchewan where weeks of fine weather at a stretch are enjoyed.

But although the prairies surrounding it are so lovely, Prince Albert's greatest beauty consists in the magnificent river that rolls its blue tides, freighted with the mysteries of former ages, past its poplar-fringed banks, with the busy little town on the one side, and the unbroken forests of the northland on the other. Passing over the great importance of the Saskatchewan for navigation, we must take a glimpse at the natural beauty of this river on whose forest-clad banks the tribes of the red men have, in bygone centuries, hunted the buffalo and deer, fought their battles and passed to their happy hunting grounds undisturbed by the intrusion of a stranger race.

In beauty and variety of scenery the Saskatchewan, with its soft Indian name,[5] is second to no river in Canada. Springing from the eternal glaciers of the Rockies, its waters, ever cold from their icy birth, and gifted,[6] so saith the legend, with magic power, sweep through Alberta and Saskatchewan, –

"A full fed river winding swift
By herds upon an endless plain" –[7]

until the shores of Lake Winnipeg are reached.

Beautiful at all times the river is – at night, when the stars are mirrored brokenly on its dark surface, like shattered flakes of light, and the roar of its current sounds distinct in the silence; or at morning, when the flushed light of eastern skies creeps over its silvery blue and the rosy mists fade from its waters; or at noon, when every ripple dances in the sunlight till it is a river of sparkling gold with clearer depths beneath its banks, and, afar up, the islands that gem it are hazy with pale blue mists. But it is beneath the sunset skies that it is most beautiful of all. The rush of the day is past, and in the dewy hush of evening, a soft stillness steals over all. The fire and orange of the western skies is reflected on the still waters, shading off into fairy tintings of blue and rose, silver and pearl, while transparent shadows chase each other swiftly over the bright expanse.

A sudden curve in the river shuts off the western glory, and here the waters are deep and clear and dark, with golden and brown undershadows, and crystalline depths along the banks where the breeze ripple of the mid stream does not disturb its perfect rest.[8]

But paler and paler grow the sunset dyes, deeper and deeper the purple glooms of twilight, more and more indistinct the swaying outlines of the distant woods. And now the golden glow has vanished, the river is a sheet of silver, broken here and there, into a whirl of gray shadows, the air is clear and sweet, the sky dusky and tender with a few early stars in its opal depths and the gleaming scimitar of a thin young moon in the south-west, and, on the opposite shore, the poplars sway eerily in the gathering gloom – all so weird and mysterious that one half expects to see a dusky warrior, clad in all his ancient panoply of war-paint and feathers, spring from their shadows, and ring his war-whoop over the waters of the river his forefathers once claimed as their own.

But the warrior never does appear. Don't think he will. He belongs to an extinct species now. Before I reached the banks of the Saskatchewan I had only very dim, vague, misty opinions concerning Indians, and the perusal of *The Last of the Mohicans*[9] and similar works had led me to half expect that I would here meet the heroes of their pages in real life. Would they, I wondered, be clad in all the historic garb of their ancestors – moccasins, deer-skin leggings, blanket, war-paint and feathers, together with the indispensable accessories of tomahawk and scalping-knife? And would they, like Cooper's braves, talk mysteriously of "palefaces" and "setting suns" and "many moons" and "happy hunting grounds," and look with disdainful hatred upon the usurping white man? Alas for my illusions! They were soon destroyed.

Doubtless, in past ages, arrayed in the before-mentioned costume, and stalking under the boughs of his native forest, the "noble red man" was a very romantic and fear-inspiring object; but as we look at the poor Indian now, clad in ragged garments fashioned after those of his conqueror, with a dirty blanket flung over his shoulder, as he shuffles through the busy streets of another race, glancing upward with cowed submission in his dark eyes, or engaged in chopping wood and other menial tasks for the white man, the last atom of romance vanishes, leaving only pity and compassion behind. But, even decayed as they are, the Indians are interesting still, and considerable amusement may be extracted from a study of their speech and habits. A fondness for exceedingly gay attire characterizes the Indian ladies (please, oh scornful masculine readers, do not exclaim that it is a failing common to the whole sex, white or red) and the dresses of the dusky belles would make Joseph's coat dull and shabby by contrast.[10] Many of the young squaws are comely – before age and hard work have coarsened the graceful litheness of their figures and roughened the round outlines of their features, while in their soft eyes, dark as shadowed lakes, they possess a beauty unowned by any paleface maiden.

The squaws are great talkers (I suppose the men will grow sarcastic here again) and it is a pleasure to listen to their soft musical language as they laugh and chatter among themselves. They are industrious too – far more so than their worse halves (here's a chance for the ladies to indulge in a spice of irony now) in whose appearance and habits there is little to excite interest.

In a few decades at most the red Indians will become extinct, and the dusky children of a race, whose origin and history are shrouded in impenetrable mystery, will have forever vanished from the land over whose plains and rivers they once held supreme control. As we thus glance over this beautiful district – a province doubtless, in the not very distant future[11] – we feel that it is indeed a country to be proud of, and a country well worth waiting and working for. It is a country where prosperity and freedom are awaiting thousands, a country where all may be happy and equal, a country where

"A man is a man
If he's willing to toil
And the humblest may gather
The fruit of the soil":[12]

and a country fit to breed a race of heroes physically and intellectually for, in the crisp, invigorating air of its wind swept prairies, and in the earnest toil that will be so abundantly rewarded, there is little to encourage sickly sentimentality or brainless indolence. Hurrah for Saskatchewan!

"God save our Queen and Heaven bless
The Maple Leaf forever."[13]

Prince Albert, June 12th, 1891.[14]

(1891)

From Prince Albert to P.E. Island

A year after fifteen-year-old Maud Montgomery travelled west by train to be reunited with her estranged father, Hugh John Montgomery, who had remarried and settled in Prince Albert, Saskatchewan, she came reluctantly to the conclusion that staying there indefinitely would not be in her best interests. Disillusioned by the toxic dynamic between her and her stepmother and disappointed by the haphazard schooling available to her, Montgomery returned to her grandparents in Cavendish, departing on 27 August 1891. This sketch, evidently written at the suggestion of one of her grandfathers and published in the Charlottetown *Daily Patriot* in October 1891,[1] provides a lively account of her journey home. According to Mary Henley Rubio, the decision for sixteen-year-old Montgomery to travel by train and boat all the way to Ottawa without a chaperone "was an extraordinary breach of custom and propriety," not to mention "downright unsafe." Also omitted from this published account is the fact that no family member went to meet her when she arrived in Prince Edward Island.[2]

WE LEAVE PRINCE ALBERT EARLY ONE FRESH AUGUST morning, just as the new born sunshine creeps over the prairies to kiss the dew from the grasses and coquette with the waters of the blue Saskatchewan. There is the usual bustle at the railway station, the good-byes, promises, reminders, the fluttering of handkerchiefs and the kissing of finger tips;[3] then the train glides slowly out, and as the last straggler on the platform vanishes, we realize that we are really off and "homeward bound!"

Quickly, familiar landmarks disappear, and soon we are flying over the virgin prairie, no trace of civilization in sight, – save where now and then we pass a little log cabin surrounded by nodding wheat fields of dead gold. The long grasses and prairie blue-bells are still damp with dew, and the shadows are black and long under the tall white-skinned poplars and straggling willows. Now and then we pass through ragged groves of pine and fir, looking dead and dismal with the gray streamers of moss clinging to their black branches, or speed by a little blue lake, rippling on its grassy shores.

We have plenty of time for inspecting the scenery! The train does not go *very* fast! It is so occupied with slowing up every few minutes, because of cows on the track, that it cannot, and our only amusement is to stick our heads out the car windows and watch said cows running, wondering meanwhile if we look as funny ourselves as do the other people whose heads are also out.

By noon we are at Saskatoon,[4] and the rest of the way there are no blue lakes, shivering poplars, yellow wheat fields, or herds of lazy cows, – in fact, there is no ANYTHING![5] A more desolate expanse could not well be imagined. Far, far, far, as the weary eye can reach, is one exasperating level, covered with grass the hot sun has scorched to a dusty brown. Here and there are bare black tracts that prairie fires have swept, and off to our left winds a river valley, whose banks, broken into round dark hills, are inexpressibly dreary. Scenery there is none, unless occasional piles of buffalo bones can be called so; neither is there any sign of life, save, once or twice, a troop of prowling jackals, and a solitary fox who tries to race with the train, but gives it up in despair! And we count the telegraph posts and the bone piles, and watch the clouds and speculate as to the possibility of the ghosts of buffalo ever revisiting their old trails that are still visible; and finally we turn round in disgust and go to sleep.

We are at length awakened by a hurrying and scurrying, shouting and banging doors, flashes of light and a general confusion from which our bewildered senses gather that we have arrived at our day's destination. We climb off in the chilly dark, and find ourselves in the surging jostling crowd at the Regina station.[6] Regina is not remarkable for beauty. The surrounding country is bare and level and the city itself is a dusty-looking place. But to do it justice, it is plucky and goaheaditive[7] and bound sooner or later to be one of the busiest and most populous of the cities that are swiftly growing up all over the bright western prairies.

It is half past eleven at night when we leave Regina. The Pullmans, they tell us, are full,[8] so we have to go in the first-class. To our dismay we find it is literally packed. In nearly every seat are two and sometimes three. Some few fortunate mortals have secured seats all to themselves, and selfishly refuse to allow any one else to disturb their naps, so we have to squeeze down into a seat with two others and bear it as philosophically as possible. Sleeping is out of the question. We take cat naps now and then, yawn, fidget, and study our fellow travellers. Anything funnier than a first class car at midnight we have never seen. If we were not feeling so sleepy and unamiable we could almost laugh. Here are some of those previously-mentioned selfish individuals stretched out on their seats in various stages of *dishabille*[9] and limpness snoring as peacefully as if on the downiest couches. There are those who are wide awake and generally glum. One man in particular growls and squirms and wonders why on earth people crowd the car so, and is so generally disagreeable that everybody is glad when he leaves.

Oh, what a long long night it is! How slowly the minutes creep away. And the train flies on, on, on, till we feel as if it never would stop, over the dark prairies. But at last far over the level, where the greens and the blues meet, we see a faint stain of orange that grows deeper and brighter, before we know it the day is born and we are on the prairies of Manitoba. On, on we speed – now by the ripe Manitoban wheat fields and snug farmhouses, now by some pretty little village and often through tracts yet free from man's dominion, where the luxuriant grasses are green and long, and the ranks of the prairie sunflowers dance and nod their impertinent yellow heads in the wandering breezes.

Rat Portage is quite a city[10] and Virden is a rapidly growing little town.[11] Brandon is a charming spot and presents quite a handsome appearance,[12] but we only see enough to wish for more, for our train, in common with its kind, has a detestable trick of starting just as we become interested in something. We have been watching a stout lady laden with innumerable parcels coming rapidly down the wet street. She has reached a muddy crossing where she suddenly slips, throws up her arms and is just in the act of falling when the train glides past and we are forever left in tantalizing ignorance as to the fate of the stout lady and her parcels.

As we approach Winnipeg the general subject of conversation changes. Previously it has been the boodling transactions recently exposed at the capital.[13] Some have moodily declared that the result will be utter ruin, confusion and general anarchy, while others have confidently assured that all these "little fusses" will blow over without serious harm to anyone. Now, however, every one discusses the recent frosts, and opinions are as varied as before. Some say the crops are ruined, others that they are unhurt. In both cases the truth seems to be between each of these extremes. We are not long in Winnipeg – just an hour! Only time to take a peep at some of the principal streets and conclude that Winnipeg is a busy, thriving city, as handsome as it is energetic.

Then we are off again, and as twilight shadows creep over us we see that the country we are in now is very different from that which we have crossed. It is rugged and hilly. Big boulders and scrubby growths of spruce and fir are seen at intervals. We are approaching the forest wilds of Northern Ontario.

It has grown raw and cold. The sun sets amid gray cloud-fringes with a cruel savage sort of splendor, and the wind that comes moaningly over the waste[14] brings with it a promise of rainy days. A promise that is fulfilled, for when we take a good-night look into the dismal night, we see nothing but a gloomy forest, with dark, sorrowful spruces looming out of the mist-like phantom trees, while afar off a line of weird firs, "like tall thin priests of storm,"[15] are outlined against the last streak of dying gold.

Morning again! and a grey, dismal morning, with rain streaming down in slanting lines over the wet, shaking trees, and splashing on the still, dark surface of the woodland streams we cross; and the train goes rocking and swaying on through the hills that rise around us, until, just as we are beginning to imagine that we must be nearing the confines of the world, lo! we pop down on a little oasis of civilization hidden away among the mountain – Fort William at last![16]

We scowl considerably on finding that we have to wait here a day for the boat; but grumbling does no good, and is productive of wrinkles besides, so we go to an hotel, and then sally out in the pouring rain to "do" Fort William. That operation does not take long. Charred stumps, wandering pigs and streets that run off into the woods are the principal sights. We say all we can, honestly, in praise of it – it is active and hardy and a "rising town," but there we stop. It is undeniably rough and ugly, and not even the limitless forests and tree-clad mountains, sheathed in gray vapor, can redeem it.

Next day, even when the sun is bright and the blue hazes wrap the rugged slopes, it is but little better, and we confess that we are heartily glad to shake the dust of Fort William from our feet, and board our boat – the palace steamer *Manitoba.*[17]

Then we steam slowly down the river of the unpronounceable name,[18] and find ourselves fairly out on the blue waters of Lake Superior. Slowly the forest slopes recede and the myriad islets become scarce until we are at last out of sight of land on that great inland sea. It is a charming day. The delightful breeze barely ripples the dancing, sunlit waters and the glorious Canadian skies are blue and tender. The beautiful boat is alive with mirth and gaiety. Everyone is in good spirits. If there are any unfortunate victims of seasickness they keep in their staterooms and nothing disturbs the general merriment. The promenade deck is the favorite resort of all – ourselves included – for here we find the best opportunities for noting the amusing characteristics of our unsuspecting fellow travellers. There are all sorts of people on the boat. The stout, elderly lady with a fondness for knitting and theological discussions, the abstracted man of business with his columns of figures, the ubiquitous spoiled small boy who tyrannizes over all the other children on board, the anxious mother of five small babies who keep her in a perpetual worry over their wanderings, the talkative Yankee who considers everything American "superb" and everything Canadian "despisable," the cynical individual with spectacles and Darwinian views – we think he really must have descended from a monkey, – the lady who hopes we will have "one real awful storm just to see what it is like you know," the timid little woman who is so afraid there will be a collision or explosion, the creature who waylays everybody, even our ignorant selves, to discuss politics, the honeymooners who "promenade" ceaselessly and run into everybody so absorbed are they, and the literary fiend[19] who prowls around, forever scribbling in an ominous black note-book. Sunset on Lake Superior! Who can describe it? The steady tramp tramp goes on around us, for in the cool evening, the deck is thronged, but we lean over the railing and watch the changing loveliness with awed rapture – the greens and blues and crimsons mingling in the translucent waters and the high hills – for we are again in sight of land – lying darkly against the golden skies. How appropriate to the scene are Scott's lines. Surely here is a lake that

"In all her length far-winding lay
Of promontory, creek and bay,
And islands that empurpled bright
Floated amid the livelier light,
And mountains that like giants stand
To sentinel enchanted land."[20]

And as it grows darker and duskier, the stars begin to peep out in the rosy sky, and on every shadowy cape and island

"Springs into life a grim gigantic shape,
Holding its lantern o'er the restless surge

A new Prometheus chained upon the rock,
Still grasping in his hand the fire of Jove,"[21]

and now and then some vessel creeps past like a huge, noiseless shadow. The deck is almost deserted, and, as a gush of laughter and music comes up from below, we shiver and suddenly realize that all the fairy light is gone, and that the Lake Superior damps are beginning to play havoc with our poetic fancies; so we retreat.

Next day is as gloriously fine as ever. We get to the "Soo" about noon.[22] We are "locked in" while at dinner, so we miss that performance and when we go on deck again we find ourselves in the lock, close to Uncle Sam's territory, with the American part of pretty Sault Ste. Marie on one hand and on the other the rapids foaming restlessly between us and our Canada.

Everyone is on deck, our American friend included. Somebody asks if this is the American side of the Sault. "Of course it is," he says loftily, "you might know that by the fine houses. You'd never see a nice house or a pretty girl in Canada." "Must be some fine looking men in the States, if *he's* a specimen," murmurs a gentleman near us, *sotto voce*,[23] and we have the satisfaction of seeing that our critic evidently overhears it, for he gets very red and immediately finds something interesting in the other side of the boat.

We are three hours at the Sault and after the novelty wears away the delay is long and tedious. We all lean over the railing and chat in a desultory fashion over one thing or another. Our American friend has digested his humor and returns to his place. A United States officer attracts his eye. "Ah," he exclaims, exultantly, "it does me good to see a blue uniform like that again after those red jackets the Canadians wear. I detest them, don't you?" turning to us. We respond indignantly that indeed we don't but instead admire them very much. "Why," he says, "they are too *flashy* for anything. And besides," he adds, with the air of one advancing a crushing argument, "they are no good! They never did anything!"

"Oh, didn't they?" we murmur innocently, "well, of course, we may be wrong, but it seems to us that, when going to school, we remember learning in a history that those same red coats *did* beat somebody – but, of course, it couldn't have been blue coats – at Queenston Heights and Lundy Lane.[24] But maybe the historian was incorrect." "Why," he gasps, "are you Canadian?" "Of *course* we are," we declare proudly, "we wouldn't be anything else for the world." At this he gives another gasp and goes away in disgust at finding us so hopelessly depraved. But in justice, be it said, the other Americans on the boat are not like this. They are kind and pleasant, thorough ladies and gentlemen, and we have a very nice time all around. Finally we get away and steam slowly down the St. Marys River,[25] where the scenery is simply exquisite, past the maple clad shores, till we emerge upon Lake Huron. Another night on the boat and at noon next day we reach Owen Sound,[26] which presents a charming appearance from the water. We have just time to hurry off the boat and scramble on board the waiting train when off she goes! What a delightful ride it is! Really Ontario is *almost* as pretty as our own dear Island! We go at a dizzy rate past the smiling farms, pretty towns, beautiful groves and green woods, where an occasional early dyed maple hangs out its scarlet flag – on, on, on till at three we reach

Toronto. Beautiful Toronto! We are only there a few hours, but in that time we see quite enough to convince us that the Queen City is indeed the most beautiful one in Canada.[27]

But nine o'clock comes, and off we are again! All night we ride! It is fearfully dismal. Just as sure as we coax ourselves into a dreamy doze, along comes a conductor to demand our tickets or make us change cars until, when we finally alight at Ottawa in the chilly gray dawn, we feel more unamiable than ever we did in our lives.

We have heard so much of the depravity and corruption that reigns at Ottawa, that we hardly know what sort of a place we looked for. We expected something very disagreeable to say the least. Therefore we are quite surprised when we find that this much-slandered place is as pretty and peaceable a city as one would wish, even if it is not as beautiful or stately as others in Canada.

Of course the Parliament buildings are the centre of attraction here. So in the afternoon we go up to them and under the guidance of a kind old veteran senator,[28] we explore all their halls and windings. We are quite lost in the labyrinth of rooms and follow our guide blindly, wondering where in the world we are ever going to come out. The House is adjourned so we go through the commons and the senate chambers and the long halls hung with portraits of departed worthies. We sit a moment in the Governor General's chair and feel at least two inches taller after this, of course.[29] Then we explore the magnificent library and finally go into the Commons gallery and hear Sir Richard Cartwright speak on the census.[30] Then we go out and ramble around beautiful Parliament Square, see the trunk of a tree that was 150 years old when Columbus discovered America, catch a glimpse of the glistening white Chaudiere Falls[31] in the distance and, in open defiance of the rules, gather a tiny bouquet to carry away as a relic. Then in the evening we go again, and listen to a debate on the census and watch the brilliant scene below and around us. It is amusing to notice how, when someone is speaking, the members of the opposite side thin out to a meagre few to come back in redoubled force when one of their own party has the floor. We, in our innocence, supposed that nothing frivolous ever disgraced the members of the House of Commons. That they all sat in solemn conclave, or at least gave strict attention to all that was in progress. But alas! they don't! They laugh, talk, doze, and throw paper balls at each other on the sly, till the bullets fall about as thick as leaves in an autumn gale.

We are very insignificant ourselves in that crowded gallery! But, nevertheless, we feel a thrill of exultant pride as we hear it whispered behind us that the finest speaker in the House of Commons comes from little Prince Edward Island. We feel as if some of his glory must be reflected on his countrymen.

Doubtless, it is unpatriotic, – but we cannot find the census debate very interesting. We are stupid enough to get very sleepy even in that temple of our country's greatness (or weakness), so we finally come away just as some energetic politician begins to pulverize the argument of the previous speaker.

The next afternoon we bid good-bye to Ottawa and by night we are in Montreal – stately, brilliant Montreal – where we stay till morning. In leaving the city we cross the famous Victoria Bridge[32] – an experience not soon forgotten. How very long it seems. All is dense darkness save when, now and then, we pass a loophole and a flash of ghostly light flits down the car, and all hands breathe more freely when we are once more out in the clear sunlight. The ride from Montreal to Quebec is very uninteresting. There is little to be seen save some sterile stony little farms and what we had never thought to see in Canada, cutting grain with the primitive reaping hook. We catch a glimpse of the Montmorency Falls,[33] looking at that distance like a moveless white snowbank, and a few minutes after we reach Point Levis.[34] Opposite us, across the blue river, is "historic Quebec," and we get a peep at the Plains of Abraham, where long ago was fought the famous battle which decided the destiny of Canada.[35] It is dark when we reach Dalhousie,[36] and then a dreary ride through the long, cold night ensues. Morning finds us at Moncton,[37] where we improve a delay by inspecting the pretty little town, which is growing rapidly. At ten we leave and are at Point du Chene by noon where the dandy little *Northumberland* is waiting for us.[38] It is rather rough crossing over, but we do not mind that, and, as the fresh breeze comes dancing up the Strait, bringing the echo of the salt seas, we realize, with a happy thrill, that we are very near home. Somebody says, "see, there is Prince Edward Island," and we eagerly rush on deck to catch a glimpse of the old sod!

Yes; there it is – the long red line of cliffs, sloping to the green uplands with villages nestled here and there – dear P.E.I. at last! Never, Canada over, have we seen a lovelier, fairer spot than this! We feel like the old Scotch Islander in Winnipeg did. He said he was from "the Island!" What Island? queried a listener. "*What Island*," repeated our honest countryman, in amazement. "Why, Prince Edward Island, man? *What other Island is there?*"[39] Nearer and nearer we come till Summerside lies before us. Slowly we steam up beside the wharf, and then, amid the bustle and the noise, we descend the ladder, realizing that our long journey is over at last and our destination reached. And as our feet press the dear red soil once more we exclaim, with heart-felt delight:–

"This is my own, my native land."[40]
Cavendish, Oct. 22nd, 1891.

(1891)

The Usual Way

While a student at Prince of Wales College during the 1893–1894 academic year, some of her classmates launched, in February 1894, a short-lived monthly paper entitled *The College Record*, which "created quite a bit of excitement," as she stated in a retrospective article, published in 1927, about her Prince of Wales year.[1] Montgomery contributed four items in three months: the next three pieces in this volume as well as a poem, "The Last Prayer," about the final moments in the life of a soldier. This first contribution, a playlet about the thwarted attempts of two first-class "co-eds" to study for their classes, a piece that takes up almost one-quarter of the eight-page second issue, apparently elicited a compliment from her Latin instructor, Dr. Alexander Anderson (1836–1925), who was reported to have called the piece "very cleverly written." As she noted in her journal, "A compliment like that from the doc is worth having."[2] In an annotation to Montgomery's journal entry dated 5 September 1893, Mary Henley Rubio and Elizabeth Hillman Waterston note that "First Class students normally attended for two years, adding Greek and Trigonometry to advanced studies in basic courses: English, history, geography, arithmetic, French, chemistry, agriculture, school management, school laws, teaching, and music."[3] Montgomery was such a student, and moreover, she elected to complete two years of study in one, as would the adolescent Anne Shirley in *Anne of Green Gables*.

CHARACTERS: MILLICENT AND ROSE, TWO P.W.C. FIRST-class girls.

Time, 4 o'clock, p.m.

Place, Millicent's room at boarding-house. Millicent looking over some books. Enter Rose.

Millicent (effusively) – Oh, I'm so glad you've come at last. I was afraid something had prevented you. And I just *can't* study alone. I never get on well.

Rose (laying aside wraps) – Nor I; I think we always get on twice as well together. Do you know, I was just making up my mind, as I was coming down the street, that I would study awfully hard the rest of the term.

M. – Wasn't I just thinking the same thing! Now, just let's both resolve that from this out we'll study as hard as ever we can.

R. – I say so, too; and let's begin this very night.

M. – All right; but hold on a minute, Rose dear, I want to show you my new coat. I just got it home an hour ago. It's real pretty, I think. There it is. Now, how do you like it?

R. – O-o-o-o-h, Milly! isn't it just sweet. Hurry and put it on. I want to see how you look in it. (Millicent puts it on). Oh, it's awfully becoming. I believe I'll get mine something like it. Let me try it on, and see how I look in it. (Puts it on and surveys herself in the glass from all points of view). Who trimmed it, Milly?

M. – Mrs. Fluffandfeathers. She's fine.

R. – I'll get her to do mine. Just see how cute that little feather is. (They begin to examine the hat, discussing shape, ribbons, feathers, etc., till Millicent glances at clock).

M. (startled) – My patience, Rose, it's half-past four. I never dreamed we'd been so long. Let's get a wiggle on. (Shoves hat hastily into box).

R. – Goodness, yes! I've got to be home by six. Let's see, to-morrow's Friday and first lesson's Cicero.[4] Where's your Cicero, Milly?

M. (frantically turning the books over). Goodness, I don't know. It was here a minute ago. Where *do* things disappear to? Oh, here it is! Well, sit down. Where does the old thing begin?

R. – Chapter 8. Oh, say, don't you hate Cicero?

M. – I guess I do! It's horrid hard. If it wasn't for those notes at the back I never could make head or tail of it; and even then I'm stuck half the time.

R. – So'm I. I declare I don't feel one bit like trying to make it out to-night; my head is kind of aching.

M. – So's mine. Say, suppose we – (looks guiltily at Rose).

R. – I believe we might. 'Tisn't likely Dr. —— will ask us anyhow.

M. – Well, let it slide. But I must see if I know that horrid chapter off by heart. You hear me say it, Rose, and I'll hear you. (Rose takes book). "Quæres a nobis, Grati –"[5] (Rose drops book and dashes to the window).

R. – Oh, Milly, come quick! Amy Lee's just gone past, and she's got the prettiest sacque[6] on you ever saw. Just look.

M. – Oh, isn't it, though? Wherever did she get it? Doesn't she look nice in it?

R. – Lovely! Aren't the streets sloppy? I declare, I just hate to move out. There's a lot of people on the go to-day. (They stand at window some time longer, discussing passers-by).

M. (returning to table with a sigh) Well, let's begin again. I don't feel like any more Cicero. Will I hear you say it, Rose?

R. (yawning) – Never mind. I guess I know it, anyhow. Geometry comes next, doesn't it?

M. – Yes, it's the 16th prop. This old sixth book is more than I can see through.

R. – Same here. What's the enunciation?

M. (reading) – If four straight lines be proportional, the rectangle contained by the extremes is equal to the rectangle contained by the means; and if the rectangle contained by the extremes be equal to the rectangle contained by the means, the four straight lines are proportionals. (Disgustedly).[7] Who in the world could ever find any sense in that?

R. (despairingly) – I don't believe I'll *ever* be able to learn geometry, anyhow. I don't understand it.

M. – Do you think Prof. Shaw'd be likely to ask us, anyhow, to-morrow?[8]

R. – I don't believe he would. We're away at the back. Anyhow, if I learned it now, I'd forget it before to-morrow.

M. (tossing books away) – So would I. Well, here's Roman History. I like it just splendid.[9]

R. (enthusiastically) – So do I. And isn't Cæsar just glorious?[10] I could read about him forever and ever. The lesson to-morrow's about him being murdered, isn't it?

M. – Yes, it's awfully interesting. But those Roman names mix me all up. I never can tell one from the other. Will I read the lesson out loud?

R. – Yes, go on. Oh, here's some chocolates, Milly. I got them at Sweetman & Co's. They do have such nice candies there.

M. – Don't they, though. Thanks, awfully. I do love chocolates. (Begins to read and eat chocolates at same time, mixing up her words, skipping Roman names, and stopping in the midst of every sentence for a fresh bite. Lays down the book at end). Those chocolates are lovely, Rose.

R. – H'm. Say, do you think Dr. —— is going to give us a week's holidays at Easter?

M. – Oh, don't I hope he will. Wouldn't it be jolly?

R. – Have some more chocolates?

M. – Don't mind if I do. Thanks. Well, there's History disposed of; what's next?

R. – English Literature; but there's nothing to learn in that. Then there's only French left for to-morrow.

M. – Oh, I'm not going to bother myself about French when we're so near the end. I know how it's going to turn out now. It's been just splendid, hasn't it? But I'm real sorry for poor Eriphile now, aren't you?[11]

R. – Indeed I am. But Iphigenia's sweet. I haven't revised half that French. Don't know what I'm ever going to do when the exam. comes on. Well, we've got on pretty well at the studies to-day. And we've sometime yet. Let's look over a little hygiene. I like it.

M. – So do I, if it wasn't for the horrid pictures in it. They give me the creeps. Say, do you really believe we'd look like that if we were skinned?

R. – I suppose so. Here, let's see if we can answer the questions for next day. Here's a funny one: "Is there any good in sighing?" Well, *is* there any good?

M. – I'm sure I can't imagine, but if there is, I know a girl who ought to be healthy. She's the worst to sigh you ever heard. She was so nice, though. She and I used to be such great chums.

R. (rather jealously) – Not any greater than you and I are now, Milly.

M. – No, indeed. You are my dearest friend, you dear thing. (They get their arms around each other).

R. – After we leave college we'll have to write to each other every week.

M. – Indeed we will. Won't it be horrid to leave college. I love going to it so.

R. – So do I.

M. – Well: "If a person is plunged under water will it enter his lungs?"

R. – Well, he'll drown anyhow, if they keep him there long enough. Well, I guess I must be going for it's a quarter to six, and I want to run up to the Bazaar before tea. Haven't we had a real nice spell studying? You'd better come up with me for a walk, Milly.

M. (weakly) – I ought to work some algebra.

R. – Never mind it. Algebra can wait.

M. – I believe I'll go. I feel sleepy, anyhow. I do think when we're studying so hard we ought to take more exercise than we do. (Puts on wraps). Are you ready? Isn't it nice to think all our lessons are learned, and we're free to enjoy ourselves.

(Exit both girls.)

(1894)

Extracts from the Diary of a Second Class Mouse

In this next piece from *The College Record*, published in the April 1894 issue,[1] Montgomery relies on the life writing and point of view of a "second class" mouse to satirize the "ins and outs of life" at Prince of Wales College. Unlike the First Class students depicted in "The Usual Way," according to Rubio and Waterston, "Second Class students took the basic courses plus algebra, geometry, physics, Latin, and scientific temperance."[2]

JAN. 9TH, 1894. – FROM THE GENERAL COMMOTION THIS morning I concluded the students must have returned, and, on creeping out from behind the wall of the Normal,[3] I found my conjecture correct. I am glad; holidays are poor times for college mice! there are never any bits of paper or crumbs around the floor then. All are swept and garnished. I have grown quite lean during vacation.

Feb. 15th. – I thought I would go over to the college to-day and see my friend, the First-Class Mouse. I performed the journey in safety and was making my way along behind the wainscotting in Prof. C——'s room[4] when I was suddenly arrested by the most unearthly noise I ever heard in my life. I cannot describe it. At first I was motionless from horror, and, on recovering the use of my limbs, I fled for my life. Oh! but wasn't I terrified! but my friend, the First Class Mouse, laughed at me and said it was only the English class yelling and hammering on their desks. I wonder if that is the way to study English. There are some things about this college I cannot understand. I always knew even from my small experience that boys are dreadful creatures to make a noise. Next to cats they are my particular aversion. But I did not think even they could have produced such sounds as those which alarmed me.

Feb. 29th.[5] – I cannot decide which are of most service to mice – the college boys, or the college girls. The boys never bring lunches, so when I find nice crumbs on the floor I know whom to thank. But then it is the boys who tear up and scatter around so many nice little bits of paper, which are so convenient when I want to make a nest. Still, as mice cannot exist solely on paper, I think after all the girls are our best friends, even if they do scream terribly and hop on the chairs if a mouse ventures to poke his poor nose out near them.

Mar. 8th. – This has been a great day in the annals of Mousedom. I was taking a nap in my nest when I was aroused by a disturbance, louder than usual. I peered out but could only see the air darkened by a cloud of something, I knew not what. As usual in my perplexities, I went to my friend, the First-Class Mouse, whose experience is very useful to me. He was a Second-Class Mouse himself last year, and so is well informed as to their customs. He told me not to be alarmed as it was only the First-Class crowd having a pea-nut party during Chemistry hour. He said they would have a lot of pea-nuts, which they would crack and eat, and then throw the shells at each other, this last being the cream of the performance.[6]

After all this was over we hurried in to explore the premises before the janitor swept them up. That floor was a caution to any mouse. Every inch was covered with shells. We found a lot of nut-meats that had been dropped, some generous slices of carrot, a lot of white beans, and a piece of smoked herring by way of a relish. I assure you we feasted royally. I hope they will have another pea-nut party soon, but my friend the First-Class Mouse said it was not probable, as the professor did not encourage that sort of thing.

Mar. 22nd. – I ventured out this evening in search of something to eat and found a lot of apple smushed over the floor, desks, and walls of the Normal. Of course I went for my friend the First-Class Mouse to share the treat. He said he supposed the Second Class had been at their old tricks again, firing rotten apples around. If they meant to leave them for me to eat, I am very much obliged, but I do not admire their taste in ornamenting the walls with them. This Normal is a queer old place. The desks look as if mice had been nibbling at them for centuries. It seems that we mice are not the only creatures fond of mincing things up.

Well, I suppose next year I will be a First-Class Mouse myself, and thus able to teach some other poor little Second-Class fellow of '95 the ins and outs of life behind these classic walls.

(1894)

High School Life in Saskatchewan

In this final piece published in *The College Record*, in May 1894, Montgomery reminisces about her experience as a high school student in Prince Albert, now the third-largest city in Saskatchewan, in 1890–1891. Given how negative her experience had been (at least according to her journals), she was careful in this piece not to identify her teacher, her classmates, the town, or the school year she attended there. Her selective account draws a good deal on a journal entry dated 19 September 1890, but it omits a number of details, including her initial liking of the school and her ambition to get a teacher's certificate; her spotty attendance record, particularly after the birth of her half-brother Bruce; and the fact that her teacher, John Mustard, whom she and her friends considered "a ninny and a bore," eventually proposed marriage. Her memory of those years was fading fast: reminiscing about her Prince Albert classmates in a journal entry dated less than two years after the publication of this piece, she confessed that "I have half forgotten their very names."[1]

IT DID NOT IN THE LEAST RESEMBLE OUR LIFE AT PRINCE of Wales. Nothing could be more dissimilar. The building itself was about as large as our college, but only one of its rooms – an apartment about half as large as Prof. Caven's room – was devoted to the use of the High School students, of which there were about sixteen. The remaining rooms served a variety of uses. The one above ours was the public ball-room, and on the occasion of a ball, our room was utilized as a ladies dressing room. On the next morning we would find numerous hair-pins, feathers, flowers etc., strewn over the floor, with very probably, a hand-mirror or two! On the other side of the big hall was The Council room and above it the Free Masons Hall. Beside these, in the back of the building were the patrol quarters where two or three red coated Mounted Policemen were always stationed to patrol the town.[2] When they arrested a drunken man they brought him in there, taking him through the hall outside our room, where very often there would be a lively scuffle and language strong enough to stand alone. Finally they would lock him up in one of the small, dark cells, a row of which ran directly back of our room. I remember venturing too rashly into an empty cell, one day, out of curiosity, and of being locked in by a Policeman, who did not know I was in it. There I had to stay, too, for a mortal hour, till he returned and the teacher told him of my whereabouts. I did not go exploring again in a hurry.

We had but one teacher and he was a firm believer in Solomon's doctrine.[3] He had a violent temper, and, as many of the High School boys had a fair share of the red man's nature,[4] we occasionally had lively times. The master, when thrashing anyone, used a murderous-looking "raw-hide" whip, as long as himself, and if the victim broke free and assumed the defensive and offensive with a stick of firewood, the thing got quite sensational, especially if, as usual, he had locked the door before beginning operations.

He could not punish the girls in this manner, but he would keep us in an hour or so after time, and give us terribly long compound interest sums to work. But, if I remember aright, very few were ever worked.

Our amusements were limited. At dinner time and recess the boys played football, while we girls (there were only two of us) wandered around the dusty old place, or sat on the balcony and watched the game. The school was beautifully situated on a hill outside of the town. The noble river[5] rolled its blue tides before it, past the mighty dark pine forests of the north land on one side, and the willow-clad banks on the other. Away to our back extended undulating sweeps of prairie, pink and golden, with roses and sheets of prairie sunflowers, and dotted with groves of slender white-skinned poplars. Or perhaps we watched the passers-by on the road beneath us – Indians for the most part, "braves" with their dirty blankets over their shoulders, or chattering dark-eyed squaws, with their glossy, blue-black hair, and probably a small-faced papoose strapped to their backs.

As for our studies, they were simply nowhere! We had a list of them as long as the Moral Law,[6] but I cannot recall ever having opened a book out of school. The work was allowed to drift along as it liked. Learning anything did not seem to be expected at all. I remember of having but one exam – in Latin – and the results of it were never known. We never heard anything more of our papers after they were given in.

I do not know what makes the memory of those times so pleasant. We did not learn anything, and they were very dull and stupid, but for all that it will be long ere I forget my High School days on the broad, fertile, wind-swept prairies of the far Northwest – the "Great Lone Land."[7]

(1894)

Valedictory

JAMES H. STEVENSON

At the end of Montgomery's year at P.W.C., the valedictory was read by New Glasgow native James H. Stevenson, who had been named "the best scholar in the school" by the Charlottetown *Daily Examiner* and who had received the Governor General's Silver Medal and ranked first in nearly every third-year subject, including Latin, Greek, algebra, geometry, English literature, and French.[1] Stevenson – whom Montgomery referred to as "Jim," "Jamie," and "Jimmy" in her journals – had shared a boarding house with her since the end of April that year and, faced with the prospect of giving the valedictory, had turned to the budding writer for help. "He wants me to write it for him," Montgomery recorded in her journal with exasperation, "simply because he is too lazy to do it himself." Her prediction upon completing it that "Jim will have the *kudos* of it and I the grind" proved to be only too true: when the *Island Guardian and Christian Chronicle* of Charlottetown reported on the convocation the following week, the unsigned article stated that "the valedictory by Mr. J.H. Stevenson[] began as most of its predecessors doubtless have done, by uttering the lament of the parting class. But before it finished, it made practical suggestions and expressed other thoughts of such value as won the praise of the principal of the P. of W. and the Premier of the Province."[2] The *Daily Examiner* ran the full text of the valedictory as part of its extensive coverage of the convocation ceremony.

ANOTHER YEAR IN THE ANNALS OF PRINCE OF WALES has rolled by, and once again its students assemble here to welcome with pleasure those who have so kindly come to witness our commencement exercises. This is an hour when joy and happiness and kindly feeling should pervade every heart, when every petty annoyance or disappointment of the past year should be forgotten, and everyone clasp hands in friendly affection, for to-night many of us must part to meet no more as fellow-students and class-mates. Some in higher colleges will steadily strive to reach that far-off, shining goal, where fame holds out her laurel crown, while some will bid farewell to college life to-night and plunge at once into the busy world's arena, there to wrest from the hands of Fate the influence and fortune ever to be won by industry and perseverance. But whatever path we may pursue, whatever pleasures await us in after life, no memory will be so dear to our hearts as that of our college course. A tie of common fellowship will forever bind those who have wandered together through classic mazes or wrestled with mathematical mysteries at Prince of Wales College.

A larger number of students than ever before has attended our college this season,[3] and lack of accommodation has been the greatest drawback to satisfactory work. It is earnestly to be hoped that the powers that be will see fit at no distant date to provide us with a more commodious building. But notwithstanding this the past year has been one of steady progress – all the various branches of the curriculum have been well sustained and drawing has been added under the able instruction of Prof. Shaw. But the year has not been one of wholly unrelieved toil. Pleasant and we also hope profitable recreation was afforded by the debating society, where our budding orators displayed their powers, and by the football contests where strength and activity of body as well as mind were promoted. A new departure has been witnessed by the publication of a monthly paper by some enterprising students.[4] This bright little periodical is devoted to the interests of the college and has formed a pleasurable feature in the history of the year.

And as regards our professors, what can we say but what has been said again and again by students who have gone out from this, our college, encouraged and strengthened by their hearty assistance and sympathy? None of us will ever forget the instruction and advice of our energetic and esteemed Principal, Dr. Anderson. The recollection of Professor Caven's genial humor will ever bring a smile to our faces and a kindly remembrance to our hearts.

Professor Harcourt, our teacher of science, has interested all and opened to our view many of the wonders of the natural world. Professors Shaw and Robertson have taken the chairs formerly occupied by Professors Robinson and West. It is superfluous to speak of the splendid work they have accomplished in their various departments, suffice it to say that deserved success has crowned their efforts. Among the athletes of the college, Prof. Shaw will be gratefully remembered for the interest he has displayed in their sports. Professors Miller and Arsenault have officiated in their several branches to the satisfaction of the students and all concerned. Owing to Mr. Lloyd's departure from the Province, we had no instructor in music until late in the term, when Prof. Earle commenced an enthusiastic and successful course of instruction, and the hours spent with him have been enjoyed and will long be remembered by us all. We take this opportunity of extending our heartiest thanks to our friends in Charlottetown who have done so much to render our sojourn among them pleasant.

And now dear fellow students we turn to each other for a last farewell. Let each and all take this as a sacred trust through life – to keep the reputation of our Alma Mater unsullied, to reflect honor on the teachers to whom we owe so much, and to help each other and our fellow men to higher planes of thought and action. Let us take the simple yet sublime motto of our college as our own – "*Ich Dien* – I serve,"[5] and let us serve, not ignoble ends, petty factions and the darker passions of human nature, but rather acknowledge as our masters only the noblest thoughts and motives, the highest aspirations and the kindliest feelings between man and man. Such a servitude would be glorious indeed. Once more friends, professors, classmates, we bid you all farewell, and yet to the end of time we will be fellow students, for what is the world but one great college where we must all learn the deepest lessons of human life. Let us then

"Go forth prepared in every clime
To love and help each other,
And know that they who counsel strife
Would bid us smite a brother."[6]

(1894)

"Portia" – A Study

Miss Montgomery's Essay at the P. of W. Convocation

LUCY MAUD MONTGOMERY

Besides ghostwriting the valedictory speech for "Jim" Stevenson, Montgomery read at her graduation ceremony one of two essays on Shakespeare's play *The Merchant of Venice*, presumably as a result of receiving the top score in her second-year "English, 'The Merchant of Venice,' &c." and English literature courses.[1] While the *Daily Examiner* gave the essay lukewarm praise ("well written and clearly and distinctly read"), the *Island Guardian and Christian Chronicle* pronounced it "the *piece de resistance* of the evening," "a character-sketch such as might have come from George Eliott [*sic*] in her 'teens. It was not only a subtle, analytical study; it was a literary gem." Praising the essay's "phrases of almost perfect art," the article concluded that "to say that Miss Montgomery in this analysis did justice to Portia's intellectual worth may seem a strong statement and undue praise, but it is simple truth." According to Montgomery's journal, she "felt pleasantly tickled" over this praise for her work.[2] The essay was published in the *Island Guardian and Christian Chronicle* and in slightly different form in the *Daily Patriot* and the *Daily Examiner*.

OF ALL SHAKESPEARE'S MANY DELIGHTFUL PLAYS SURELY the *Merchant of Venice* is the most delightful. The scenes of this charming comedy are for the most part laid in that fairy city of romance, Venice, the queen of the Adriatic; and some of its characters are ranked among the great dramatist's master pieces. Of these characters, Portia the beautiful heroine is, perhaps, the one who appeals most strongly to our sympathies, and, from first to last, fascinates us by her beauty, grace and intellect.

There are three female characters in this play, all perfect portraits after their mind, but there is a great difference in the kind. Jessica, the pretty, dark-eyed Jewess, is indeed, piquant and sprightly, but too heartless and deceitful to win our love; and Nerissa, the confidential waiting maid has all of an indulged servant's garrulity in her sharp tongue. But who will find a fault with Portia – this stately, graceful heiress of a long-past age? An age far removed from us now, in customs and in manners as in time and yet here brought vividly near to us in these pictured passions of the human heart, which is the same to-day as it was when Venice was in her glory's prime.

And yet Portia is not absolutely without a flaw, – a little touch of human frailty now and then endears her still more to our hearts. For one thing, she is somewhat sarcastic and does not at all spare the weaknesses of the suitors, whom her golden tresses, and no less, her golden ducats, have brought to her feet. When we first see her in the play, she is gaily discussing with Nerissa the faults and virtues of her unfortunate admirers, with a sportive carelessness which tells us that her heart is as yet untouched. But withal, her sparkling wit is without malice or bitterness – it is merely that of a light-hearted, joyous girl, with no cares to trouble her, except, perhaps, those same lovers whom she may neither accept nor refuse, being bound by the terms of her father's will, to marry whoever chooses from three caskets the one containing her picture.

But Portia, though quick to see their foibles, is never anything but perfectly considerate and thoughtful of them. In her interviews with her princely suitors we are always impressed by her delicate tact and graceful courtesy. Affection for any she never simulates – there is no affectation of an interest she does not feel, but never, by word or look, does she wound the feelings or hurt the vanity of any aspirant for her hand. And even if after they fail in their choice and depart, she expresses her relief in some laughing jest with Nerissa, who shall blame her?

But still in time to Portia comes the true fairy prince – he who, alone of all others, has the power to awaken in her heart a woman's tenderest love. No titled lover he, with princely retinue or haughty lineage.[3] Only a handsome young Venetian, with no fortune and nothing save his noble birth, courtly manners and manly spirit to recommend him. But Portia's wayward heart has found its master, and her speech to Bassanio in the casket scene is a marvel of mingled maidenly delicacy and womanly love. Our hearts thrill with sympathetic joy when Bassanio chooses the right casket and wins both the picture and the beautiful original.

But over their bridal happiness comes a sudden chill – ill tidings for Bassanio. Antonio, his dearest friend, is in danger, and his presence is requested at once. Portia nobly rises to meet the occasion. With gentle firmness she tells Bassanio that he must go at once – with no word or look does she seek to keep him by her side, when duty calls him away. With true thoughtfulness, she conceals her own sorrow at the parting and strives to encourage him with her hopeful assurance and sympathy.

Then comes the grand climax of the play – the famous trial scene where all the tragic issues find their centre. And here we see Portia in a new light. We have beheld and loved her as the happy maiden, the loving woman and the gentle bride, now she claims our admiration as the possessor of a magnificent intellect. The friend to whom her husband owes most is in danger of his life at the hands of relentless Shylock. All efforts to save him have been fruitless. Never was woman's quick wit more sorely needed and never did it come more promptly to the rescue.[4] Disguised as a doctor of laws, Portia enters the court. Her pleading for mercy is unrivalled – grandly eloquent, tenderly sublime. And when it is of no avail, her subtle logic and keen judgment succeed where all the learned heads in Venice have failed, and Antonio is saved.[5]

Then comes the last beautiful scene, where, in the moonlit gardens of her home, Portia welcomes back her husband.[6] A charming picture she presents in truth, this sweet bride of long ago, than whom no nineteenth century maiden can find a higher ideal of womanhood to emulate.

And as we turn away from the fairy scene of light and music with which the play concludes, we feel that Bassanio has indeed, won for his bride a woman worthy of his love. For as long as the English language is spoken or read, as long as genius is admired and womanly sweetness praised, the character of Portia will be regarded as one of the truest, noblest, fairest creations of Shakespeare's master genius.

(1894)

"Which Has the Most Patience under the Ordinary Cares and Trials of Life – Man or Woman?"

BELINDA BLUEGRASS/ENID

In February 1896, in the midst of her year as an undergraduate student at Dalhousie University, Montgomery reported in her journal that she had won the top prize of five dollars in a contest sponsored by the Halifax *Evening Mail* for a letter answering this question: "Which Has the Most Patience under the Ordinary Cares and Trials of Life – Man or Woman?"[1] After hearing through the grapevine that her submission signed "Enid" could not be considered for the prize because it did not put forth an argument, she made a second submission as "Belinda Bluegrass."[2]

All entries were submitted evidently using pseudonyms to ensure anonymity – which was just as well, because the judge for the contest, Archibald MacMechan (1862–1933), happened to be Montgomery's English literature instructor. As MacMechan reported in a letter also printed in the *Evening Mail*, "After careful consideration, it seems to me that the verses signed 'Belinda Bluegrass' are the best expression of what I personally believe to be the truth. They show thought as well as point and vivacity. The second place I would assign to the verses of 'Eve.' The prose letter signed 'Enid' also deserves honorable mention, on account of the sentiment expressed and the care taken in the composition." In fact, it was because of MacMechan's enthusiasm for the work of "Eve" that the *Mail* added a second-place prize of two dollars. It is worth noting, however, that while MacMechan described both of Montgomery's submissions in some detail, he said nothing about the second-prize winner, whose work was not signed "Eve" at all but "Lilith" and whose views are remarkably similar to ones Montgomery would express in a 1909 letter to Ephraim Weber: "If woman has really more patience than man, it is, I believe, because her capacity for patience, at first no greater than his, is more developed by the circumstances of her life ... I think the impartial decision must be that man, *in his own sphere*, is as patient as woman in hers."[3]

Montgomery also pasted into her scrapbook an undated and unidentified clipping entitled "Personals" that suggested that the identity of the prize winners did not stay secret for long: "Miss Montgomery won the prize offered by the *Evening Mail* for the best letter on 'Which has the more patience; man or woman?' Fame cleaveth unto 'they of Dalhousie.'" MacMechan, whom Montgomery categorized in an 1895 journal entry as "rather a weak man," would later pan Montgomery's work in his book *The Headwaters of Canadian Literature* (1924).[4]

As my letter must be brief,
I'll at once state my belief.
And this it is – that, since the world began,
And Adam first did say,
"'Twas Eve led me astray,"[5]
A woman hath more patience than a man.

If a man's obliged to wait
For some one who's rather late,
No mortal ever got in such a stew,
And if something can't be found
That he's sure should be around,[6]
The listening air sometimes grows fairly blue.

Just watch a man who tries
To soothe a baby's cries,
Or put a stove pipe up in weather cold,
Into what a state he'll get;
How he'll fuss and fume and fret
And stamp and bluster round and storm and scold!

Some point to Job with pride,
As an argument for their side![7]
Why, it was so rare a patient man to see,
That when one was really found,[8]
His discoverers were bound
To preserve for him a place in history!

And while I admit it's true
That man has *some* patience too,
And that woman isn't *always* sweetly calm,
Still I think all must agree
On this central fact – that she
For general all-round patience bears the palm.

BELINDA BLUEGRASS

IT WAS THE DAY WHEN ALL THE GUARDIAN ANGELS CAME to the Benign Giver to ask a boon for each several charge. One by one they came, in bright procession, and departed rejoicing; but one stood apart with drooping wings and veiled face.

Last of all he, too, approached the Giver and knelt in reverence before Him.

"Oh, Benign Giver," murmured the sorrowing spirit, "I am woman's guardian angel, nor know I what boon to crave for her who needeth all. From cradle to grave her path is through sorrow and pain and self-sacrifice. She brings man's children forth in agony, she rears them in anxiety, she gives them up to the world in bitterness and anguish of heart. Daily she is beset with unnumbered trials. Grant then, most Benign Giver, some boon to compensate and strengthen."

He ceased. All heaven was hushed. Through the silence sounded the Giver's voice. "Sad spirit," He said, tenderly, "take from My hand this most precious boon for woman, this boon bestowed on none other of My creatures – the gift of long-suffering, all-forgiving, divine patience."

Then the guardian angel unveiled his face and passed from the shining multitude with joy on his radiant brow.

ENID

(1896)

Crooked Answers

L.M.M.

In November 1896, Montgomery recorded in her journal that she had received a letter from her second cousin Edwin Simpson (1872–1955), asking if she would like to correspond with him. Montgomery had mentioned Simpson in passing in her journal on a few occasions prior to this – she ended up taking over his school in Belmont during the 1896–1897 academic year while he attended Prince of Wales College in Charlottetown – but he would play an increasing role in this record of her life after she reluctantly accepted his marriage proposal in June 1897 (despite the growing physical repulsion she felt for him) and then spent the better part of a year trying to extricate herself from that promise.[1] Although during this period Montgomery mentioned in her journal the publication of several short stories and poems in North American periodicals, absent from this record of her life and her career is any mention of the publication in the spring of 1896 (while she was studying at Dalhousie University in Halifax) of two sketches in *The Prince of Wales College Observer*, a follow-up student publication to *The College Record* – on whose masthead Edwin Simpson leads as "Manager."[2] The extent to which this piece or the two that follow are autobiographical is impossible to ascertain, given that Montgomery rarely went into details in her journal about her actual experience teaching; that said, the form of the personal essay makes these pieces seem like fact rather than fiction. Several of these "crooked answers" would appear again in "Half an Hour with Canadian Mothers" later in this volume and in "Facts and Fancies," chapter 11 of *Anne of Avonlea*.

WHEN, ABOUT A YEAR AND A HALF AGO, I LEFT P.W.C., the proud possessor of a first-class license, I had some ideas about school teaching, which experience has rubbed out of my mind. For one thing I did not believe that the amazing answers of pupils one sometimes reads in the funny columns of papers, ever did or could have any foundation in fact. But a year's experience as a teacher in a country school soon convinced me to the contrary.

All the crooked answers to be recorded below I can vouch for as genuine, and too hopelessly original ever to be forgotten.[3]

One boy in the primer class was noted for his startling answers. It was very hard on my nerves at first; after some time I got used to it. The first day I took him in hand I asked him what the sheep gave us, having first carefully led the subject up to the expected answer, "wool." He looked up cheerfully.

"Lambs," he piped confidently, and I collapsed. Well, he was certainly right. Nobody could deny that, though it wasn't just what I expected. It was the same boy who, being asked to spell "catch," in the presence of a certain critical visitor,[4] shouted out with all the energy of conscious correctness, "S-n-o-w-catch!"

But it was another lad who tried to spell "speckled" one day, and couldn't manage it.

"Well," he said, after many futile efforts, "I can't spell it, but I know what it means."

"Well, what," I asked with all the unsuspecting rashness of an inexperienced schoolma'am.

"Tom Jones' face," he said with a guileless look at the aforesaid Tom, whose freckles were famous in the school. Tom took it out of him at recess though; and I was careful of calling for impromptu meanings after that.

It was not only in the lower grades such answers were given. The fourth class pupils were especially noted for their *bon mots*.[5] I shall never forget one boy's definition of "ecclesiastic." He spelled the word correctly, and then announced triumphantly that it meant "a tremendous teacher." I have sometimes thought that he got "religious" and "tremendous" mixed up, but it is a subject that does not respond to speculation. It was another fourth-class boy who said that a glacier was "a man who put in window frames."

In history that class generally surpassed themselves. It was certainly startling to hear that Thomas a Becket was "canonized as a *snake*;"[6] and it gave my faith a sad blow to discover that "William Tyndale *wrote* the New Testament."[7]

In one examination paper I recollect a particularly striking answer to the question, "What did Charles do after the battle of Dunbar?" The answer, "He ran away and went up a tree," was written in perfect good faith, mind you, and I dare say that pupil has been wondering ever since why she didn't get full marks for that question.[8]

In geography the discoveries they made were amazing. I found out that "the Suez canal connected Nova Scotia and New Brunswick,"[9] and that "the Isthmus of Panama joined South America and Greenland."[10] One patriotic boy said that the "Atlantic Ocean was *in* P.E. Island." In definitions they were equally felicitous. One boy said that a *cape* "was a portion of land that had caved in," and a girl, after much serious thought on the subject, announced that a continent was "a piece of water with some land in it." It was the same girl who solemnly assured me that there were 365 days in a month!

When I sat down to correct their compositions I generally had a treat. How deliciously original some of them were! One boy, I remember, took "Courting" as an optional subject, and with all the wisdom of twelve years, declared in his opening paragraph that "courting is a very pleasant thing, which a great many people go too far with." That composition bore evidence of deep and searching thought.

Another boy – the one who gave "crab-apple" as a noun, which was the name of an animal – started out to write a composition on "Birds." His first sentence was "Our cat catches birds." From that he branched out and gave me the history, character, habits and accomplishments, not only of his own particular and individual cat, but of every other feline in the neighborhood. But not another word did he say about "birds."[11]

The invariable closing sentence of most of those compositions will serve admirably to conclude this article:

"This is all I can think of, and so no more at present from

L.M.M."[12]

(1896)

The Bad Boy of Blanktown School

L.M.M.

Written in close proximity to "Crooked Answers," this sketch likewise takes teaching as its subject, although once again, it is difficult to ascertain to what extent the piece is autobiographical. In a journal entry dated 18 September 1894, Montgomery mentioned welcoming two new students to her class, including "George Howells, the traditional 'bad boy' of the district," whose grandfather had "served a life sentence in prison for shooting another man," but there is no further mention of him in that record.[1] In this sketch, she anonymized the name of her school and omitted its location; but while she introduced her subject as "George" within quotation marks, implying that she had changed his name to protect his identity, the mention of a student named George Howells in her journals indicates that she had not actually done so. This piece appeared in *The Dalhousie Gazette*, Dalhousie's student newspaper (which is still published today), in March 1896, toward the end of Montgomery's sojourn as a student at that institution. George anticipates "bad boy" Anthony Pye in *Anne of Avonlea*, except that Montgomery does not have the success Anne has in reforming him.

His shadow darkened over my path on the very first day on which I was installed as mistress of Blanktown school. The trustees said that the children were pretty easy to manage, but solemnly warned me that I would have serious trouble with "George." They added that I might depend on them to back me in any emergency that might arise in my dealings with that obstreperous youth.

For the next two months, though George did not materialize, I heard enough about him to drive any teacher, just entering on professional life, to the verge of insanity. Not a day passed but some of George's characteristics were impressed upon me. In the first place, he was reputed to be "not all there." There was something terrible in the vagueness of this; and I never could see the point because, when I did fall in with George, I rather thought there was a little too much of him there for my peace of mind. George's grandfather had killed a man; George's father had a most unsavory reputation; and George would appear to have inherited all the shining virtues of his ancestors, with a few of his own thrown in. I was informed that he had been expelled from the school regularly once a year, since his A, B, C days, after many desperate conflicts with the reigning pedagogue, and that he was a thief, liar, braggart and bully, all in one. In short, so far as I could discover, George's mission in life seemed to be to keep school teachers in perpetual remembrance of the fact that earth is not their home. George evidently did not shine in the haunts of civilized life, for weeks passed by and I saw him not. I had almost begun to think that George was some mythical bugbear for frightening inexperienced schoolma'ms, when, one gloomy November day, he came.

I was trying to impress on a five-year-old the ancient and immemorial fact that "the cat caught the mouse," when the door was thrown violently open, and a tall, loose-jointed, raw-boned lad strode into the room, slammed his books on a desk, and flung himself into a seat with an expression that said, "Here I am, and there you are. Which of us is going to come off best?"

I have always been proud of the fact that I kept calm at this trying crisis. I disposed of my small student leisurely, and then sailed down the aisle to interview George, who awaited me with an appalling grin. George's physiognomy was not exactly prepossessing, but it had the merit of uniqueness. Nobody ever looked quite like George. Freckles! You never saw so many large, well-developed, healthy-looking freckles on any one face in your life. His eyes could look three ways at once, his hair stood straight up on end in aggressive defiance, and as for his mouth – you could have cut mouths for a dozen boys from it and still have a good piece left over. He generally went about with it wide open; it was hard on your nerves till you got used to it. Once in a while he would remember and shut it. If, through the hum of the schoolroom, came now and then a sharp, sudden snap, suggestive of a rat-trap going off, everybody knew it was George closing his mouth, and didn't stop to investigate. George's voice, however, was his main attraction. It was of great compass, was cracked in three distinct places, and regularly fell all to pieces at the end of every sentence, when he was reading.

I thought I had been sufficiently warned about George, but ere long I discovered that the half had not been told me. When George entered one door of Blanktown school, peace and order and law fled out of the other. George's most striking peculiarity was a passionate love of fighting. George considered that day wasted on which he didn't have a good, solid, all-round, impartial fight. Not long after his arrival, I entered the schoolroom one morning to find George and another boy in a furious tussle on the floor. The other boys stood around in glee, and the girls were shrieking on the tops of their desks. As nobody paid the least attention to my questions or commands, my only resource was to fly at the cloud of dust and drag the combatants apart by their coat-collars. While I lectured the first, George wriggled from my grasp, and at roll-call I missed him. I appointed a deputy to govern in my absence, and went in search of him. I found him sulking in a corner of the porch.

Now, I was really very sorry for George. He had had no chances, and his training had been sadly deficient. I was honestly desirous of reforming him. In how many hundreds of Sunday-school books had I not read how bad boys, influenced by their teachers, turned from their evil ways, and grew up to be governors and bank-presidents, and a credit to their country generally. So I talked to George just beautifully – you'd be surprised. I didn't altogether expect him to burst into penitential tears, and develop into a wingless angel on the spot, but I didn't see how he could help being impressed. I never was more surprised in my life than when George, having heard me through, looked me squarely in the face and remarked, "You are a confounded fool," in a tone of infinite contempt!

Polite, wasn't it? Encouraging, too! I went back to the schoolroom a sadder and a wiser girl; I thought there must be something astray in the logic of Sunday-school books. Since moral suasion had so poor an effect on George, I thought the birch might bring the argument more forcibly home to him, though I hated to think of using it. So a few days afterwards when he had thrown a smelt[2] at one of the girls, I called him up to my desk and said, "Hold out your hand," in a very terrible tone of voice, that quite concealed my inward quaking. I didn't expect to be obeyed. In fact I rather expected to be instantly annihilated. It was the second great surprise of my life when George quietly held out his dirty paw and took his punishment without a word. Then he went home, and for a month we saw no more of him. I fondly hoped he had gone for good.

But, alas! just as the remembrance of his misconduct had begun to fade away like a bad dream, George returned, as cheerful and irrepressible as ever, and in a mood that reminded me of the man in the Scripture, whose house had been swept and garnished.[3] From that out George's record was phenomenal. He really surpassed himself. Our mutual conflicts became so common that the pupils hardly stopped their work to look on. George's sole merit was punctuality – he never missed a day – and you may well believe I almost regarded it as an additional vice.

Finally, matters reached a climax, just in time to save my reason. One morning, I took upon myself, without consulting George, to change the seats of the fourth class further front. When he came in, rather late, he emphatically informed me that he didn't approve of this arrangement. We had a sharp argument, my patience suddenly gave way, and I curtly informed him that I would see the trustees at once, and have him expelled from the school again.

George's dignity was mortally offended. He snatched his cap, knocked over a bench, shied his slate at an inoffensive pupil who was wrestling with decimals in a remote corner, kicked over a pile of wood by the stove, and shook the dust of that unhallowed place from his feet, never to return to it while I was teacher in Blanktown school! He was a very peculiar youth – that George.

(1896)

James Henry, Truant

L.

In this sketch, published in *The Prince of Wales College Observer* a month after "Crooked Answers," Montgomery draws once again on her teaching experiences to tell a story of yet another troublemaking boy. But while both this piece and "Crooked Answers" focus on teaching and were published in two issues in a row, each appears with its own byline – "L.M.M." in the first piece, "L." in this one – both designed presumably to protect her anonymity.

IT WAS CHRONIC WITH HIM, SO THEY SAID,[1] BORN IN HIM and incurable, but you would never have thought it to look at him. He had the most guileless, open countenance you could possibly imagine; his big, pale blue eyes could look you squarely in the face with an expression of utter innocence; his uneven whitish hair had not one lawless kink or curl in it. He had a most engaging smile, and altogether a stranger would certainly have taken him for the model boy of the school; appearances were never more illusive than in the case of James Henry. James Henry had reduced the practice of mischief to a fine art, but he particularly excelled in playing truant. It was an everyday performance with him, and there was a legend current in the educational circles of Blanktown that on the very first day that James Henry, with a brand new jacket and primer, and a clean face for once in his life, had been sent to school, he had – accidently, of course – dropped his primer over the bridge and spent the day, meditating upon his loss, in the woods. Since then, if ever a week had passed in which James Henry had not played truant, the teacher I was assured, always chalked it carefully up, that he who ran might read and remember the unusual occurrence.

Very small inducements were sufficient to allure James Henry from the path of duty. A good chance to go trouting, a rumor of ripe raspberries over at Sandy Plains, an opportunity to go bird-nesting or steal a ride to the station, or even the mere fact that the day was warm and the water in the creek just right for swimming – let any of these come in his way and we saw nothing of James Henry in school that day, trying to borrow a slate pencil or driving live crickets, harnessed to strings up and down the aisle when my back was turned, or trying to trade a sour apple for a chew of gum.

When James Henry answered "Present," at morning roll-call it generally took me till recess to recover from my surprise. If he did not, however, there was nothing to do but wait till he came shambling in at noon, with his innocent smile and bland blue eyes, as if he had not his pockets stored with imprisoned crickets at that very moment. No punishment ever had any effect on James Henry. He took it, as he took everything else, with a cheerful resignation, and an apologetic smile that seemed to ask pardon for the trouble he was giving you.

One day in August was particularly warm and stifling. Not a breath of wind stirred, and a smoky, blue haze slept on the brows of the hills, and blurred sky and sea on the far pearly horizon. The blue waters of the creek, shimmered and creamed invitingly down beneath the willows on its banks. It was very, very warm and James Henry, eating his bread and molasses on the fence at dinner time, looked down across the clover pastures, thought what a fine day it was for a swim, was tempted and fell. He put his last crust in his pocket and started for the creek; and, when school went in for the afternoon James Henry was neither at his desk nor under it, nor hiding behind the porch door, nor sunning himself on the woodpile.

A warm day in school tries a teacher's patience severely, and I lost mine just then. With a grim smile that boded no good to James Henry, I asked where he was. A dozen grimy hands went up and as many voices shouted out that he had gone swimming in the creek, in defiance of the express warnings and reminders of the owners of the said voices. Thereupon I despatched Tom Merrybone to the creek, with orders to bring James Henry back, dead or alive; and Tom went out, followed by the envious looks of the others. Soon Bob Sly asked to go out and slipped off, after Tom and two boys who had gone for water, left their bucket on the road and joined in the chase. The four ministers of justice, Tom at their head, arrived on the banks of the creek just as James Henry scrambled out on the other side and proceeded to hurry into his scanty garments. Tom shouted across that if he didn't instantly return to the school, it would be worse for him; and the other boys looked mysterious and said that they just guessed they wouldn't be in his shoes for a good deal, and advised him to "just wait and see."

The unfortunate James Henry did not want to wait and see. He turned, scrambled up the bank, and made off across the fields.

Tom and his confederates gazed at each other blankly; but "teacher" had ordered them not to return without James Henry, and she must be obeyed at any cost – more particularly when such obedience meant a lively chase through woods and fields, instead of sweltering over fractions in a close room.

So they resolutely waded across the creek and gave chase to the fugitive. When James Henry saw them coming in full pursuit, he changed his course and made for the blueberry barrens over at Sandy Plains; there he would have a better chance of eluding his pursuers among the spruce copses. He ran and they ran, across fields, over fences, through brush and under-growth, with perspiration streaming from every pore, and a firm determination to win or die. James Henry had the start and, fear lending him wings, he kept it. Like a hunted animal, he flew through the barrens of Sandy Plains, up the railroad track for half a mile, then through the woods between Sandy Plains and Blanktown, and out again into the fields far back of the school. But James Henry's strength was failing him; his pursuers gained on him foot by foot, till at last they seized him, half over a knotty longer fence,[2] and dragged him forcibly to the ground, much to the detriment of his already tattered garments.

Meanwhile at Blanktown school, we had given up hope of seeing any of them back that day. James Henry must have succeeded in winning the enemy over to his side; probably he had bribed them with apples or trained crickets – crickets were marketable commodities in Blanktown school – and they had basely betrayed their trust. Tom Merrybone's defection vexed me most; I had always thought I could depend on Tom.

It was well on in the afternoon when, glancing out of the back window, I saw the four victors marching down across the fields, half leading, half dragging the exhausted and shrinking James Henry. But within one field of the school the latter's legs, or conscience, or both, failed him utterly, and he lay flatly down on the ground and refused to stir. The others stood over him and argued, but seemingly with no effect and, when I tapped imperatively on the window, they decided that it was time for prompt measures. Each one seized poor James Henry by a leg or arm and, despite his kickings and squirmings, swept down the field with him, in at the door and up the aisle to deposit their victim triumphantly at my feet, where he lay breathless and hatless, torn, dusty and in tears.

I looked at the poor little object and my anger melted away. Tom Merrybone and company were remanded to their seats with a severe rebuke, and James Henry was told to go and work an addition sum for penance – a mild punishment, which disappointed those who had expected some excitement.

But James Henry was cured forever and a day. He had had enough of playing truant to last him for the last of his natural life; and though he continued to barter apples and lose his pencils and drive crickets, he never again played truant while I was mistress of Blanktown school.

(1896)

A Girl's Place at Dalhousie College

LUCY M. MONTGOMERY

This article appeared in the *Halifax Herald* in late April 1896 as part of a multi-page coverage of "The Thirty Sweet Girl Graduates of Dalhousie University" – a term from Tennyson's "The Princess" that had been central to L.T. Meade's popular school novel *A Sweet Girl Graduate* (1891). It seems rather odd that the editors asked Montgomery to contribute this piece, given that she was not about to graduate and that she knew she would not be able to continue with her undergraduate studies beyond her one year. Cecily Devereux notes that Montgomery's journal entry dated the day of the publication of this piece omits any mention of it and describes her journey back to Prince Edward Island: "This article's appearance on the day of the conclusion of her academic career suggests that it is also interesting as a kind of valediction."[1] For the ever pragmatic Montgomery, the stated challenge with writing the piece was not philosophical but practical: "I want to do it but the request couldn't have come at a more inconvenient time." It is worth noting, too, that of all the pieces appearing in this cluster of articles, Montgomery's is the only one that is signed.[2]

Devereux, introducing this piece in her critical edition of *Anne of Green Gables*, notes that it contains "the full ambivalence of Montgomery's feminism, conveying her sense of the importance of 'advancement' for exceptional women, and of the maintenance of the status quo for everyone else." More specifically, in Devereux's view, Montgomery "makes the somewhat compromised point that an educated woman makes a better wife and mother – that is, that education for women is valuable for men and society, rather than for women as individuals."[3] Devereux's assessment of Montgomery's feminism in this essay can be contrasted with the unsigned headnote to a reprint of this article in a 1979 issue of *Atlantis: A Women's Studies Journal*, which finds this article far more compelling in terms of its treatment of "the pride and independence of her spirit" compared with what is found in the novels *Anne of Avonlea* and *Anne of the Island*, which are "disappointing to feminists" in terms of their "treatment of women's education" because they focus on "Anne's romantic aspirations to find a mate who would suit all the vagaries of her imagination and personality." As the unsigned headnote adds, "Montgomery's own aspirations and concerns at Dalhousie College in 1896 were closer to her original concept of Anne as the independent and responsible young woman who emerges from her first novel."[4]

"Why, sirs, they do all this as well as we."
*　　*　　*　　*　　*
"Girls,
Knowledge is now no more a fountain sealed;
Drink deep until the habits of the slave,
The sins of emptiness, gossip and spite
And slander, die. Better not be at all
Than not be noble."
*　　*　　*　　*　　*
"Pretty were the sight,
If our old halls could change their sex and flaunt
With prudes for proctors, dowagers for deans,
And sweet girl graduates in their golden hair."
Tennyson – "The Princess"[5]

IT IS NOT A VERY LONG TIME, AS TIME GOES IN THE world's history, since the idea of educating a girl beyond her "three r's"[6] would have been greeted with up lifted hands and shocked countenances. What! Could any girl, in her right and proper senses, ask for any higher, more advanced education than that accorded her by tradition and custom? Could any girl presume to think the attainments of her mother and grandmother before her, insufficient for her?[7] Above all, could she dream of opposing her weak feminine mind to the mighty masculine intellect which had been dominating the world of knowledge from a date long preceding the time when Hypatia was torn to pieces by the mob of Alexandria?[8]

"Never," was the approved answer to all such questions. Girls were "educated" according to the standard of the time. That is they were taught reading and writing and a small smattering of foreign languages; they "took" music and were trained to warble pretty little songs and instructed in the mysteries of embroidery and drawing. The larger proportion of them, of course, married, and we are quite ready to admit that they made none the poorer wives and mothers because they could not conjugate a Greek verb or demonstrate a proposition in Euclid.[9] It is not the purpose of this article to discuss whether, with a broader education, they might not have fulfilled the duties of wifehood and motherhood equally well and with much more of ease to themselves and others.

OLD TRADITIONS DIE HARD

and we will step very gently around their death bed. But there was always a certain number of unfortunates – let us call them so since the world persists in using the term[10] – who, for no fault of their own probably, were left to braid St. Catherine's tresses for the term of their natural lives;[11] and a hard lot truly was theirs in the past. If they did not live in meek dependence with some compassionate relative, eating the bitter bread of unappreciated drudgery, it was because they could earn a meagre and precarious subsistence in the few and underpaid occupations then open to women. They could do nothing else! Their education had not fitted them to cope with any and every destiny; they were helpless straws, swept along the merciless current of existence.

If some woman, with the courage of her convictions, dared to make a stand against the popular prejudice, she was sneered at as a "blue-stocking,"[12] and prudent mothers held her up as a warning example to their pretty, frivolous daughters, and looked askance at her as a not altogether desirable curiosity.

But, nowadays, all this is so changed that we are inclined to wonder if it has not taken longer than a generation to effect the change. The "higher education of women" has passed into a common place phrase.

A GIRL'S PLACE AT DALHOUSIE COLLEGE

A GIRL IS NO LONGER SHUT OUT FROM THE TEMPLE OF KNOWLEDGE

simply because she is a girl; she can compete, and has competed, successfully with her brother in all his classes. The way is made easy before her feet; there is no struggle to render her less sweet and womanly, and the society of to-day is proud of its "sweet girl-graduates."

If they marry, their husbands find in their wives an increased capacity for assistance and sympathy; their children can look up to their mothers for the clearest judgment and the wisest guidance. If they do not marry, their lives are still full and happy and useful; they have something to do and can do it well, and the world is better off from their having been born in it.

In England there have been two particularly brilliant examples of what a girl can do when she is given an equal chance with her brother; these are so widely known that it is hardly necessary to name them. Every one has read and heard of Miss Fawcett, the brilliant mathematician, who came out ahead of the senior wrangler at Cambridge,[13] and of Miss Ramsay, who led the classical tripos at the same university.[14]

In the new world, too, many girl students have made for themselves a brilliant record. Here, every opportunity and aid is offered to the girl who longs for the best education the age can yield her. There are splendidly equipped colleges for women, equal in every respect to those for men; or, if a girl prefers co-education and

WISHES TO MATCH HER INTELLECT WITH MAN'S ON A COMMON FOOTING,

the doors of many universities are open to her. Canada is well to the front in this respect and Dalhousie college, Halifax, claims, I believe, to have been the second college in the Dominion to admit girl students, if we can use the word "admit" of an institution which was never barred to them. Girls, had they so elected, might have paced, with note-book and lexicon, Dalhousie's classic halls from the time of its founding. When the first application for the admission of a girl to the college was received, the powers that were met together in solemn conclave to deliberate thereon, and it was found that there was nothing in the charter of the college to prevent the admission of a girl.

Accordingly, in 1881 two girls, Miss Newcombe and Miss Calkin,[15] were enrolled as students at Dalhousie. Miss Calkin did not complete her course, but Miss Newcombe did and graduated in 1885 with honors in English and English history, – the first of a goodly number who have followed in her footsteps. Miss Newcombe afterwards became Mrs. Trueman and is now on the staff of the Halifax ladies' college.[16] In 1882 Miss Stewart entered, took the science course and graduated in 1886 as B.Sc. with honors in mathematics and mathematical physics.

In 1887 three girls graduated. Miss Forbes and Miss MacNeill each took their degree of B.A., the latter with high honors in English and English history. The third, Miss Ritchie,

THE MOST BRILLIANT OF DALHOUSIE'S GIRL GRADUATES

took her B.L.,[17] she then took her Ph.D., at Cornell university and is now associate professor of philosophy in Wellesley college.[18] Then occurs a hiatus in the list, for we find no girls graduating till 1891 when there were four who received their degrees, Miss Goodwin, Miss McNaughton and Miss Baxter in arts; Miss Muir took her degree of B.L.

In 1892 Miss Baxter, who had graduated with high honors in mathematics and mathematical physics, took her degree of M.A., after which she went to Cornell and there gained a Ph.D.

Miss Muir took her M.L.,[19] in 1893 and has since been studying for a Ph.D., at Cornell. In 1892 three girls, Miss Weaton, Miss Archibald and Miss Harrington, obtained their B.A. degree. Miss Archibald graduated with great distinction and took her M.A. in 1894. Afterwards she went to Bryn Mawr college,[20] winning a scholarship at her entrance. Miss Harrington graduated with high honors in English and English literature and became M.A. in 1894. She also won a scholarship at Bryn Mawr, where she is at present studying.

In 1893 the two girl graduates were Miss McDonald and Miss Murray, the latter of whom took high honors in philosophy and is now on the staff of the Ladies college. The graduates of 1894 were Miss Hebb, B.A., Miss Hobrecker, B.A., Miss Jamieson, B.A., and Miss Ross, B.A. Miss Hobrecker took honors in English and German. Miss Jamieson and Miss McKenzie each took their M.A. in 1895. Miss Ross graduated with high honors in mathematics and mathematical physics.

IN 1895 THREE GIRLS GRADUATED B.A.

Miss McDonald took honors in mathematics and mathematical physics; Miss Ross was the second Dalhousie girl to graduate with "great distinction," and takes her M.A. this year. Miss Bent is at present studying for M.A.

It will be seen, from these statements, that, out of the twenty-five girls who have graduated from Dalhousie, nearly all have done remarkably well in their studies, and attained to striking success in their examinations. This, in itself, testifies to their ability to compete with masculine minds on a common level. This year there is a larger number of girls in attendance at Dalhousie than there has been in any previous year. In all, there are about fifty-eight, including the lady medical students. Of course, out of these fifty-eight a large proportion are not undergraduates. They are merely general students taking classes in some favorite subject, usually languages and history.

In all, there are about twenty-nine undergraduate girls in attendance this session. The number of girls in the freshman class is the largest that has yet been seen at Dalhousie. Out of the twenty-six girls, at whom

DISDAINFUL SOPHS ARE PRIVILEGED TO HURL ALL THE OLD JOKES

that have been dedicated to freshmen since time immemorial, there are nine undergraduates. In the second year are eleven girls, eight of whom are undergraduates; and in the third year six out of the nine girls are also undergraduates.

There are also nine girls in the fourth year, seven of whom graduate this session. This is the largest class of girls which has yet graduated from Dalhousie. Several of these are taking honors and will, it is expected, amply sustain the reputation which girl students have won for themselves at the university. No girl has as yet attempted to take a full course in law at Dalhousie. Not that any one doubts or disputes the ability of a girl to master the mysteries of "contracts" or even the intricacies of "equity jurisprudence;" but the Barristers' act, we believe, stands ruthlessly in the way of any enterprising maiden who might wish to choose law for a profession.

However, we did hear a different reason advanced not long ago by one who had thought the subject over – he was a lawyer himself, by the way, so no one need bring an action against us for libel. "Oh, girls," he said,

"GIRLS WERE NEVER CUT OUT FOR LAWYERS.

They've got too much conscience." We have been trying ever since to find out if he were speaking sarcastically or in good faith.

But, if shut out from the bar, they are admitted to the study and practise of medicine and two girls have graduated from the Halifax medical college as full fledged M.D.'s. One of these, Miss Hamilton, obtained her degree in 1894 and has since been practising in Halifax.[21] In 1895 Miss McKay graduated and is now, we understand, practising in New Glasgow. There are at present three girl students at the medical college. One will graduate this year; of the other two one is in the third, and one in the first year.

Dalhousie is strictly co-educational. The girls enter on exactly the same footing as the men and are admitted to an equal share in all the privileges of the institution. The only places from which they are barred are the gymnasium and reading room. They are really excluded from the former, but there is nothing to keep them out of the reading room save custom and tradition. It is

THE DOMAIN SACRED TO MASCULINE SCRIMMAGES AND GOSSIPS

and the girls religiously avoid it, never doing more than cast speculative glances at its door as they scurry past into the library. We have not been able to discover what the penalty would be if a girl should venture into the reading room.[22] It may be death or it may be only banishment for life.

The library, however is free to all. The girls can prowl around there in peace, bury themselves in encyclopedias, pore over biographies and excercise their wits on logic, or else they can get into a group and carry on whispered discussions which may have reference to their work or may not.

They take prominent part in some of the college societies. In the Y.M.C.A. their assistance is limited to preparing papers on subjects connected with missions and reading them on the public nights; in the Philomathic society they are more actively engaged. The object of this society is to stimulate interest and inquiry in literature, science and philosophy. Girls are elected on the executive committee and papers on literary subjects are prepared and read by them throughout the session.

They are also

INITIATED INTO THE RITES AND CEREMONIES OF THE PHILOSOPHICAL CLUB

and are very much in demand in the Glee club. Once in a while, too, a girl is found on the editorial staff of the *Dalhousie Gazette*, and what the jokes column would do, if stripped of allusions to them, is beyond our comprehension.

The athletic club, however, numbers no girls among its devotees and it does not seem probable that will change – certainly not in this generation, at least.[23] The question of the higher education of girls involves a great many interesting problems which are frequently discussed but which time alone can solve satisfactorily.[24] Woman has asserted her claim to an equal educational standing with man and that claim has been conceded to her. What use then, will she make of her privileges? Will she take full advantage of them or will she merely play with them until, tired of the novelty, she drops them for some mere fad? Every year since girls first entered Dalhousie, has witnessed a steady increase in the number of them in attendance; and it is to be expected that, in the years to come, the number will be very much larger. But beyond a certain point we do not think it will go. It is not likely that the day will ever come when the number of girl students at Dalhousie, or at any other co-educational university, will be equal to the number of men. There will

ALWAYS BE A CERTAIN NUMBER OF CLEVER, AMBITIOUS GIRLS

who, feeling that their best life work can be accomplished only when backed up by a broad and thorough education, will take a university course, will work conscientiously and earnestly and will share all the honors and successes of their brothers. There will, however, always be a limit to the number of such girls.

Again, we have frequently heard this question asked: "Is it, in the end *worth while* for a girl to take a university course with all its attendant expenses, hard work, and risk of health? How many girls, out of those who graduate from the universities, are ever heard of prominently again, many of them marrying or teaching school? Would not an ordinarily good education have benefited them quite as much? Is it then worth while, from this standpoint, for any girl who is not exceptionally brilliant, to take a university course?"

The individual question of "worth while" or "not worth while" is one which every girl must settle for herself. It is only in its general aspect that we must look at the subject. In the first place,

AS FAR AS DISTINGUISHING THEMSELVES IN AFTER LIFE GOES,

take the number of girls who have graduated from Dalhousie – say thirty, most of whom are yet in their twenties and have their whole lives before them. Out of that thirty, eight or nine at the very least have not stood still but have gone forward successfully and are known to the public as brilliant, efficient workers. Out of any thirty men who graduate, how many in the same time do better or even as well? This, however, is looking at the question from the standpoint that the main object of a girl in taking a university course is to keep herself before the public as a distinguished worker. But is it? No! At least it should not be. Such an ambition is not the end and all of a true education.

A girl does not – or, at least, should not – go to a university merely to shine as a clever student, take honors, "get through," and then do something very brilliant. Nay; she goes – or should go – to prepare herself for living, not alone in the finite but in the infinite.

SHE GOES TO HAVE HER MIND BROADENED

and her powers of observation cultivated. She goes to study her own race in all the bewildering perplexities of its being. In short, she goes to find out the best, easiest and most effective way of living the life that God and nature planned out for her to live.

If a girl gets this out of her college course, it is of little consequence whether her after "career" be brilliant, as the world defines brilliancy, or not. She has obtained that from her studies which will stand by her all her life, and future generations will rise up and call her blessed,[25] who handed down to them the clear insight, the broad sympathy with their fellow creatures, the energy of purpose and the self-control that such a woman must transmit to those who come after her.

(1896)

To the Editor

In this letter published in *The Editor: A Journal of Information for Literary Workers* in March 1899, Montgomery made a request for a copy of her short story "A Little Accident," about a group of schoolboys who regret their ill treatment of a new classmate after they are all involved in a sledding accident. A copy of the story appears in Montgomery's Scrapbook 2, suggesting that her request was answered.

TO THE EDITOR:–

I wonder if any reader of the highly prized *Editor* pages can help me out of a little predicament of a sort I do not often get into. In November I had a short story entitled "A Little Accident," accepted by the *Youth's Advocate* – now the *Youth and Age* – of Nashville, Tennessee. It was published in their issue of December 1st., but as I was not a subscriber to the paper I did not know of this until late in January. I at once sent for the paper but was informed that the issue of December 1st. was completely exhausted. There is no other way I can get the paper here. Now, like most writers I suppose I like to see my scribblings in print, as well as preserve them, and if any of the readers of *The Editor* happens to possess a copy of *Youth and Age*, of December 1st., 1898, which he or she does not need, I should be exceedingly grateful to said reader if he or she would send it to me, and will return the favor in any way or at any time possible.

L.M. MONTGOMERY, Cavendish, P.E. Island, Canada.

(1899)

PART 2

Maud Montgomery, Newspaper Woman

FIGURE 3 The office of the *Halifax Daily Echo* and the *Morning Chronicle*, at 10 and 12 Prince St., Halifax. Undated photograph. (Courtesy of the L.M. Montgomery Collection, Archival and Special Collections, University of Guelph Library.)

A Half-Hour in an Old Cemetery

M.M.

In September 1901, after living again with her widowed grandmother in Cavendish for three years, Montgomery accepted the position of proofreader for the *Halifax Daily Echo*, in spite of its salary of five dollars a week, which, as Carole Gerson notes, was "considerably less than the wages of most contemporary Ontario women journalists." Still, "it was not so much money I was after as experience and a *start* in journalism," Montgomery declared in an extract from her journal not included in her account of her *Daily Echo* experience in "The Alpine Path."[1] Initially, the only writing assignments she was expecting to be given would involve fake society letters, but ten days after her start at the paper, an essay appeared under the byline "M.M." It describes a "ramble" in the cemetery of St. Paul's Anglican Church (better known as the Old Burying Ground) in downtown Halifax, founded in 1749 and closed in 1844; it is now considered a National Historic Site of Canada. Montgomery would draw on parts of this essay to describe Anne's impressions of a Kingsport cemetery in chapter 4 of *Anne of the Island*. This essay appeared mere days before the launch of her weekly column, "Around the Table," included later in this volume.

As a general thing, a graveyard is not considered a cheerful spot for a ramble! Yet there is a certain kind of pleasure in it for some minds and moods; and when the place in question is garbed in the glamor of history and "unhappy, far-off things"[2] the pleasure is increased.

Nothing could be fuller of interest than a half-hour spent in old St. Paul's graveyard, that city of the dead set in the heart of the busy town, while the waves of life surge unceasingly around it, and its dwellers lie in the dreamless slumber that never wakens to recurring dawns of labor. Here, in the very domain of the strenuous present, is the realm of the past!

For the most part no great art or skill was lavished on the old tombstones here. The larger number are of roughly-chiseled gray or brown stone, with here and there a white marble striking an almost jarring note in this subdued harmony of funereal tints. In few cases is there any attempt at ornamentation. Some are adorned with skull and crossbones and this grisly decoration is frequently coupled with a winged cherub head. Many are prostrate or in ruins. In almost all Time's tooth has been gnawing into the inscriptions until some are completely effaced and others can only be deciphered with difficulty. The tombstones vary little in design or sentiment, yet one and all voice two of the most deeply-rooted instincts of humanity – the hope of immortality and the dread of oblivion. These monuments were erected to perpetuate the memory of men and women wholly forgotten a generation ago!

What unconscious pathos there is in some of them! Here, is one "erected to the memory" of one who is buried elsewhere, far from the graves of his kindred. There, is another marking the burial place of a "favorite child." Yonder is a cluster of gray slabs where a whole family rest – father, mother, sisters, brothers, together in death as in life.

Here we find a tombstone inscribed thus:

"To the memory of George Reeves, who died on the 22nd of September, 1840, aged 43 years. This is raised as a tribute of affection by one whom he served so faithfully for 27 years that he was regarded as a friend, deserving the fullest confidence and attachment."

A very good epitaph! Who of us deserves or desires a better? We are all servants of some sort and surely if the fact that we were faithful might be truthfully inscribed on our tombstones nothing more need be added.

One would scarcely look for irony in a graveyard; yet that selfsame epitaph is really an ironical commentary on the contrast between the present and the past. The "servant question" could not have been a burning one in those days.

On one gray slab is a condensed biography of the pulseless clay it covers:

"Here lieth the body of John Morden, Esq., for many years storekeeper of His Majesty's Ordnance at Halifax. He served in the army until the peace of 1763, when he retired from bad health. He was a brave officer, the best of husbands, the best of fathers, the best of friends. He died October 29th, 1792, aged 84 years."[3]

There is scope for imagination here.[4] How full such a life might have been of adventure! And, as for his personal qualities, could human eulogy go further?

But what is this? We pause by a plain little headstone, covered from top to bottom by lettering that is blurred and worn. The cemetery with its overarching trees and long aisles of shadows, fades from sight. We see the Halifax harbor of nearly a century agone. Out of the mist comes slowly a great frigate, brilliant with "the meteor flag of England."[5] Behind her is another with the Stars and Stripes reversed floating beneath St. George's cross,[6] and a still, silent form, wrapped in that same starry flag, lying on his own quarter-deck. Surely Time's finger has turned back his pages and that is the *Shannon* sailing triumphant up the bay with the *Chesapeake* as her prize![7]

This little monument is a memento of that famous sea duel. Two officers of the *Shannon*, a boyish middy of 18 and a man well past middle age, are buried here. They "died of desperate wounds received in the gallant action" – so reads their epitaph. It is such as a soldier might wish for!

And so our half-hour ramble ends as we pass out by the beautiful tribute to Nova Scotia's dead heroes that guards the gates, with its memories of Inkerman and Alma and Balaklava,[8] those "bleak heights that are famous in story,"[9] out into the busy streets again, leaving behind those passionless shades where autumn leaves are drifting noiselessly down over the old forgotten graves of men and women who lived and loved and joyed and suffered when the last century was young.

"After life's fitful fever they sleep well."[10]

(1901)

FIGURE 4 Visual heading for "Cynthia's" newspaper column "Around the Table," published in thirty-five instalments in the *Halifax Daily Echo* (many of them reprinted in the *Morning Chronicle*) from September 1901 to May 1902. (Microfilm at Library and Archives Canada.)

Around the Table

CYNTHIA

This newspaper column, which appeared in thirty-five instalments between September 1901 and May 1902 in the *Halifax Daily Echo* and which is reprinted in its entirety for the first time in this volume, contains some of Montgomery's most innovative work. It is signed "Cynthia," an unmarried woman who lives with "Polly," "Theodosia," "Ted," and "Aunt Janet" in a Halifax home. Together, they form a virtual family even when their personalities clash. They play practical jokes on each other, start an "anti-slang" society, discuss reading materials, and try to amuse themselves on their limited budgets.

Montgomery referred to these pieces as "a column or so of giddy stuff" for which "everything is fish that comes to *Cynthia*'s net – fun, fashions, fads, fancies."[1] After publishing a first instalment under the title "Over the Tea Cups," she settled on the name "Around the Table"; a *Daily Echo* staff artist "made a heading for it in which four or five rather melancholy and spinsterish maidens sit around a table, presumably talking gossip" (see figure 4). Given that she commented frequently on the fast pace of the newspaper office, it is fortunate that her ability to write the witty column did not depend on her mood: as she noted in a journal entry dated November about her "sparkling" column, "I can always write brilliantly when I'm in the dismals."[2]

Montgomery did not record how this newspaper column came about or how it was received by her colleagues or by the general public, except for the cryptic remark that "I think it rather goes."[3] A few publication details can illuminate this at least in part, however. Out of the thirty-five columns, twenty-three were reprinted in the *Morning Chronicle*, which was published in the same building and often used the same material, within days of their publication in the *Daily Echo*.

Moreover, in contrast with the women's columns that Janice Fiamengo studies in her book *The Woman's Page: Journalism and Rhetoric in Early Canada* (2008), thirteen of the columns appeared or at least began on the front page of the newspaper. These columns also anticipate some of Montgomery's hallmarks as a novelist: her fascination with word play, her parody of people's foibles and prejudices (including her own), and her strategy of couching social criticism in humour. Many of the anecdotes told here would be reworked into key moments in her novels, particularly in *Anne of Avonlea* and *Anne of the Island.*

Over the Tea Cups

Saturday, 28 September 1901

The Art of Selecting a New Hat –
This Season's Creations.

Autumn at the Public Gardens
and the Passing of the Old Garden.

Don't Get in a Panic Unless You Have To.

How a Young Man Proposed to His Best Girl and
Why the Engagement Was Broken.[4]

(Written Specially for Saturday's *Daily Echo.*)

THIS IS THE TIME OF YEAR WHEN A WOMAN STARTS TO get or make a new hat. Now comes one of our chances for pitying the men. They never have the fun in selecting new hats that we have – at least, it doesn't seem possible that they have. I suppose men do get new hats occasionally; but there can't really be much excitement in it for them – their hats are so plain and so much alike.

Now, when a woman gets a new hat it is always exciting – it is more exciting than ever this season, when the "picture" hat has come to its own.[5] The variety where from to choose is bewildering – so, too, are the prices, sometimes.

"Sweet simplicity"[6] is out of date, and lavish use of material is the hall-mark of a fashionable hat today. Some of the hats on exhibition are dreams.

The greatest trouble is, that the folks who designed this season's hats seem to have had in mind only goddess-like creatures, "divinely tall and most divinely fair."[7] On such the new hats must look bewitching – if it be not incongruous to speak of a goddess as being bewitching. But what of the small women? There are a few of us left, despite the vogue of the Gibson girl,[8] and as one of them I rise to make my feeble protest. Oh powers that be in the world of fashion, do please give us something that won't eclipse us altogether.

A word of warning! Don't – if you can possibly avoid it – don't try to trim your own hat this fall. You will find it a delusion and a snare.[9] It looks easy. It really seems as if anyone ought to be able to jumble silk and velvet and feathers and frills together into the seemingly careless creations of fall millinery. Nothing was ever more deceptive. That seeming carelessness calls for heaven-born genius. If you don't possess this don't let even precious economy beguile you into trimming your own hat. Nine times out of ten it would be, not a "dream," but a nightmare.

By the way, who ever originated that expression, "Beautiful as a dream"?[10] Some dreams are perfectly horrible. Just eat a bedtime snack of mince pie and Welsh rabbit and fruit cake, and see for yourself.

The Public Gardens are very beautiful just now, and so apparently think the crowds who frequent them.[11] The color harmonies are exquisite – the greens of the trees, ranging from darkest emerald to golden, the sparkle of fountains and the moonlight gleam of shadowy pools, the bright tints of the flowers and the brighter tints of ladies' dresses. Everyone, from the babies who toddle delightedly along the paths, to the octogenarian, who basks contentedly on the bench, seems to find the place a garden of delight.

Somebody has said that who ever loves a garden is a good person. So there must be lots of good people in Halifax.

Speaking of gardens, somebody ought to write a treatise on "The Passing of the Old-Fashioned Garden." It is almost a thing of ancient history now – worse luck, for it was a beautiful place. There are a few old-timey gardens left yet, here and there in some remote country village, and to go into one of them seems like entering into a different world "where all things always seemed the same."[12] There is such dignity and repose about an old-fashioned garden. It seems like a desecration to think of "the strenuous life"[13] in such a place.

Old-fashioned gardens were all pretty much alike. Perennials flourished there, coming up faithfully every year like tried and true old friends, poking their green heads bravely up in sunny nooks before the last snow bank had dwindled away in the shadow of the firs at the north. There were holly-hocks in gay, stiff, soldierly ranks under the parlor windows, tiger lilies in gorgeous cuirasses to guard the gate, groups of nodding poppies like fine ladies in frilled silken gowns, clumps of southern wood that great grandmother planted two generations ago, strips of ribbon-grass, rows of cabbage roses down the central path and a tangle of sweet briars by the fence, honeysuckle climbing over the front porch and two big lilac trees before the door with day lilies at their roots.

There were flowers there, too, that you never hear of nowadays. They exist still, no doubt, but in the new order of things they seem ashamed of their plebeian names. You can find some of them in the catalogues masquerading under weird Latinized appellations. In olden days they were content to be known as "Clove Pinks," "Adam and Eve," "Bouncing Bess," "Scarlet Lightning," "Sweet Balm," "Butter and Eggs," "Bride's Bouquet," "Prince's Feather" and "Bleeding Heart."[14] But those names seem to have passed with the passing of the old garden.

Don't, if your little finger aches, straightway imagine that you have the smallpox.[15] The chances are that you haven't.

When the diphtheria was around Polly thought she had it.[16] One day she was talking to a friend and the next day she heard that that friend had diphtheria. That night she came to my room at one o'clock and roused me out of the sleep of the just[17] to tell me she had diphtheria – she knew she had it because her throat was sore and she just felt shivery all over. She made me hunt out a medical treatise on infectious diseases and read her the symptoms of diphtheria in its incipient stages while she checked them off on her fingers. She said she had 'em every one, too.

I began to get scared myself and went to the glass and peered down my throat. It seemed normal. Polly knew she was going to die and said she wished she hadn't been in such a hurry getting her new winter hat and would I promise faithfully to give Jack the message she would leave for him? And did I think she would be black in the face if she choked to death?

We didn't sleep any all the rest of the night and we cried a good deal and kept examining each other's throats. Next day Polly found out it wasn't her friend who was sick and the person who was sick hadn't diphtheria.

Moral: Don't get in a panic until you have to.

This story was told me the other day by a person who assured me it happened not a hundred miles from Halifax. I can't vouch for it, but here it is:

He was one of those systematic fiends who eat and sleep and make love by rule and method. The other night he called on his best girl, proposed and was accepted. After he had gone she found this memorandum which he had accidentally dropped:

"Things I must do this evening."

1. Shave myself.

2. Borrow $5 to buy roses for Dorothy.

3. Call at the laundry to get my collars and cuffs.

4. Propose to Dorothy. (a) Tell her I've loved her ever since that day I saw her in the park wearing that little red coat – make that strong. (b) Mention that when I look into her beautiful eyes I realize how unworthy I am – that's the conventional thing to say. (c) Get my arm gradually around her waist. (d) Ask her if she thinks she can like me just a little. (e) Kiss her.

5. Stop in at Jimmy's and have a game of poker with the boys.

6. Wind up my alarm clock and put it close to my ear so that it will go off at 7 tomorrow morning.

The young lady, it is said, concluded that she didn't care for so methodical a husband and the engagement is off.

To wind up with here is a new wrinkle Polly has got for hair dressing. She brushes her hair into a very fluffy pompadour and twists it into a loose 8 at the back.[18] On the left of this she fastens crookedwise a plump velvet bow. Then she takes a black velvet ribbon and passes it through a loop of hair directly in front of her pompadour where she ties it in a small bow above her forehead. With Polly's piquant features the effect is charming.

[Letters, Books, and Neckwear]

Saturday, 5 October 1901

ONE OF THE MOST NOTICEABLE THINGS IN THIS SEASON's fashions is the dainty neckwear. The display in the stores is bewildering and it is a liberal education to walk down Barrington street[19] and look at all the pretty things that are destined to nestle under dimpled chins and encircle white throats. It really seems as if the homeliest woman in the world ought to be able to make herself pretty with the aid of these charming confections.

There are ties and fichus[20] and collars of lace and gauze, fine as cobwebs; ruffs and boas of chiffon and feathers; and the loveliest of ribbons. Polly went uptown yesterday and squandered some of her substance[21] on two new ties that she didn't need in the world – for her top bureau drawer is crammed with all sorts and conditions of neckwear already.[22] She said the temptation was irresistible and when I saw the ties I didn't blame her. One was a wide plaid ribbon in delicate shades of blue and the other was of lovely old rose hemstitched silk.

I think I have more moral backbone in these matters than Polly has, but I always take the precaution of leaving my purse at home when I sally forth to look at the new neckwear.

Polly has been reading a recently published volume of somebody's love-letters – I forget whose, but it doesn't matter.[23] As a result she has burned all hers – a very wise precaution. Nowadays, when we are bombarded with such literature, the people who preserve love-letters are only one degree less foolish than the people who write them. Nobody is safe. Because you are not a Browning[24] or a Bismarck[25] or a Hugo[26] is no guarantee that some excavating fiend will not get hold of your soul-outpourings when you are dead and gone and straightway inflict them on a public that suffereth long and is kind.[27] The interest of love-letters doesn't depend on the eminence of the writers. We have had "Love Letters of a King,"[28] "Love Letters of a Worldly Woman,"[29] "Love Letters of an English Woman,"[30] and so on. Next thing, we will have "Love Letters of a Cook," or "Love Letters of Tommy the Policeman." And, doubtless, they will be just as interesting as the others.

But to those people who don't like the idea of a posthumous edition of their affections I give Punch's advice – "don't."[31]

With the exception of love-letters which are perennial and will probably continue to be despite all warnings, correspondence seems to be in a parlous state nowadays[32] – at least so say those who are always lamenting the good old times. Letter writing is numbered among the lost arts.

This is doubtless true in a measure. The telegraph and telephone, quick travelling and cheap postal rates have all contributed to do away with the long, leisurely, sometimes stilted but oftentime delightful epistle of "ye olden tyme."[33]

Besides we have no time nowadays to inscribe our thoughts in friendly correspondence. Mostly we haven't time to even think the thoughts.

But there are one or two points in which modern letter-writers might improve. One of these is in answering questions. You write to a friend asking about several little matters in which you are interested. Can anything be more exasperating than to receive a reply, telling you lots of news, perhaps, but ignoring your questions completely?

I confess with shame and contrition that I have not been always blameless in this respect myself and Polly pulled me up right smartly when she returned from her last vacation.

When she came back I asked her how Aunt Eliza's rheumatism was. Polly responded that the baby had an attack of croup. I said:

"Is it true that Edith and Ted are engaged?"

Said Polly:

"Millicent is coming to Halifax for the winter."

After this had gone on for some minutes I anxiously asked Polly if she had been dissipating too muchly during vacation and didn't think she ought to consult a brain specialist at once?

Polly said she had meant to ask me the same thing. She had asked so many questions in her letters and I had answered them in just the same way.

I took the lesson to heart and I have reformed to such an extent that I feel at liberty to preach to other people.

Speaking of Polly's vacation here is something she told me about it:

"You know Kitty Felix. She always has a joke to fill up one of those horrid silences that sometimes fall on a roomful of people and she is always reminded of a good story at the right time. I've often envied her for my mind always becomes a perfect blank on such occasions. She has worked up a reputation for brightness just on that.

Well, when we were at the L——s in Kentville[34] Kit was scintillating as usual and one day I came across a book she'd dropped. Cynthia, you'd never guess! It was a collection of jokes and conundrums. Kit had marked off those she had used and the rest were divided into sections – one for every day of her visit. Well, I just learned by heart all those she had marked for that evening and I sprung them all before she had a chance. Of course she was simply furious, but she couldn't say a thing without giving herself away."

[Charitable Fits and Desperate Measures]

Saturday, 12 October 1901

POLLY HAD ONE OF HER CHARITABLE FITS LAST SUNDAY, and spent the afternoon at the Poor's Asylum.[35] She got herself up regardless in a befrilled and beflounced organdy and a picture hat. When I protested she silenced me by declaring that the poor old folks out there just loved to see pretty things, and that she always put on her very spiffiest when she went to see them.

Then she rifled her window garden – and mine, too, I may add – for flowers to take with her, and departed with them and a whole armful of miscellaneous literature which she had begged, borrowed or stolen.[36] Among the rest she had about three dozen religious tracts. Goodness knows where she got them, but I suppose from the cook. Our cook's idea of wild and frenzied dissipation and excitement is simply to revel in tracts.

That evening, around the tea-table, Polly gave us an account of her afternoon.

"They were all so glad to see me," she said, "and I sang hymns to them and read the tracts to three old bodies. And then I talked with Nora. Nora was a housemaid in grandmother's family thirty years ago, you know. She looks exactly like the pictures you see of George Eliot.[37] Well, Nora has an excellent memory, and she delights to tell me tales of long ago, when mother was a girl, and had simply dozens of beaux. I store them all up in my head, and when mummy begins to lecture me on my flirtatiousness I silence her by springing some of Nora's reminiscences on her. She just colors up beautifully, and doesn't say another word. Nora says mother was the prettiest girl in Halifax in her time.

"There is one dear little old lady out there who just looks like a doll. Today she was sitting there, wearing a real dressy little black velvet bonnet, a lace-trimmed apron, a red waist, a black lace collar and a necklace of beads. Her little corner is neat as a pin, and all prettied up with mottoes and cards and nicnacs.[38] I just sat down and told her all about the new party dresses I was getting for the winter, and she was as pleased as Punch.[39]

"One woman there has a son in the South African Constabulary. She proudly showed me his photograph in uniform, and she just beamed when I said, 'What a nice-looking boy!' He was, too.

"Oh, I had a very interesting afternoon, and I'm going every single Sunday after this to sing to them and read tracts to them. I think it is my duty."

Polly talks like that, you know, and she really meant it at the time. But it will be six months before she thinks of the Poor's Asylum again.

From the foregoing you'd think that Polly was rather a kind hearted and amiable creature, wouldn't you? But listen to this.

"You know," she said, pensively, "I've been thinking about when the Duke and Duchess come.[40] I'm so small, and just as sure as I get a good spot to see the procession some great, big man will plant himself squarely in front of me. That was the way it was when the first contingent came home.[41] But I have evolved a really brilliant idea this time. I mean to arm myself with half a dozen good, stout hat-pins. Then if any brute of a man gets in my way I'm just going to jab one into him clear up to the head. I don't care if it does hurt. I'm not going to stick at trifles when the chance of a lifetime to see a genuine Prince of the blood comes."

"But a policeman will take you in hand," I objected.

"No, he won't," said Polly triumphantly. "If he tries to I'll make at him with another hat-pin. Do you suppose any policeman on earth could stand his ground before such a weapon in the hands of a desperate girl?"

I think it's not a half bad idea, and I'd try it myself only I know quite well that my nerve would fail me at the critical moment. But Polly's won't, and I hereby warn each and every member of the "male sect"[42] in Halifax that, when the procession passes, he would better not get in front of a small girl with brown eyes, tip-tilted nose and a red hat. That's Polly, and she will be in a dangerous mood.

Somehow, the other evening, the conversation turned on the comparative vanity of men and women. Ted and I got quite excited over it. Ted, of course, took the part of his sex. He declared men were not half so vain as women.

"Why, look here! You never see men daubing all those nasty, beautifying messes on their faces that girls do – creams and bleaches and glycerine, and that sort of stuff. Catch them!"

Then I told a little tale.

One day last summer I was in a Halifax drugstore. Before the counter stood a strapping, six-foot youth talking to the clerk in tones that were audible a block away.

"I'm off on a camping bat," he said, "and I want a few little creams and things to keep me from looking like a fright when I get back. Just give me" – here he read from a list – "a box of Blank's cold cream, a tube of cucumber jelly, a bottle of Oriental face bleach, a piece of camphor ice, a bottle of vaseline, a tube of lanolin, a bottle of violet toilet water, two ounces simple tincture of benzoin, a bottle of witch-hazel extract, a box of borated talcum, some cocoa butter sticks, a bottle of rum and quinine hair tonic and a package of Jones' infant powder.

"Those are all right, aren't they?" he queried anxiously. "Girl gave me that list and told me I'd come home fit as a fiddle if I used 'em. Last year when I got back I looked like a battle-scarred veteran, and I'm determined to come out better this time, if it takes a fortune. Just send all those things over to the house, won't you, old fellow? And wrap 'em up so they won't break, and the contents ooze out." Then he went out as smug as you please.

"There's no use judging all men by one fool sample," growled Ted grumpily.

I read something the other day which called back to memory sundry recollections of childhood hours spent at a brown desk in a certain little white-washed country schoolhouse. Out of all the "mental exercises" which the powers that were inflicted on us, worst of all did we dread "paraphrasing," in which we had to take an innocent passage from a poet who had never done us any harm, and write its sense out in our own words. What untold wear and tear of gray matter I might have been spared, had I but possessed the gift of condensation indicated by the youth in this story.

A boy was asked to paraphrase these lines from the ballad of Lochinvar.[43]

"She is won – we are gone over bank, bush and scar.
They'll have fleet steeds that follow, quoth young Lochinvar.
There was mounting 'mong Graemes of the Netherby clan,
Fosters, Fenwicks and Musgraves, they rode and they ran.
There was racing and chasing on Canobie Lea."

The lad reflected a while, and then wrote:– "Loch left, followed by the whole gang."

Here is a conundrum Ted sprang on me the other day – when I hadn't been doing a thing to him either, mind you:

"Why do we honor Royalty?"

I said:

"That is one of the problems of history, sonny, I give it up."

"Because a British Sovereign is eleven-twelfths fine gold," said Ted.[44]

What should be done to the man who carries concealed conundrums about with him! Suggestions called for.

When Polly came home from the Marine Band concert the other evening she was uplifted over a new idea in sashes.

"There was a tall, slender girl sitting before me," she said, "and she wore a soft-sash of shaded blue silk. This was tied in two bows about five inches apart. The top one was the smallest, and its ends were carried down to form the other one, the ends of which reached the floor. I'm going to have one tied like that for Genevieve's party next week."

[Collisions and Crossed Wires]

Saturday, 19 October 1901

FOR THE PAST FEW DAYS HALIFAX HAS PRESENTED A weird, half-finished appearance, very much as might a beauty who is dressing for a festivity, and has her toilet only half completed. Skeleton-like structures have sprung up on the streets; here and there vivid patches of color have blossomed out startlingly along the sombre blocks; and at every step you have met people rushing along with armfuls of queer things and bunting. Then, as for running into people – bless me, I couldn't begin to count all the people I've caromed into, or been caromed into by, while I was gazing skyward or twisting my neck half off trying to see the latest thing in decorations. I count myself lucky to have escaped with a few bruises. But Polly had her new hat almost spoiled by colliding with somebody – she declares he was walking backwards – and she is furious over it.

Some of the decorations are very nice; others remind you of the things you sometimes see in bad dreams. A frantic outburst of color without any clearly apparent design is not bound to be beautiful. But at the present moment of writing the decorating is only well under way and children and fools should never judge work half done.[45] By the time this appears in print – when there will be nobody to read it because everybody will be staring at something else – Halifax will have got all her finery on, and doubtless the general effect will be very gay and gorgeous. Only, as Ted says, I do hope the Provincial Building, when completed,[46] will look a little less like a venerable octogenarian tricked out in the fripperies and abbreviated skirt of a chorus girl than it does at this very moment.

Nature has been doing a little quiet decoration on her own account after her ancient fashion. Not in honor of the Royal visitors, perhaps, because she does it every year for prince and peasant, and anybody who has eyes to see. She is an unrivalled colonist, that same old nature. What magnificent tones of maple crimson and birchen gold and chestnut amber she is lavishing on us in this "moon of falling leaves"![47] And the vines! Is there anything in the world more satisfyingly beautiful than a tangle of vines, vivid wine-reds and bronzes and purples, creeping over a ruddy old brick wall? Even Ted, who hasn't a spark of poetry in his soul at all, admits that such a sight "goes to the right spot somehow."

Polly's soul is all harrowed up at present. She is so deep in the slough of despond[48] that even the prospect of the Royal visit can't pull her out. I'm going to tell you why, because I think her misfortune may give a needed warning to other people.

Polly has got into trouble about a postscript.[49] Myself, I think postscripts were invented to get people into trouble, and for no other purpose whatever. Being a woman, I always put postscripts to my letters, and I suppose I shall go on in the same old abandoned way to the end, albeit I know it is a bad, bad practice. Somehow, a letter doesn't seem properly rounded up without a P.S., does it? And then I'm always sure to think of the most important piece of news after I've signed my name.

But to return to Polly. Last Sunday she wrote a couple of letters to two of her friends of the sterner sex. Polly always writes that kind of letter on Sunday. I've lectured her and lectured her, but it doesn't do any good. She is properly punished for it now, however.[50] Well, she put her letters into envelopes and addressed them – one to Tom and 'tother to Jack – but didn't seal them up. That evening something funny happened. That is, Polly thought it funny, and so would Jack, but it seems that Tom would not be likely to see the humor of it. Next morning Polly, in a hurry to mail her letters, snatched one from its envelope, scrawled down a postscript – three pages long – and sent it off. That afternoon she came to me like one of the heroines in Laura Jean Libbey's novels[51] – dissolved in floods of tears. It had just dawned on her that she had put Jack's postscript to Tom's letter, and she was sure it would make Tom furious. It did, too. Polly got a letter from him yesterday, and since then she has been a woebegone damsel.

The moral of all this is: Don't write postscripts. But if you must write them, if the laws of your being absolutely necessitate postscripts, be careful that you never match the right P.S. with the wrong letter.

In reading a fashion review the other day I came across an announcement that filled me with joy. It was that the dressmakers were going to put pockets in women's dresses again. Delightful! For years we have gone pocketless. We have wandered forlornly around with handkerchiefs sticking out at the corners, pocket-books hanging here and memoranda tucked away there. And we have lost these things with religious regularity. But, if this announcement be reliable and not a heart-breaking will-o'-the-wisp, our trials in this respect are over, glory be!

Of course the men, who seem to have an unaccountable liking for old, threadbare jokes, say it wouldn't be any use for us to have pockets because we couldn't find them if we did have them. But that is a masculine delusion. Trust a woman to find her pocket – and a man's too, if it comes to that! If the pocket comes back to its own I shall throw up my hat with joy in its honor.

Another thing men are always poking fun at is the hair-pin. I'm sure I don't know why. There isn't a more useful thing to be found on the face of the earth. The origin of hair-pins is lost in antiquity. Probably Eve sat down outside the gates of Eden and twisted a convenient twig into the first hair-pin, and by doing so she did much to mitigate the unpleasant inheritance consequent on her indiscreet tampering with green fruit.

Let me tell you the things I saw Polly do with a hair-pin in just one half hour.

She buttoned her boots and gloves with one; she cut the leaves of her magazines and opened her letters with it; having mislaid the key of her jewel box she picked the lock with a hair-pin; she fished up a stick-pin that had fallen into a crack in the floor; she picked the meats out of a lot of walnuts; she impaled marshmallows to toast over the gas; she trimmed her lamp wick; she straightened one out and propped up a straggly flower in her window garden with it; she took a cork out of a bottle with one, and she pegged down a loose cord in her sweet-pea pyramid with another.

And yet some people imagine that all a hair-pin is good for is to pin up hair![52]

Young man, do you want to be right up-to-date in the matter of signet rings?[53] If so, have a tiny photograph of "her" framed in a narrow gold border, take the place of the usual engraved device.

A laugh is as good as a dose of medicine, say the folks who know. Here's your laugh. I saw it in a newspaper the other day so it must be true:

A Sunday school teacher was in the habit of telling her little pupils about some incident which had come under her notice during the week, commenting on it, and then asking them to quote a verse of Scripture appropriate to it. One Sunday she told of a poor cat which had its tail cut off by some bad boys. After talking about the cruelty of this she asked for the usual quotation. After a moment's reflection a little girl raised her hand and said gravely:

"That which God hath joined together let not man put asunder."[54]

["After the Ball"]

Saturday, 26 October 1901

It is "after the ball"[55] with Halifax now. The Duke and Duchess have come and gone, the decorations have been stripped away and the frenzy of patriotic enthusiasm has simmered down to its usual comfortable glow. After all, it's nice. A Royal visit stirs up our gray matter pleasantly and forms a picturesque incident to tell our grandchildren, but after it is at an end it is also pleasant to settle back comfortably into our respective little grooves again with a sigh of something very like thankfulness that the whole fuss is over and done with. Dukes and Duchesses may come and go, but the work-a-day goes on forever.

Polly got a good look at the Duchess – without the aid of any hat-pins, fortunately – and she declares that she is royally beautiful. Polly likes to enthuse, you know; she thinks it is a sort of patriotic duty to say things like that. Ted remarks patronizingly that the Duchess was a rather fine-looking woman, but he really wouldn't take the trouble to look at her twice if he met her without knowing who she was.[56]

"It's just the beaux yeux of her crown that Polly admires,"[57] he declares.

Anyhow, the Duchess had her hair done just beautifully. Everybody is agreed upon that.

The illuminations were very beautiful. Those of the warships in particular made us think of our childhood dreams of fairyland. Thousands of people were on the streets last Saturday night in spite of the rain and there was as much fun in looking at them as at the illuminations. Ted declares he had the good time of his life.

"It was the greatest fun out," he says, "to watch the women who were clinging to the railing in front of the Provincial building, hoping to catch a glimpse of Royalty when it came to the reception. It must have been fearfully wearisome, but they hung on there like grim death for over an hour. The manoeuvres of some who were down to get up were amazing examples of grit and persistency. And such black looks as those who were trying to climb up got from those already in place."

Polly and I got dripping wet and had our Sunday-go-to-meeting hats ruined. But bless me, what odds? We will have plenty of time to get new ones before the next itinerant Prince comes our way.

Is there anything in the world more lovely than a fine October morning? When I ask questions like this Polly and Ted laugh heartlessly and say that if I try to describe an October sunrise I must do it by dead reckoning, because I never get up early enough to see. But that's a libel – born of their mean malice, you know. I do get up early sometimes – and I always enjoy it so much that I make a resolution on the spot that I will rise with the lark every morning thereafter for the space of my natural life. And the next morning I sleep so late that I have to gobble down my breakfast standing, and pin my hat and put my gloves on as I tear down the street![58] There ought to be a law against making resolutions.

But to return to my mutton![59] A really fine October morning is a glorious thing. All the valleys and the purple basins among the hills are filled to the brim with delicate mists as if the spirit of the autumn had poured them in for the sun to drain. Such ethereal colors, too – amethyst and pearl and silver and rose and smoke-gray; and they trickle over the edges of the valleys and scarf the russet shoulders of sere slopes.

There is such a heavy dew that the fields glisten like cloth of silver and baby winds are ruffling the crisp leaves in elfin dances along the lanes or sending them spinning down the river like a fleet of fairy shallops.

One must be out in the really, truly country to see these elusive lovelinesses at their best. But the early morning is charming, even in the city, when the ends of the streets run off into blue hazes through which the harbor waters cream and sparkle, and the crisp leaves rustle under our feet, and there is all around us the pleasant stir of awakening life and labor.

Next week comes All Hallowe'en.[60] We are going to try lots of tricks at our house. We always do. There is any amount of fun in it, although I don't believe any of us ever saw anything yet, for all our pains.

Last year Polly and I tried a Hallowe'en dodge. We promised each other afterwards, "cross our hearts solemn and true," that we would never, never tell anybody about it. Well, I've kept silence on it a whole year, and that's as much as anyone could expect of a woman and a secret. I'm going to tell it now. Polly is out of town in some unearthly place, where *Echoes* are few and far between, so I am in hopes she'll never see this. Please don't anybody tell her when she comes home, for if she finds out she'll never forgive me.

The trick is this. You take a hard-boiled egg, cut it in two and scoop out the shells. Then you each – there must be two of you – this is the good feature of it – there is no eerie nonsense about going off to encounter spooks alone – take half the egg and fill the shell with salt. You have to eat the egg and the salt, and if you can manage to devour the shell also your chances are so much better. Then you take off your shoes and stockings and go upstairs backward, on your bare feet, without speaking a word. If you speak the spell is broken. Then, of course, you get awfully thirsty in the night, and when the clock strikes twelve, the spirit of your future partner of weal and woe will appear and bring you a drink of water.[61]

Well, Polly and I ate the egg and the salt, and took off our shoes and stockings, all in melodramatic silence. Then we started to go upstairs backward. It happened that the stairs were uncarpeted, having been newly varnished that day. The soles of our feet stuck to every step, and it seemed as if the skin must come off when we pulled them loose. I shall never forget that ascent. It would have been such a relief to have been able to say, "Oh, dear," when we stuck extra fast, but we couldn't, because speaking would spoil everything.

And, after all, it was all in vain. Polly suffered agonies of thirst, but no obliging apparition came to her relief, and, as for myself, I went right to sleep, and never felt thirsty or woke up at all. Perhaps it was because we didn't eat the shells. And we couldn't walk comfortably for a week.

Now that the chilly days have come we can revel in the luxury of open fires again. I do so love an open fire. It is delightful to sit before it in the dusk and watch the flames flickering and glowing, and darting up in their cheery, companionable way. When I am curled up in a cosy arm-chair before a purring fire every bit of malice and uncharitableness goes out of my heart, and I feel that I can forgive everybody, even my dearest friends. Autumn twilights and open fires and friendly gossip and delicious daydreams all belong together in the eternal fitness of things.[62]

This didn't happen in Halifax, but it might. I recommend it to the thoughtful consideration of "stern paryrunts"[63] as an improvement on the old brutal methods.

The girl was rather young, and so was he, but he nevertheless called formally on the object of his affections. One evening her father and mother entered the room at an early hour, the latter carrying a glass of milk and a huge slice of bread spread with jam.

"Now, dear, run away to bed," she said kindly to her daughter. "It's time that all good little girls should be in bed."

Then the father addressed the amazed young man.

"Now, youngster, you drink that glass of milk and take that slice of bread and jam to eat on the way home. And hurry, for your mother must be anxious about your being out so late by yourself."

The young man did not call again.[64]

Polly has taken to perfuming her golden tresses with orris root.[65] She sprinkles it over them with a sugar sifter, and then brushes them vigorously for an hour – Polly has any amount of spare time lying around, you know – until the perfume is thoroughly assimilated into the roots. The fragrance thus imparted will last for fully two weeks.

[Dismal November]

Saturday, 2 November 1901

WELL, NOVEMBER IS HERE. IT'S THE MOST DISMAL month in the whole year, isn't it? Polly says that is why she was born in it. Some of us at times put it the other way, and say it is dismal because Polly was born in it. But that is just when we are cross and Polly has been disagreeable.

November seems to be an outcast among the months – the threadbare tramp of the calendar. The mellowness and drowsy charm of autumn have gone, and the crisp sparkle of winter hasn't yet come. It is a sort of betwixt-and-between time, and that is always abominable. The trees are ragged, the fields sullen and the world seems out at the elbows generally. Of course, there are compensations – everything, even November, has compensations.[66] But they don't appear on the surface. Ted says the reason Thanksgiving is celebrated in this month is because people are so thankful there is only one November in the year.[67]

Just now Polly has a special grievance against Max O'Rell.[68] Max is one of those delightful people who know everything about everything, and air their knowledge in print mercilessly. I believe the real reason why Polly detests him is that she saw an article of his the other day on "What a Woman Should Be," and discovered that she fell short of every one of Max's requirements. But, as I told her, Max O'Rell is only one man, so what need she care?

Max O'Rell is full of opinions about women. I always feel so sorry for his wife when I read them. But, in spite of his complacent reflections on and about our sex, I have a comforting suspicion that Max doesn't really know much about us after all. He is too sure of his knowledge to be dangerous.

Lately he has been giving columns of good advice to "the engaged girl." Goodness only knows what will happen if she follows his advice, but there's one comfort – she won't.

Every now and then you read things purporting to be the naive and truthful utterances of children on various subjects. Most of them are very funny, especially if they are true – but sometimes you are haunted by a doubt that they have a made-to-order flavor. Hence, when you meet with something "really truly" so, it is all the more enjoyable. A friend of mine gave me a very good illustration of a childish misunderstanding the other night.

In one of the elementary catechisms used in Sunday Schools for infant classes occurs the question, "Why should we honor and love God?" or words to that effect, the answer being, "Because He makes, preserves and redeems us." The comma after "makes" is, of course, vital to the proper meaning of the sentence. My friend said that until she was ten years of age she honestly thought that the answer was, "Because He makes preserves, and redeems us."[69]

One day last week Polly laid down the magazine she had been reading with a groan.

"What's the matter?" I queried sympathetically.

Polly made a wry face.

"I've been reading an article by one of those detestable creatures who tell you what you ought not to eat. He has given here a whole list of eatables to be avoided, and I don't believe there is a thing in the world that I like which is not tabooed."

Then I crossed my hands at the back of my head, leaned back luxuriously in my easy chair and gave Polly a bit of a preachment.

"My child," I said – I always talk like that when I want to impress Polly with my superiority in years and wisdom – "don't let articles of that stripe disturb you. They really don't amount to a row of pins. Tomorrow you will probably read another which will contradict every word of the one you have just read. People would never eat anything at all if they started out to live by the hygienic rules in the magazines. The people who tell you what you ought to eat, and the people who tell you what you ought to read are members one of another. The best plan, as I've found it, is to go ahead and eat the things you like, and read what books you want to. Even if you have a weakness for the Duchess' novels[70] or for mince pies and doughnuts, that doesn't argue that you are in a parlous state, mentally or physically. Not at all, in spite of the hygienic writers.

"Just because a thing is printed in the papers, Polly," I went on – waxing eloquent – "you are not bound to believe it. Some dreadful fibs do creep into the papers now and then. As for the perpetrators of those what-you-oughtn't-to-eat articles, they always remind me of the fox-who-lost-his-tail story.[71] I firmly believe that they are cranks who have lost their own digestions beyond finding, while fooling with health foods or something of the kind, and now want to prevent everybody else from enjoying themselves. Time was when I used to put some faith in their teachings and try spasmodically to live up to them, but oh, I'm wiser now! Life is too short, and there isn't much use in starving yourself to keep yourself alive.

"Of course," I hastened to add – not wishing Polly to rush off and squander her quarter's allowance in a wild, soulless revel of caramels and almond rock – "there's no sense in going to extremes. As Josiah Allen's wife says, 'Be mejum,'[72] and then you'll have a good digestion and a clear conscience, both of which are inestimable blessings."

When I paused, out of breath, Polly beamed and said:

"What a comforting old dear you are, Cynthia. Let's go out and have some ice-cream."

After all it takes a woman to find a way out of a difficulty. For example here is a little tale of the course of true love in the Emerald Isle,[73] which I read somewhere not long ago.

A poor couple went to the priest for marriage and were met with the demand for the marriage fee. It was not forthcoming. Both the consenting parties were rich in love and little else. The father was obdurate.

"No money, no marriage."

"Give me lave, your riverence," said the blushing bride, "to go and get the money."

It was given. After a short interval she returned with the sum of money and the ceremony was completed to the satisfaction of all. But the newly-made wife seemed a little uneasy.

"Anything on your mind, Catherine?" inquired the father.

"Well, your riverence, I would like to know if this marriage could not be spoiled now."

"Certainly not, Catherine. No man can put you asunder."

"Not even yourself, father?"

"No, no, Catherine. You are past me now. I have nothing more to do with your marriage."

"That aises me mind," said Catherine, "and God bless your riverence. There's the ticket for your hat. I picked it up in the lobby and pawned it."

[Wedding Bells]

Monday, 11 November 1901

REALLY, IT SEEMS AS IF EVERYBODY WERE GETTING MARried. In every paper I pick up I see headings such as these: "Interesting Event," "Wedding Bells," "Two Hearts Made Happy," "United in Marriage," and so on. In all instances, of course, the bride looked beautiful, and was charmingly dressed, and the wedding was quiet but pretty. Wouldn't it be a positive relief to hear of a noisy wedding or an ugly bride.

AROUND THE TABLE.
BY CYNTHIA.
WILL APPEAR IN MON-
DAY'S ECHO.

FIGURE 5 Advertisement for "Around the Table," *Halifax Daily Echo*, 9 November 1901, 9. (Microfilm located at Library and Archives Canada.)

This reminds me of a story I read once upon a time about a reporter who had just secured a position upon the staff of a newspaper. The editor told him that in reporting imagination was at a discount, and that he must stick to plain, unvarnished facts. The first assignment given him was to report a local wedding. The guileless youth, faithful to his instructions, stuck to plain, unvarnished facts. He said the bride's red hair and freckles showed to rather worse advantage than usual in her white dress, but that, owing to her down-dropped eyes, her squint was not greatly in evidence, and, on the whole, she presented a better appearance than the bridegroom, who looked frightened to death, and had never amounted to much in the community anyhow. The whole account was in a similar vein, and the reporter thought he had done his duty. But, alas, he lost his job, and the editor nearly lost his head when the irate relatives of the bride and groom invaded his sanctum.

The moral of this is that it is best to stand by the good old way, in the matter of weddings, at least.

But the interest in weddings is perennial. Folks like to see them and hear about them. The bride, for once in her life, if never again, is the central figure of her world. It is her day and hour of triumph. How she looked, how she was dressed, how she carried herself through the ceremony – these are the echoes of the conversation that buzzes about her. All the world loves a lover, it is said,[74] and it is equally true that all the world loves a bride.

Then, again, there is a never-fading charm in the dainty details of the trousseau, and the pretty gifts and household plenishings that are to adorn the new home. The charm cannot be defined, but is none the less powerful. The woman who doesn't delight in seeing the belongings of a bride must be a weird sort of creature indeed.

Long live the dear brides! Cynthia wishes them every happiness and a lifelong honeymoon.

The meanest man alive has been discovered again. He is always being discovered in a new place. This time it isn't in Halifax, fortunately. Polly and I read this story in a Detroit paper the other day, and Polly said she just wished she had been that girl, and wouldn't she have taught that young man a lesson! I've no doubt she would, too.

But here's the story. It may serve as a warning.

"The wretch! I'd like to have his blood," snapped the pretty girl in blue. "I would, so there! I'd like to know what he did mean, hanging around here, if he didn't mean business. Mad? Of course I'm mad! You'd be mad if you'd had to put up with what I had. He was here the other evening, and something told me that the supreme moment had arrived. He was awfully nervous and fidgetty. No, it wasn't a case of tight shoes, stupid. Don't be silly! Do you think I was born yesterday? I got ready my oh-this-is-so-sudden look, and none too soon, for he leaned over and said tenderly:

"'Would you marry me if I proposed?'

"You needn't tell me what I should have said. I know just as well as you do that I should have told him to ask me if he wanted to find out. But he is the only eligible young man I know, and I couldn't afford to take any chances, so I murmured 'yes!'

"'By Jove,' said he, 'I've won the bet. You see, one of the boys at the club bet the cigars that you wouldn't have me and I took him up.'

"What followed is a mere blank. For the life of me I can't remember whether I sent for the police or turned on a fire alarm."

Somebody once said a woman is at the bottom of every bit of mischief that goes on in the world.[75] I don't know who it was; but, of course, it was a man. It is really dreadful the way men blame everything on us. I suppose they can't help it – heredity is too strong for them. Adam began it when he hadn't backbone enough to take his shortcomings on his own shoulders, and it has come down through the ages until it has got chronic with them now.

But, really, the line ought to be drawn somewhere. The other day, while reading the September *Bookman*, I came across an article – written by a man? Oh, yes! – in which it said that women are responsible "for the deterioration of heroes."[76]

Now, I call that adding insult to injury![77]

The writer of the article in question says that women have dragged the novel down by reason of their liking for "the cheaply heroic type of hero."[78] Masculine heroes have to be made to fit feminine ideals. He says that if a writer dares to depict a man as he really is – for instance, the Tommy of Barrie's *Tommy and Grizel*[79] – the feminine critics rise up in bitter denunciation.

Well, all I can say is, that if Barrie's "Tommy" is a faithful delineation of the average man, as he really is, heaven help the poor creature. Men must be far sillier and more egotistic than – not than I've always thought them, because I have a very good opinion of them, after all – but than what Aunt Janet always declares they are, and she is a professed man-hater.

I could say lots more about this, but I won't. I will refrain.

This is one of Polly's trouble-saving devices. She says she invented it herself, and as I never heard of it before, I daresay she did. I was patiently and laboriously threading ribbon through the interminable holes of some beading when Polly came in and looked me scornfully over.

"Well," she said, "I can't write absurdities for the papers as you do, but I have more gumption about everyday matters than you have, Cynthia. See here! Fasten a small shield pin in the end of that ribbon and you can slip it through that beading with much less weariness to the flesh."[80]

I meekly followed her advice, and found it good, so I hereby pass it on.

Here is a conundrum for you all. "What verse in Genesis proves that the people who lived in those days used to do sums on the ground?"[81]

I'll tell you the answer next week, if you haven't found out for yourselves before then.

[Bad Luck and Bad Advice]

Saturday, 16 November 1901

BY SPELLS THIS WEEK IT HAS LOOKED AS IF WE HAD JUST about come to the end of our fine weather, hasn't it? And oh, the grumbling that I've heard! Really, we human creatures are never satisfied. No matter how many weeks and weeks of fine weather we have when just one rainy day comes look out for scowls and growls.

To be sure, a rainy day in the city is rather grimy and grubby. Out in the country it is really pleasant – if you don't want to go anywhere. When I'm out there I like the rain. I like to see the little valleys all brimful of mist and the rain coming down in slanting lines over the tops of the spruces and making little dimples in the pools and great, widening rings on the pond. I like to hear it, too, tinkling among the boughs or rat-tatting against the windows. When I waken in the night I like to hear it pattering on the roof – that is to say, if the roof doesn't leak, as it did one time last summer when Polly and I were spending a fortnight in an old upcountry farmhouse. The rain came right down on us and we had to get up in the "mirk midnight"[82] and chivy around to pull our bedstead out of the way. Then the old thing kept drip-dripping all night until our nerves just went to pieces. You've no idea what an eerie noise a great drop of rain falling from the ceiling on a bare floor with a mushy little thud makes in the dead of night. It sounds like ghostly footsteps and all that sort of thing you know.

November is the month when shooting stars are in vogue. For the last two years we have been promised an especially fine display because the "Leonids" were due.[83] I suppose something went wrong with celestial machinery because they didn't turn up. This year the astronomers are looking for them with undiminished faith, but meteors seem to be like comets – rather tricky folk to pin your belief to.

Comet hunting is the pet hobby of astronomers. It must be a decidedly exciting sport, with the tail of a comet instead of a fox as a trophy of the chase. It has the charm of uncertainty, too, because, as there is no known way of branding comets,[84] an astronomer who has run a comet to earth can't be sure that it hasn't been already discovered by somebody else. In this connection let me tell you a little smile I read 'tother day.

Once upon a time there was a famous scientist – I daresay he is yet, but it sounds better that way – more fairy-tale-ish, you know – who was a noted comet-hunter, but he had an ambitious rival. Twice had this rival patiently hunted down a comet, only to find that the famous man had been there before him. The third time he thought he was sure of his prize, and gave out to the world that he had really and truly discovered a comet.

"I think," wired the famous man to him, "you will find that it is my comet of six years ago that has returned."

The disgusted rival, in a fearful passion, wired back:

"Why don't you keep your old comets chained up?"

Some time ago, in this department, I gave my opinion on the subject of hygienic rules as suggested by Polly's perplexity over them.[85] I think one thing I told her was that she would probably pick up an article next day which would contradict every word that she had just read. Since then, for my own amusement, I've been collecting a few of these contradictory statements from various journals, and here they are, suitably coupled together:

"Eat only a light breakfast" and "Breakfast should be the best meal of the day."

"Always take a good walk before breakfast," and "Never attempt to do anything on an empty stomach."

"Take a cold bath the first thing in the morning," and "The shock to the system in suddenly encountering cold or heat is very injurious."

"Do not get in the habit of sleeping during the day," and "Always take a nap in the afternoon."

"Eat only at meal times," and "Always eat whenever you feel hungry."

"Eat no meat," and "If you would be strong eat plenty of meat."

"Never eat before going to bed," and "Always take a light lunch before retiring."

"Accustom yourself to scanty indulgence in fluids," and "Drink all the water you can."

"Make a practice of rising early," and "Sleep until thoroughly rested no matter how late it is."

There you are! Just suppose anybody tried to live up to those rules! What would be her fate?

Polly broke her hand-mirror the other day and quarrelled with Jack the same evening – the latter being, to her mind, the logical consequence of the former. "No luck for seven years," says Polly.

It worries me to think how superstitious Polly is. The idea of anybody in this enlightened age believing that bad luck is attendant on breaking mirrors. Of course, I wouldn't sit down with thirteen at a table for anything you could give me – but that is an entirely different thing!

We discussed the subject around the table last night, and everybody laughed at Polly. Aunt Janet said that if Polly had passed under a ladder she might make moan, but that it was all nonsense about breaking mirrors. Theodosia said of course it was; the only thing that really brought bad luck was seeing the new moon over your left shoulder. She said she had seen the last moon that way, and she'd never had a bit of luck since.

"My new dress doesn't fit, and my new hat doesn't become me, and Jim admires that horrid girl who is visiting the B's," she said dolefully.

Ted howled at us and said we were all idiots "except Cynthia." You see, I hadn't said a word about my little odd-number belief.

It is wonderful what a reputation for wisdom you can gain if you only keep mum!

But I happen to know that Ted carries a four-leaf clover about in his pocket-book.

Speaking of the new moon reminds me that I saw it over the right shoulder, and a very pretty picture into the bargain, when I was going down Pleasant street the other evening. There was the moon, right over the dark head of the lion on the monument,[86] like a golden fairy boat piloted by one great white star, afloat in a sea of silvery blue sky, against which the graceful boughs of the leafless trees in the old cemetery came out like a delicate etching.

But, really, Polly has been unlucky of late. The other night, at the M—'s dance, she forgot and sat down on her new tulle sash, and of course it was done for.

Those tulle sashes are lovely things, however, and I advise you to get one if you can remember always to pull it aside before you sit down. Polly's is – or was – of tulle, brought down to a point in front, where it is held by a rhinestone slide. In the back it is gathered into a huge rosette, with long ends reaching to the bottom of the skirt. These ends are knotted twice, and in each knot is a tiny rhinestone slide. In the centre of the rosette there is also a rhinestone buckle!

But remember – don't – sit – down – on – it.

Here is the answer to that conundrum I propounded last week: "What verse in Genesis proves that the people in those days did sums on the ground?" The first verse of the sixth chapter, where it says, "Men began to multiply on the face of the earth."

[A Walk in the Park]

Saturday, 23 November 1901

LAST SUNDAY AFTERNOON I WENT FOR A WALK IN THE Park.[87] I took Theodosia with me, because Theodosia has been known to keep silence for as much as ten minutes at a time. Polly wanted to go, too, but I sternly said "No!" I wanted to think, and I knew that would be impossible if Polly went along. Likely as not, just as I would be getting into a rapture over the aroma of the pines or enthusing over a glimpse of the Arm[88] framed in feathery boughs, Polly would say,

"Cynthia, what color do you think I would better select for my new coat – automobile red or bottle green?"

And all my soul-inspiring visions would come down with a crash then and there.

So Theodosia and I went alone.

I suppose the Park is not so beautiful in November as in June. But the woods have charms of their own in every season. Just now they look as if they had hooded themselves in russet and brown, and fallen asleep to dream of future springs. All the ferns and countless little green wood things that carpeted the aisles of the pine-lands have turned sere and brown or vanished altogether. But the pines are still there, green and beautiful and unchanging, with gauzy veils of vapor clinging to their brows, and ripely purple shadows lurking beneath them.

Theodosia and I wandered around dreamily and enjoyed ourselves, drinking in deep breaths of the crisp, resinous autumn air. When we were tired we went and sat down by the shore. In the clump of spruce behind us several sparrows were making a great commotion – chattering and scolding and screaming. I suspect they were holding a Sparrows' Rights Convention or something of that sort. Before us was the silver-gray harbor and on our left the city, scarfed in its mists. Theodosia softly quoted Kipling's lines about "the warden of the honor of the North,"[89] as we watched the sun, breaking suddenly from a dark, low-hung cloud behind us, send a flood of splendor over the tossing waters and the purpling hills beyond.

And we both felt that our afternoon had not been wasted, and told each other so. It's good to creep away once in a while to talk with the trees and find out what rare companions they can be.

Thanksgiving comes next week, so if I want to do any moralizing about it now is my chance. Yesterday Polly said in a dismal voice that she really didn't know what she had to be thankful for. But she has lots of things, and so we all have, if we would only count them up. The trouble is, we would rather count up our troubles and groan and growl about them. That is human nature!

Thanksgiving ought to be celebrated royally, not only in the letter, but in the spirit. At least, as some historic character has remarked, we can all be thankful "that things ain't no wuss."[90]

Thanksgiving can, of course, be well and truly celebrated everywhere, but I think the Thanksgiving par excellence is one that is held in an old homestead. Thanksgiving in a new or rented house can't have the same flavor as it has in a home where the very walls are permeated with the joys and sorrows of three or four generations. When the grown-up children come home to spend the day under the old roof, with perhaps a vacant chair to remind them of one who has gone to "a far country"[91] – too far to even turn his footsteps back for that reunion – Thanksgiving is or ought to be all that its name implies.

Aunt Janet is making mince meat for Thanksgiving up at our house already. Mince meat needs to be mellowed by age, you know. What would Thanksgiving be without mince pie? This is not a conundrum, but a serious, sober question. Well, it wouldn't be Thanksgiving, that's all. When folks leave mince pie out of the day it will be time for the Government to interfere.

Polly and Theodosia and I took in the display of art needlework yesterday, and, of course, we enjoyed ourselves hugely. We would have been less than human – feminine human – if we hadn't. If there be one thing more than another over which the average woman is inclined to gloat it is fancy work. There is a perennial charm in it. Since the dawn of history, from the tent-dwellers down, the needle has played an important part in the decoration of palace and cottage. The ancient tapestries, as well as the carefully preserved samplers our great-grandmothers worked, bear testimony to that.

Oh, what pretty things can be made by skilful fingers – things so dainty that their beauty would be "their own excuse for being" even if they were of no use at all.[92]

Some of the cushions we saw yesterday were lovely – "perfectly sweet," as Polly says. Three of them, representing flowers, were especially beautiful. Theodosia liked the red one; Polly, being sentimental, liked the pink one, while I coveted the yellow one with the big purple pansy in the centre.

To be sure, when we went home and told Ted about them he sniffed in his aggravating masculine way, and said that, for his part, he wanted a cushion that you needn't be scared of – one that you could sit down on or double up under your head, or shy at the other fellow, or generally jam about to your heart's content. He said his life of late years had been a burden to him because of the elaborate cushions in the drawing-rooms and cosy corners of his lady friends.

"It takes all the zest out of existence," said Ted, "to feel that your hostess is watching out of the corner of her eye to see that you don't lean up against her favorite cushion. As for me, give me plain, comfortable, every-day cushions or give me death."[93]

That's the way the men talk, you know. Isn't it funny?

Most young ladies, at one period in their lives, seemed possessed by a desire to alter and improve upon the original spelling of their names. Ethel becomes Ethyl – suggestive of chemistry, isn't it?[94] – Lilian blossoms out as Lylian, and Mabel evolves into Maebelle. I had a very virulent attack of it myself once, and while it lasted I wrote myself down as Synthea.[95] But it's all over now, and – like measles – you never take it twice. I was left to recover from it gradually, not being blessed with a brother like the girl's in the following story, who might have cured me quickly by a similar heroic method.

A lad received a letter from his sister, Jessie, who was at a fashionable boarding school. It was signed "Jessica." He replied:

"Dear Sister, Jessica:

"Your welcome letter received. Papaica and Uncle Georgica started for Halifaxica yesterday. I have a new horse. It is a beauty. Its name is Maudica.

"Your affec. brother,

SAMICA."

The sister's next letter was signed Jessie.

Polly has very pretty little feet. That is why she has dared to adopt the new fad for lacing shoes. She laces them from the top downward, and ties the strings in a natty little bow across her foot. That is all very nice if you don't go above Number Twos.

[Cakes and Dresses]

Monday, 2 December 1901

WE HAVE HAD SOME FOREWARNINGS OF WINTER THIS last week, haven't we? The air grew cold and crisp and the poor little sparrows twittered and fluffed out their feathers; and one morning the good folks of Halifax wakened up to see a filmy scarf of white over their city – not much of a snowfall, but just enough to pick the roofs out in dark lines and make the streets for a few brief moments into avenues of marble and invest the glimpses of distant hills with an unreal, fairy-like beauty. The first snowfall of every year has a perennial novelty. There is always a certain suggestion of miracle or magic about it. We go to bed some night, looking out on a dull, gray, lifeless world from which all zest and sparkle seem to have departed. Next morning, presto, change![96]

Somebody – something – has been at work in the hours of darkness and the sad old world is transformed. And we look upon it with as much delight as if we had never seen it before – this wonderful white loveliness that came while we slept and vanishes again before the morning is far spent.

One day last week Polly and I were ambling down Pleasant street together, feeling at peace with ourselves, each other and all the world. We overtook Marian and Marian opened up enthusiastically on her new hobby – reading people's characters by their walk.

By the way, it's simply gruesome to reflect how many methods there are of giving ourselves away!

"I've been noting the characteristic gait of everybody I've met to-day," declared Marian, "and I know what sort of people they are just as well as if I'd lived with them all my life."

"Well, what is that woman like?" asked Polly, indicating a tall lady in black who was gliding up Spring Garden Road.

"She has a feline walk," said Marian sagely. "Your reputation wouldn't be safe a minute with her. She'd tear it all to little bits in her gentle, purring way."

"What about that lady in gray who just came out of the Academy of Music?" I asked.[97]

"Good erect bearing – firm, easy step," catalogued Marian. "She's just and fair and seldom fails in anything she undertakes. She has enough motion and not too much. You may be sure her household is well managed."

Just then a girl passed us in a walking hat and heavy boots with half-inch soles.

"See that stride?" said Marian. "Oh, she's aggressive – overdoes everything just as she does her walk. Too much energy – or rather, doesn't know how to use it – no tact – thumps the world into giving her what she asks."

A little woman skipped past us at the Prince street crossing and Marian exclaimed,

"That's the hen walk – short, jerky steps go with a fussy, important manner. That woman is discontented and couldn't think a big thought to save her life."

When a tall girl with a dreamy face under a gray velvet hat passed us Marian murmured,

"Notice that little hitch in her walk. She doesn't step evenly. That girl is always halting between two opinions. She can never make up her mind to anything. When she buys a new hat she tries on every one in the shop and the milliner has to pick one for her after all. Oh, going down George street, are you? Well, bi-bi. You ought to study this thing up, Cynthia – you'd find it interesting."

Polly and I went on, feeling uncomfortable. We knew Marian was looking after us and sizing us up from our gait in turn.

At the last church fair he attended Ted bought a typewritten recipe for "scripture cake." He paid a quarter for the recipe and a slice of the cake wrapped up in tissue paper. Ted didn't eat the cake – he says he intends to preserve it as a souvenir.[98] This is not meant for a reflection on the cake or the builders thereof, because it is good.

To be sure, Polly made one next day. I helped her and obeyed her orders meekly, and she says – but never mind! The ingratitude of human nature is proverbial.

Anyhow, the cake was a dismal failure. But that wasn't the fault of the recipe. Here it is:

4½ cups of 1 Kings, 4.22.[99]

1½ cups of Judges, 5.25 (last clause).[100]
2 cups of Jeremiah, 6.20.[101]
2 cups of 1 Samuel, 30.12.[102]
2 cups of Nahum, 3.18.[103]
1 cup of Nahum, 17.8.[104]
2 tablespoons of 1 Sam., 14.25.[105]
6 of Jeremiah, 17.11.[106]
2 Chronicles, 9.9, to taste.[107]
½ cup Judges, 4.19 (last clause).[108]
A pinch of Leviticus, 2.13.[109]
2 teaspoons Amos, 4.5 (baking powder).[110]

Follow Solomon's prescription for making a good boy (Proverbs 23.14),[111] and you will have a good cake.

I imagine that the secret of Polly's failure lurks in the last injunction.

The other day Ted went to a wedding in Truro, which Polly and I were unable to attend. He will never do such a rash thing again. When he got home we took him in hand, and made him tell us about it – at least, we tried to.

Of course, the first question was, "What did the bride wear?"

Ted looked wise.

"Oh," he said, in a triumphant, that-is-an-easy-one tone. "She looked fine. She wore – why, she wore a dress. It was between a cream and a blue and a brown. And she had a bonnet on."

"I suppose you mean a hat," said Theodosia, blandly. "It is one of the mysteries of life why men will persist in lumping all kinds of feminine headgear together as 'bonnets.' What was her hat like?"

"Well," said Ted, meekly. "It was – it was – well, it looked fine. It was made of fur and lace, and things."

"What was her dress trimmed with?" I asked.

"Oh, some ribbons and things," replied Ted vaguely. "And it had a lot of fuzzy stuff let in in front, and kind of three-pointed things with lace over them."

"What had the bridesmaid on?" queried Polly, undauntedly.

Ted brightened up.

"Well, I can tell you that because I took particular notice of her. She looked just fine. Her dress was of gray, flimsy stuff, with shiny trimming and those upside-down sleeves, and she had one of those fluffy, chuffy what-do-you-call-em's at the back of her neck."

"What did Fan wear?" demanded Theodosia.

"Fan looked great. She had on one of those boleros of ostrich feathers, and it was tremendously fetching."

"A bolero of ostrich feathers!" I exclaimed. "Why, Teddy-boy, there never was such a thing heard of! At least – of course – well, Fan has very original ideas. But a bolero of ostrich feathers!"

"Well," said Ted, miserably, "I don't know what it was if it wasn't a bolero. She had it round her neck."

"O-o-h, a boa!" exclaimed Polly, light breaking in at last. "Ted, you'll be the death of me yet. What did Kitty wear?"

"She had a floppy sort of hat, and one of those muslin shoulder shawls – only it looked kind of thin for muslin."

"He means a chiffon fichu," said Theodosia, pityingly. "Kitty told me she was going to get one. And what had –"

"Excuse me," said Ted, hastily. "There's a man going down the street whom I positively must see."

When Ted had gone we three looked at each other and softly, sadly sighed.

"Can we squeeze in here?" said a young man, as he and a young lady climbed into a crowded car on Hollis street the other evening.

"Well, you can if you want to, mister," said the man from the country, "but I'm thinking it would look a trifle better if you reserved that mark of affection until you reached the girl's home."[112]

[Presents and Secrets]

Saturday, 7 December 1901

THE OLD WOMAN IN THE SKY IS SHAKING HER FEATHER beds while I write, and the feathers are flying down over the world.[113] There's a Christmassy look about them. This is only the first week in December, but the air is charged with Christmas already. When you see a group of girls in solemn conclave over fancy work you may know by that token that they are exuding and imbibing new ideas about Christmas presents.

At our house an air of mystery reigns. It is considered very bad form to ask any one what she is making, and a discreet blindness is the best way of avoiding pitfalls. When I enter a room unexpectedly and see Polly or Theodosia hustling something guiltily out of sight my feelings don't dream of being hurt as they would at any other time. I just smile knowingly and begin to talk about the weather.

Then the shop windows are overflowing with Christmas. It is delightful – Polly says "scrumptious" – to stroll along the streets and gloat over all the pretty things that are going to gladden lucky people's hearts later on. The variety is bewildering, and the only trouble is where to choose. No sooner do you find something you think is just what you're looking for than you catch sight of something still nicer, and so on until you are ready to declare that the only way is to walk into a shop with your eyes shut and buy the first thing you happen to pick up.

The designs in calendars seem lovelier this year than ever before – some of them are things of beauty and joys forever.[114] The prettiest one that I have seen this year is the "Sweet Lavender" one – a drop calendar of lavender-tinted cards with a dainty girlish face smiling forth from each.

To be sure, Ted, in his usual reckless way, scoffs at these calendars. He says they are of no real use at all, and he has warned Polly and Theodosia and me that if we each give him a calendar this Christmas – as we did last year, unfortunately, not having consulted each other beforehand – we are to select big advertising calendars with good, honest figures, that you can see across the room without having to hunt them out amid a maze of flowers and pictures and things.

Ted is so deplorably practical.

There are books, dainty volumes in dainty bindings, books that you can put on your shelves lovingly and read and cherish, and re-read until they become as old friends to you, blent with memories of all fair Christmastides.

Books are among the nicest Christmas presents possible. But exercise due gumption in selecting them. Don't give Thomas a Kempis[115] or "Daily Comforts" to the society bud, or the Visits of Elizabeth[116] to your devotional aunty. Don't give a girly-boarding-school story to your football brother, or Omar Khayyam[117] to your cook, or *How to Be Happy though Married*[118] to a henpecked husband. These are the misfits that turn Christmas cheer sour.

Speaking of books. Some day I am going to promulgate a Society for the Prevention of Cruelty to Books.[119] It is sadly needed. Not long ago I lent a book to a friend of mine. It was a favorite book. When it came back, and I beheld its mutilated condition I could have cried had not fiery indignation scorched up my fount of tears. It had seventeen dog-ears and a big blister on the cover. The binding was loose, and on every page were marks that suggested a baby with sticky fingers. My poor, dear book!

But, at least, it did come back. Some books never do. They vanish mysteriously, and though at times we hear a vague rumor of their wanderings, they never return to us. Their empty spaces yawn upon our shelves, but the places thereof know them no more forever.

Oh, folks, why will you do such things? Why can't you realize that it is every whit as dishonest to keep or lend a borrowed book as it would be to keep or lend your neighbors' kettle, if you had borrowed it? People who wouldn't "steal a pin"[120] for the world seem to have absolutely no conscience as regards books.

If I were asked what is the hardest worked word in the language I should, without hesitation, answer "perfectly." If something doesn't soon occur to give it a rest the poor word will have nervous prostration.[121]

I was at a wedding the other day where it was on everybody's tongue. The bride was perfectly sweet, the church looked perfectly lovely, the groom was perfectly splendid, the flowers were perfectly superb, the bridesmaids' hats perfectly fascinating, and the dress of the bride's mother perfectly gorgeous.

I felt perfectly bewildered.

I'm glad I'm not famous. So is Polly. We came to this conclusion the other night when we were reading a newspaper article upon "What Noted Women Eat."

"Imagine how horrid it would be," remarked Polly reflectively, "to pick up a paper and see blazoned in headlines across it, 'Cynthia Crunches Cookies,' or 'Polly Prefers Peanuts.' Fancy having all your little pet foibles of diet exploited for the curiosity of the public."

Yes, there are compensations for the unknown!

Polly is making for Jack's Christmas present one of those pretty double photo frames, devoted to "My Summer Girl" and "My Winter Girl." It is of heavy cardboard, hand-painted and tied together by silk cords. The summer divinity is enshrined in daisies and forget-me-nots, and the winter goddess smiles from holly berries and leaves with a sprig of mistletoe among them.

Polly has wisely taken no chances. She has put her own photo in both places – one taken in June-time attire of lace and muslin, and one in the smartest of hats and furs.

[Preachments on Christmastide]

Saturday, 14 December 1901

(1) "I MUST GIVE JENNIE SOMETHING THIS CHRISTMAS because she gave me a present last year."

(2) "Oh, I have to give Lou a present, too, because I want to give Dot something, and Lou would be offended if she were left out."

(3) "I am not going to give Winnie anything this year because I simply can't afford a present that would be equal to the other things she will receive."

(4) "I shall make one of those big bunches of crepe paper oranges for Kitty. It's so much nicer to give something of your own handiwork, you know."

(5) "I'll be glad when Christmas is over. I have been working myself blind making presents or going a weary round of shopping every afternoon until I'm really worn out."

Now, all these foregoing remarks, heard by myself at different times during the last two weeks are to serve as pegs upon which

I mean to hang several little preachments for the benefit of humanity in general and *Echo* readers in particular.

In number one the "for value received" spirit crops up – one of the most unlovely manifestations of gift-giving. Jennie must be remembered, not because she is a dear and valued friend, or because, perchance, she is a lonely soul to whom a gift might bring a cheering realization of the real meaning of Christmas, but simply and solely because she gave you a present last year and so put you under what you consider an obligation to return it. Now, this way of looking at the matter is opposed to the very essence of Christmastide.

No gift should be given from a sense of obligation – and a false sense at that. If Jennie knew the motive of your gift do you think she would care to receive it? I am very sure she would not. "The gift without the giver is bare,"[122] and if it be tainted with the stain of commercialism it is worse than bare – it is an insult to the recipient. There is nothing on earth so abominable as a "duty" gift.

Then, number two indicates a still baser motive. Lou must have a gift, and one equally as nice as Dot's, or she will be offended. Well, my Christmas giver, ask yourself this question. Is Lou's friendship, if dependent on the giving or not giving of a gift, worth retaining? Is it even a real friendship at all? I would not consider it so. The friend who is worth having is not going to be alienated from you because you do not give her a Christmas box. Don't desecrate your friendship and the spirit of Christmas by giving somebody something just because you fear she will be annoyed if you don't. Let all the Lous get offended if they will be so foolish, but don't let yourself cater to this one of the little foxes who are doing their utmost to gnaw the very heart out of a beautiful and better-deserving old custom.

Number three reeks with positive snobbishness. You are not going to give Winnie anything because you have a selfish, unworthy fear that your inexpensive little gift will seem trifling and poor to her compared to those which her wealthier friends will give her.

Leaving out the wrong to yourself which springs from all such motives, you are doing a wrong to your friend. You imply that all she cares for is the intrinsic value of her gifts – that the love and real friendship that may have prompted them count for nothing at all. Certainly, you are not very complimentary. And if your implied estimate of her be false and if she honestly value her gifts for the givers' sakes then you are going to deprive her of a very real joy and pleasure when you refuse to give her any token of your affection for her. She will have a perfect right to feel grieved and hurt at your omission. Oh, don't let snobbishness, that vilest of all small vices, creep into your heart now of all times. There are good and excellent reasons for not giving a gift at some times, but number three is not among them.

Number four has a comical aspect to me.

I am not decrying the idea that a gift which you make yourself, putting into it dainty handiwork and that individuality which is lacking so often in a purchased gift, makes the very nicest Christmas present possible. It is true. What I am laughing at is the perversion of this idea that obtains in some people's minds. There is no sense in supposing that a bunch of crepe paper oranges which are neither useful nor ornamental and like no oranges that ever grew on any tree, is better than a "boughten" thing can be simply because you "made it yourself" and – in a whisper – "it didn't cost you much." Kitty has my sympathy. Were I she I would make a bonfire of the oranges and so get minutes of fun out of them anyway.

To my mind, my "fifthly" is the most serious of all, and indicates the plague spot which, if not checked, sooner or later will destroy all real happiness and pleasure in the Christmas season. There is something wrong when people are glad that Christmas is over. When Christmas becomes a burden and strain on health, purse or nerves it is time to call a halt.

The woman who overtasks herself in making Christmas presents has lost sight of the fundamental truth of Christmas. It ought to be a season of peace and good-will. But there can be no peace about it when your nerves are all on end through bending for hours over needlework or poring over the problem of how to make one dollar do the work of two at the bargain counter. And as for the good-will there will be none of it either. More likely you will be out of temper with everybody and everything. Take things easier, dear fellow creatures. Make or buy only such Christmas gifts as you can afford in time and money and give them with all sincerity of motive to the friends you are fortunate enough to have and to value.

I believe that in the foregoing paragraphs I have narrowly escaped being serious. To redeem my reputation for frivolity, I must tell you about some of the new shoes. They are so dainty this year, rivalling Cinderella's famous slippers. Black velvet has become fashionable and the results are charming. Black velvet slippers are not only becoming, but comfortable – a combination not always found. Polly has a new pair – Polly's feet are "one of her weak points, don't you know" – which are very plain, having only a small silver buckle to relieve their sombre richness. On Polly's toes they look as the slippers of a French beauty of the Louis reigns might have looked.[123]

Theodosia has a lovely pair for dancing of white brocade, embroidered with gold thread, with a sparkling buckle on the toe. They're so pretty I don't see how she can ever have the heart to spoil them by dancing in them.

I have come to the conclusion –

That when anyone says that she "thinks it is her duty to tell you," you may prepare for something disagreeable.

That to confer a favor ungracefully is a good way to make its recipient your mortal foe.

That while it may be hard to keep your illusions it is harder to lose them.

That photographs and epitaphs are not to be trusted.

That if everybody at all times and upon every occasion told the truth, the whole truth, and nothing but the truth,[124] life wouldn't be worth living.

That it doesn't pay to be always cheerful moralists to the contrary notwithstanding.

That most folks hate to be surprised.

That a flattering mirror is a promoter of amiability.

That gossip is an aid to digestion.

That tact is the spice of life.[125]

And, finally, that it is of no use coming to conclusions because when you think you have arrived at one you find out it isn't the right one after all.

[Illusions of Christmas]

Monday, 23 December 1901

I BELIEVE WE ARE GOING TO HAVE A WHITE CHRISTMAS after all. I'm so glad. I hate a "green" Christmas. You know, when a Christmas is a dirty-grayey-browney affair, looking as if it had been left over about a hundred years ago, and had been in soak ever since it is called a green Christmas. Don't ask me why! As Lord Dundreary says, "There are thome thingth no fellow can underthtand."[126]

We don't get a white Christmas oftener than once in a blue moon, so it is something to be duly thankful for. It is the only real, guaranteed Christmas. Any other kind is a fraud and imitation. Always ask your dealer for a white Christmas and insist on having it.

Lots of snow, making the world look like a magnified Christmas card, crisp, exhilarating air and jingles of sleigh bells everywhere – that's as it should be. No "green" Christmas for me, an it please ye.[127]

I hear that Santa Claus is coming around on an automobile this year. The 20th century is certainly going to do away with all the little romance that is yet left us. There was a subtle charm about a benevolent, itinerant old saint roaming at large on Christmas eve with a sleigh and bells and reindeer. When we were very, very small, and deluded and happy, how we used to sit up in the bed and listen for the pawing of those reindeer's feet on the roof – wondering dreamily at the same time how they managed to get up there at all, or hang on when they did, so steep was the sloping roof of the old house. But then, of course, they were fairy reindeer, and fairy reindeer can do anything. When we heard the snow slip from the eaves we knew they had dislodged it, and at any louder creak than usual we knew it was Santa Claus coming down the chimney, and hoped that the fire would be quite out so that the good old soul wouldn't burn himself or get singed.

In the morning we used to go out and look for the prints of the reindeer's feet in the snow. We never found them, alas! Once we thought we did, but a scoffing older brother, who was nine and a cynic, said they were only sheep tracks. I suppose they were.

But now Santa Claus comes on the automobile!!!!

My belief in Santa Claus was the first illusion to be stripped away from me. The process has been going on ever since, and is always painful, but not nearly as much so as it was that first time. We get hardened to it in time; as the Irishman said, you can get used to anything, even to being hanged.[128] But who of us ever forgets the cruel agony we feel when we first behold a beloved illusion lying stone-dead before our eyes – murdered, most likely, by some brutal creature a year or so older than ourselves. All the philosophy in the world can't cure that sting.

And how we hate the people who destroy our illusions. This is illogical, of course. We ought to be grateful to them – oh, very! But human nature is always illogical. I have forgiven – and forgotten – a great many people, but I shall never forgive the girl who told me that there was no such person as Santa Claus – that it was just my father and mother who put the things in my stockings.[129]

I was six years old and she was eight. I thought she was grown up. I had admired and liked her before that – she was my pet idol among the "big girls." After that I hated her. I was afraid of her, too. She represented to me a person to be avoided, because of the power she might possess of inflicting more pain. The next thing she would tell me might be that there were no fairies.

Perhaps she wondered why I so suddenly gave over worshipping at her shrine. If ever the time arrives when I feel that I can really forgive that girl I shall know that I have attained to a high level of Christian virtue.

Don't destroy other people's illusions – this is the moral of the foregoing. I am as fond of morals as the "Duchess" in Wonderland![130] They will never forgive you for it probably. It will make them unhappy, and it doesn't do you any good. Just because you are so unfortunate as to have lost all your own illusions don't, out of mean malice and envy, try to rob other people of theirs. There is no need. The world will do it soon enough for them. An illusion is a brittle thing. The least little rude touch and – w-r-r-r – it is gone forever, into dust and fragments. Handle other people's illusions very tenderly, or – better still – leave them alone. And if you have a few of your own left yet cherish and guard them jealously. When you have lost them all you will become a cynic and a nuisance. If ever the time comes when everybody has become too wise and logical to have illusions "may the present scribe be dead."[131]

What a power Christmas has, to be sure! How the heart thrills to it and all it stands for – sweet old memories, the knitting closer of cords that may have strained slack through time or absence, and the realization of our common brotherhood. There is nothing in all the world so beautiful as the spirit of Christmastide. Friendly messages and gifts wing their way over many lands and seas, joyous family reunions take place in sacred old homesteads, and for one day at least the sad old world rejoices and dreams that it is young again.

Just suppose, if Christmas were to be blotted out of the calendar! Would the most daring iconoclast in the world think of trying to do it?

Are you going home for Christmas? That is the question everybody is asking everybody else. I hope you are. Christmas anywhere else than home has a sour flavor like an unripe orange.[132]

At our house we are resting on our oars[133] – what time we are not wrapping up and addressing Christmas presents. Our work is done. Everybody is remembered that we haven't forgotten, and we have tried to have as few misfits as possible. Theodosia undertook to pilot Ted through the mazes of his Christmas shopping. I did it last year in the integrity of my heart and the innocency of my hands. I'm wiser this year. When Ted asked me to go I said I had a very pressing engagement, and wouldn't he ask Theodosia. Theodosia likes to be obliging and, besides, she didn't know, so she went off gaily enough, poor thing.

That evening, after Polly and I had fanned her, and given her hot drinks, and rubbed her head with menthol[134] Theodosia recovered sufficiently to sit up and give us a detailed account, partly pantomimic, of her experiences Christmas shopping with Ted. She said I ought to have warned her. But I didn't see the necessity. It's such fun, after you've fallen into a trap yourself, to watch the next person being neatly nipped in it.

Speaking of traps. Ted came home the other evening from a call, and told us this story.

"I was down to see the T's this evening, and some other fellows were in, and the girls got us to run an obstacle race. We all went out to the hall, and a lot of things were strewn down its length – baskets and footstools and things like that. Then we blindfolded one of the chaps and started him to walk down the hall. The point was to avoid touching any of the 'obstacles.' He did pretty well, and then came my turn. I thought the girl who was tying up my eyes took rather long over it, but she got it done at last, and I started. I went down the hall slowly and deliberately, lifting my feet as high as I could at every step, and putting them down as carefully as if I were treading on eggshells. I didn't touch a thing, and thought I was getting on splendidly and I couldn't imagine why all the rest were shouting with laughter. But when I got to the end, and took the bandage from my eyes, I understood. All the 'obstacles' had been removed, and I had walked painstakingly down an empty hall."

To each and all Cynthia wishes the merriest of merry Christmases, peace, joy and good-will, and gifts galore.

[Retrospection and Resolutions]

Monday, 30 December 1901

WELL, CHRISTMAS IS OVER. POLLY AND THEODOSIA and I have just begun to recover from the effects. I am afraid that deep down in our hearts we are glad that it will be a whole year before another Christmas. But do you think that we would admit it? No, indeed. Perish the thought! We had a splendid time, of course! And now that we have partially recovered from the day-after-Christmas indigestion, and have counted up the spoil we are ready to go on our way rejoicing.[135] To be sure, our nerves are still in a bad condition. Theodosia is sleepy, Polly is snappy and I am stupid. Ted says – but there! Men can never understand these things!

I hope you all hung up your stockings and got them full. We didn't have a white Christmas after all, but that wasn't my fault. I prophesied one and that was all I could do.

Did you get any calendars given you? I got seven, Polly got six and Theodosia didn't even get one. So are things unevenly divided up on this planet.

It is about time now that we were thinking about our New Year resolutions, isn't it? You always make some of course. I do. Who doesn't? But do you keep them? Ah! As Kipling says, "that's another story."[136] Besides, there would be no fun in making New Year resolutions if one couldn't break them.

Folks work off their Christmas indigestion making vows of reformation for the New Year. Your conscience always troubles you when your stomach isn't in good working order. If we never overate at this season of the year we would never feel that we wanted to make resolutions. Then, when we have recovered our normal health, we break them all as cheerfully as possible.

The making of many resolutions is a sign of extreme youth. As our years increase our resolutions decrease. Time was when I made a solemn business of it. I wrote all my resolutions elaborately down on a sheet of foolscap, with the date and a verse of Scripture at the top. They used to fill one sheet and sometimes overflow on another.

"Now," I used to say, gravely, "I will tack this document up on the wall over my writing desk. When I break a resolution I will mark a cross against it. It will be my one great aim during the coming year to have as few crosses as possible on this paper."

Well, about the middle of February I would take that list of resolutions and sneak down to the kitchen fire with it. There would be so many crosses on it by that time that you couldn't see the resolutions.

Nowadays, I don't write my resolutions out. I still make a few from force of habit, of course, but I keep mum about them, so that nobody knows when they are broken. This year I am just going to make one, and I am also going to make what somebody has called a "Herculaneum" effort to keep it.[137]

Ted heard Polly and me discussing our New Year resolutions the other night, and he said if we were so anxious to keep them why not fine ourselves five cents every time we broke one. Polly said it would be bad enough to break your resolutions without breaking yourself, too. I demanded tragically, if he thought resolutions were made to be kept?

Ted never makes any himself. He says that whenever he makes a resolution he is immediately possessed with a wild, frenzied desire to rush out and break it. Consequently, he says, New Year resolutions are a menace to the well-being of the State.

But if you want to make some don't let the foregoing remarks discourage you. Probably they are more the outcome of my post-Christmas cynicism than of my real belief. Even if you do break them in the long run the effort to keep them is worth something. Here's luck to you in the keeping of yours.

In old-fashioned debating clubs and rural "literary societies" a favorite subject about this season used to be, "The year that has just passed." The local orators thrashed it out exhaustively, and drew all the morals possible from it.

The end of the year is, as a general thing, somewhat given over to retrospection. We like to overhaul our memories as well as our consciences, on New Year's eve, as we sit before a dying fire – it must always be dying to be properly romantic – watching the Old Year out. We grow dreamy and sad and a wee bit sentimental. We recall the loves and hatreds, the pleasures and sorrows, the successes and failures of the past twelve months. We think of our flirtations, and wonder where the Toms, Dicks and Harrys[138] are now, and if they have forgotten. We sigh softly, and quote scraps of poetry that occur to us as appropriate. In short, we get out Memory's treasure-box and rummage among its motley contents. We have the vague regret that everyone experiences at the turning of a life page. Good or bad, earnest or frivolous, it is written and filed away in the archives of Eternity. We will never have a chance to correct its mistakes. Old Father Time has no proof-readers.[139]

Then the clock strikes twelve and we open the door to let the Old Year go limping out and the New Year come joyously in. "The King is dead. Long live the King!"[140]

Here are some adjustable New Year resolutions:

During the coming year:

I will not lose my temper, but only mislay it occasionally.

I will never repeat gossip save to a trustworthy person.

I will try to improve other people's minds.

I will not get into debt if I can help it.

I will not tell any fibs except in the way of business.

I will be kind and amiable when I feel like it.

I will early to bed and early to rise at least once a week.

I will try to bear other people's misfortunes with equanimity.

I will be cheerful and smiley when everything is going right.

I will accomplish a great deal if nothing interferes to prevent me.

I will go to church regularly on fine Sundays.

I will not tell anybody that she has a cold.

I will never use slang except under great provocation.

I will not growl at the weather when it is fine.

I will never say anything to my friends' faces that I would not say behind their backs.

I will not make puns except when the temptation is irresistible.

A happy New Year to you all is Cynthia's wish for her readers.

[Mistakes and Blunders]

Monday, 6 January 1902

One must say something about the weather, if only from a sense of duty. Like the poor, we have it always with us, and it is a blessing, for without it what would we find to help along a conversation that had struck a snag? A sapient remark about the weather will bridge over many of "those awful silences."[141] Without it we would be lost, not having revolutions to help us out. In Chile and Venezuela, I have heard, they never talk about the weather. Instead of saying, as we do, "Isn't it a lovely day?" or "Do you think it is going to rain?" they say, "What are the prospects for a revolution today?" or "Wasn't that a fine revolution we had yesterday?"

But really, just now it isn't safe to commit yourself to an opinion about the weather. It reminds me of nothing so much as the alligator in the old rhyme who "wouldn't go along and wouldn't stand still, but just kept bobbing up and down."[142]

The other night we were talking about psychology, and Theodosia told us a bicycle story in her own inimitable way. You may not all at once see the connection between psychology and bicycles, but Theodosia evidently did.

"It is queer," she remarked, dreamily, "what thoughts will flash into a person's mind at times. For instance, now, the time that bicycle ran away with me last summer. What bicycle? Oh, I forgot! I never told you – I was afraid you'd laugh at me.

"Well, it was while I was out at Bridgetown in September, and a lot of us went on a bicycle picnic over North Mountain.[143] I hadn't my own wheel, so I had to borrow one, and the only one to be had was an old thing that a summer boarder had left at the M——s. I didn't like the look of it a bit – somehow it made me think of those horses who are always putting their ears back, don't you know? But beggars can't be choosers,[144] so I started off with it, and for a while it did very well.

"Finally, Charley and I got separated from the rest – somehow – and we were wheeling down a slight incline, when I made the horrible discovery that my wheel was running away with me. There was no doubt about it. I kept going faster and faster, and the harder I backpedalled the faster I went. Charley was left behind in no time. I lost my nerve, and the next thing I lost was the pedals. I had to hold my feet up then, and I held them up until I really thought they'd drop off at the ankles. At last I had to let them down, expecting they'd be dragged clean off. But the wheel was so high they didn't touch the ground, and still I kept on in my mad career.

"Presently I saw a simply awful hill right before me. It looked as steep as the side of a house. I knew for a certainty that I would be killed if I kept on. I also knew that I would be killed if I jumped. But I thought to be killed at the top of the hill would be more convenient for my friends than half way down, because they would not have so far to carry me. So I shut my eyes, bid farewell to life and jumped.

"I landed under a clump of young spruce trees. I opened my eyes. I knew when I jumped that I was going to be killed, and so my first clear and distinct thought was 'I am dead!' I quite believed it at the time, but after a few minutes I came to the conclusion that I really could not be dead after all, because I found myself wondering if I had spoiled my hat in my fall, and that would be absurd if one were dead. But, of course, something must have happened, and my next brilliant thought was, 'No, I am not dead, but I am unconscious.'[145] I kept still for a while, and then it dawned upon me that there was really nothing the matter with me. So I crawled up in a rather dusty condition, and assured Charley, who had just arrived on the scene, that I wasn't a bit hurt.

"Charley found that fiendish wheel half way down the hill, but nothing in the world would have induced me to mount it again. So I walked home and pushed it along. But what I want you psychologists to tell me is this. What made me think those queer thoughts when I fell?"

None of us could tell her, but we discussed the matter as wisely as if we knew all about it. Ted discovered the moral this time. It is, that you shouldn't ride on a borrowed bicycle.

Did any of you ever write "friendship letters"? If you haven't never do. Those of you who have will know why I give this advice. "Friendship letters" are worse than ghosts!

Perhaps some of you don't know what friendship letters are. Well, this is how they are built. You and some friend decide to write each other a letter, to be read at some future date – five, eight or ten years from the date of writing. The letters are written and sealed up; the name and date of opening are written on the envelope; they are exchanged and kept inviolate until the time comes when they are to be opened and read – that is, if your curiosity doesn't compel you to open them the day after you get them.

When Polly and I were at school the poetical girl of our class had an inspiration, as she thought. At a class symposium we were holding in her room – aided by chocolate caramels and other unlawful eatables – she proposed that the whole eight of us should exchange "friendship letters" – to be read a certain number of years – Polly has forbidden me to tell how many – from that night.

We thought it such a fine romantic idea then, and we put it into effect straightway. Ever since, seven letters have been reposing in a box at the bottom of my rubbish trunk. The other night the anniversary came around. Polly and I remembered our letters just in time, hunted them out and read them.

It was really a horrible experience. There was nothing romantic about it. Those letters seemed like ghostly visitations from the past. They emphasized all the little changes that had come about since they were written. Some of the writers were married; others were far away, busy women of the working world. Some we had quarrelled with and didn't love any more. Yet here in these mocking letters they were vowing undying affection. One girl was dead, and her letters gave us the uncanny feeling of a missive from the spirit world[146] – a voice calling to us across the grave – calling jokes and frivolity, too, which increased the uncanniness. Altogether we felt blue and disgruntled when we finished with those letters, jolly as most of them were, and we vowed we would never write any more.

"They've made me feel as if I were about a hundred years old and haunted by spectres of a mis-spent past," said Polly, plaintively.

Some people accuse Theodosia of being strong-minded, but she isn't. As a proof of my statement here is a way she has invented, all out of her own sleek brown head, to perfume her gown. When nearly ready to go out she hangs her gown upon a chair back and then, taking her chafing dish,[147] she heats water to the boiling point and pours in a few drops of lavender. When the whole is simmering she sets it on the floor, minus the chafing dish, putting the flame out first, and shakes her dress over the fumes until the whole garment is infused with a delicious elusive hint of perfume. Then Theodosia puts it on and thus, arrayed in sweetness, goes forth conquering and to conquer.[148]

"Yes, he made a big mistake," said Polly with a sigh.

"I don't call it a mistake," said Ted majestically. "I call it a blunder."

"Well, isn't that the same thing?" asked Polly.

"No, there is a difference," said Ted. "For instance, suppose a fellow went to call on a friend, put an old umbrella on the stand and took away a new one when he left, that would be a mistake; but suppose he put down a new one and took away an old one, that would be a blunder, d'ye see?"

Polly admitted that Ted had scored a point.

[Unlikeable People]

Monday, 13 January 1902

EVERYBODY SEEMS TO HAVE COLDS JUST AT PRESENT. I have one. I know that I have – not so much on account of the discomfort it causes me, although that is bad enough, as because every single person I have met since I caught it – or since it caught me – has informed me that I have a cold!

It's terribly aggravating. My informants' intentions are good, so I cannot retaliate by some bitingly sarcastic speech which might hurt their feelings, even when it relieved mine. Besides, I can never think of my sarcasms in time. When I do think of them I say them then and there under my breath, and it is a relief, but it does not prevent the next person I meet from cheerfully saying, "Why, you've got a cold," in a tone which implies that they have just made an astonishing new discovery.

But the worm will turn. I have reached my last bound of endurance. I am not going to say what I will do to the next person who tells me I have a cold – but be very sure of this, he or she – for I shall be no respecter of sex or age – will never make a like remark to me again.

I dare say I've said the same thing to people lots of times myself. If so, I beg their pardon, individually and collectively, now, and promise that I won't ever be so bad again – 'deed and 'deedy, I won't. I've found out what it is like. My friends and acquaintances may go on contracting cold after cold, to the lasting injury of their health and temper, but I shall never tell them what they are doing.

Neither will I tell people what to do for a cold – unless they ask me, of course. In that case I shall begin at A and go through the whole alphabet of the remedies that people have advised me to try for a cold. I never used any of them myself, so they will be as good as new. They are all reliable, and will cure the most obstinate cold in the world. I know this is so because the folks who advised them said so. And they are good people who speak the truth.

When we were around the fire the other evening at our house, in a purple winter dusk, with the firelight playing hide-and-seek in the corners, we fell to talking about the people we didn't like – in a general way, of course.[149] We didn't particularize. That is always dangerous. Theodosia led off.

"Preserve me from the candid friend," she exclaimed.[150] "I don't claim this remark as original. Somebody said it or something very like it before. But that was an accident. If he had not said it I would have.

"The candid friend is the one who sets out to reform you. Now, I don't like being reformed – nobody does. It is also her province to pull you up on all points of dress and behavior. I have a candid friend. When I see her coming in time I always run, but sometimes she pounces on me unexpectedly.

"'Now, my dear Theodosia,' she says, 'I hope you won't mind me speaking about it, but really I wouldn't wear that hat if I were you. It doesn't become you at all – it makes your nose look puggier than usual.'

"I am expected to be grateful for this. Another time it is,

"'Now, my dear, do you know if I were you I'd not go around quite so much. You're overdoing yourself, and you're looking frightfully thin and miserable. Everybody is noticing it.'

"Every time I see her she has some speech like this to make about my dress or appearance or doings. She prides herself on saying these things to her friends' faces and not behind their backs. Now, I wouldn't care a bit what she said behind my back because then I wouldn't have to look as if I were pleased and thankful. Some day, when I have scraped up enough moral courage I am going to be candid with her. Perhaps it will cure her. They say that like is apt to cure like."[151]

Aunt Janet's pet aversion was the meddler. Being a woman Aunt Janet personified her type in the feminine gender, but masculine meddlers may also ponder her protest in their hearts.

"When I say 'Good Lord deliver us' in church," said Aunt Janet solemnly, "I always add under my breath 'from the meddler.' A certain meddling person I know is my besetting sin.[152] I never can feel a bit like a Christian with her. All the old heathen in me comes right to the surface. She is always loaded with good advice. She knows what I ought to do much better than I know myself. Her way is always the best and she means to make me take it. The more a thing isn't any of her business the more she mixes herself up in it. But there, children, I'm going to stop. I shall say too much if I don't. The mere thought of that kind of people gets on my nerves."

"I can get along with anybody except the person who tells me how ill she is or was and how many pills she had to take and what the doctor said and how she used to feel in the mornings," said Polly in a breath.

"'A bore is a person who insists on talking about himself when I want to be talking about myself,'" quoted Ted oracularly.[153]

"No," said Polly severely, "that cap doesn't fit me, Ted, so I'm not going to wear it.[154] I know I've lots of faults – you take care of that – but telling people about my pains and aches and woeses is not among them. At the C——s party the other evening Mrs. So-and-so kept me one whole hour telling me about her attack of illness last spring and its consequences. She enjoyed it so much I hadn't the heart to stop her even if I could have. But I had an ache in every one of my bones myself by the time she got through."

Marian, who had dropped in, stopped pulling Bobs' ears – Bobs is our cat, so christened the day after Paardeberg[155] – long enough to say that she hated people who were always smiling.

"You know the kind," she said. "They have what Jack calls an 'everlasting grin.' I don't think they ever take it off even when they're asleep. They smile in season and out of season.[156] They never laugh heartily – because it might disturb their smile, I suppose. I've never read Dante's *Inferno*,[157] but I hope he had a special circle for the professional smilers."

Ted didn't like the gag man.

"One of these chaps who go about propounding conundrums and catches to all and sundry. If you ever hear of me being tried for manslaughter know all men by these presents[158] that the victim is one of those fellows. I'm a patient, long-suffering chap – Polly knows that – which is the only reason I haven't done it before."

For my own part I do not like the people who are always right. Not, mind you, the people who merely think they are always right. I can afford to disregard them. But the people who really and truly are always right. They are terrible because they are so infallible. You know beforehand that there is no chance for you if you differ from them and your respect deserts you then and there.

How we would love them if they made even one weeny teeny mistake! But they never do. They are incapable of it. And so, of course the rest of us, who are always blundering in some way or another cordially detest them for their unlikeness.

I suppose the law of the association of ideas is remotely responsible for the story that has just popped into my head in connection with the foregoing paragraph. I read or heard it somewhere recently.

A woman who believed in the possibility of attaining to sinless perfection was arguing with one who didn't.

"Well," said the latter, "did you ever hear of any human being who was really perfect?"

The former nodded and looked sad.

"Yes," she said, "I did – just one. She was my husband's first wife."[159]

All my foregoing remarks are just bristling with morals, but I will refrain from commenting on them. I will leave them to point themselves.

How are your New Year resolutions coming on?

[The Fierce White Light of Perfect Truth]

Saturday, 18 January 1902

THESE ARE THE DAYS WHEN WE HEAR THE SLEIGH BELLS tinkling along city streets and winding country roads, in the daytime and beneath the stars. Don't they sound exhilarating? Especially if you are behind them! I have always thought that the very soul of music was expressed in the clear far-away tinkles of sleigh bells drifting across snowy hills on the clear, crisp air of a moonlit winter night or in that perfect half hour that follows the rose and saffron of a fine sunset.

There are different kinds of sleigh drives. Polly now, likes the snug, furry little cutter, "built for two,"[160] behind a sleek-coated nag with a "half-past two" record. Well, that isn't a bad way. But there are others!

I think the way to get the most real, genuine fun out of a sleigh drive is for about a dozen cheerful folks to pile into what is known in country districts as a "pung," with plenty of straw and fur robes, and start off somewhere in a happy-go-lucky fashion, singing all the good old sleighing glees you can think of – or hymns if you are going to prayer-meeting. Of course in town you can't very well do this – you would probably get run in as public nuisances and at least would attract a good deal of undesirable attention.

Speaking of hymns reminds me. Once upon a time I was with a party of friends out to just such a sleigh drive. We had just escaped from the thralldom of high school examinations and we felt very light-hearted. It was a pitchy dark night – that is to say the night was dark and the roads pitchy, oh very – and we were all singing merrily and enjoying ourselves. It was "Old Hundred"[161] we finally struck into and we were making such a noise that we never heard or saw a sleigh coming towards us until we were all tangled up with it. The driver thereof was an honest old farmer from Wayback and I suppose he didn't like to have his meditations so rudely disturbed. He was very cross and he said some horrid swear-words, really and truly he did. They hurt our feelings so much that when we finally got sorted out and started on our way again we didn't sing any more of

"Old Hundred," but struck up instead, "Hark from the Tombs a Doleful Sound" as being more appropriate.[162]

The next time you are out in the country on a good snowy road full of pitches get your driver to gallop through them. It's the most exciting sport I know of. You get about sixteen different kinds of exercise all at once, including the vocal chords. Because, of course, you must scream at every pitch. There's no fun if you don't.

Did you ever stop to think how hard it is to tell "the truth, the whole truth and nothing but the truth"?[163] Of course, I don't mean that you or I deliberately tell falsehoods in our daily walk and conversation, or even concoct more than our necessary share of little cream-colored fibs. Neither do I mean those rash statements we make in moments of irritation, such as "I'd give the world for something-or-other," when we know perfectly well we would make a terrible fuss if we had to pay a dollar for it. I just mean that probably hardly a day passes in which all we say would bear investigation in the fierce white light of perfect truth.

Don't get angry, please. I'm just as bad as the rest. I'll tell you how I found it out.

The other night, around the table, we were talking of this, and Ted gave utterances to the views recorded above. Polly and Theodosia and I were very angry.

Theodosia said, just a little bit priggishly:

"Ted, I always tell the truth. I am very careful to – the plain, unvarnished truth. It is horrid for you to insinuate that I do not."

Ted's eyes twinkled.

"That's because you never caught yourself. Do you girls really suppose that you can go through a day without telling a little fib unless you want to get yourselves into hot water?"

"Why, of course we can," I said indignantly.

"Well, I dare you to," said Ted.

Of course that was unbearable. We couldn't take a dare. So the three of us vowed that the next day we would watch every word we said and prove Ted's statements to be false.

You know, I thought it would be easy.

Well, the next morning I started out confidently; and I did really get on pretty well through the morning, although I meditated so long before answering any question put to me that people all thought something was the matter. But at lunch time my troubles began. I went to lunch with Jen. She had on a new hat. Really, it was the worst-looking hat I've seen for a long time. It was in glaring taste and it made her look like a fright – there is no other way of putting it.

Well, presently Jen said:

"Cynthia, how do you like my new hat? I trimmed it myself and I am quite proud of my success.[164] Don't you think it is very becoming. Tell me honestly what your opinion of it is."

Wasn't I in a nice fix? I knew Jen would never forgive me if I did tell her my honest opinion. I hesitated. We all know that the woman who hesitates is lost.[165]

"I – I – think it's very pretty," I said feebly.

"And becoming?" persisted Jen.

"Very," I said shamelessly. The second step is always so much easier than the first. But as I said it I thought I could see Ted's impish grin over Jen's shoulder.

Then I met Mrs. B. Mrs. B. is not a favorite of mine. Speaking candidly I do not like her. She wanted me to do something for her. I didn't want to do it but to refuse without any good reason would have stamped me as a crank. So I said I would.

"You don't mind, do you?" she said. "Oh, not at all," I answered.

When I went home Great-Aunt Rachel was there. The next day was my birthday and she had brought me a present. It was an ugly old-fashioned brooch with a lock of Great-Uncle Hezekiah's hair in it. I had never seen Great-Uncle Hezekiah, who died years before I was born, and I couldn't feel very enthusiastic. Besides, I knew that I would have to wear that brooch continually, or the donor would never forgive me. I had to thank her for it and I didn't feel one bit thankful.

When I went upstairs I found Polly crying in her snuggery.[166] She was a poor little woe-begone Polly. It seems that she had told the truth all day and in some very trying situations. Polly has a good deal of moral backbone, you know.

"But oh, Cynthia," she sobbed. "I've made more enemies to-day than I did in all my life before. And they will never forgive me, I am sure. And, oh dear! Jack came in this evening – and – and – we got to talking about – about faults – and Jack said wouldn't I honestly tell him what – what I thought was his most g-glaring fault – s-so he could correct it – and I d-did – and he got so angry – and we quarrelled – and I wish – I were dead – I do."

Then Theodosia came in and told her experience. She had got into a peck of troubles too and had not even Polly's consolation of success, for at the last she had told her hostess at an afternoon tea that she had had a lovely time when the truth was she had been bored to death.

"I never thought what I was saying until it was out," she declared. "Won't Ted exult."

But Ted was good as gold. He didn't rub it in a bit and he praised Polly's grit and told her Jack would be all right again soon.

It's all very sad when one thinks of it.

Do you want to read your friends' characters from their handwriting? Here are a few hints:

Lines standing upward indicate a hopeful disposition; downward, the writer easily desponds. Straight across the page, a well-balanced mind. If the o's and a's are always well closed the writer is secretive; if open, inclined to be confidential. Heavy down-strokes, dashes or cross marks indicate strong will and intensity. Unnecessary flourishes indicate vanity or conceit. If the letters grow smaller towards the end of a word, don't trust the writer. If larger, a good disposition is indicated. Extreme care in punctuation, etc., means a finicky bent. Many dashes indicate a rollicking temperament. Letters straight up and down are the sign of a logical mind; slanted, of a sentimental turn. Large, free running hand means generosity; sometimes extravagance; small, cramped writing, the reverse. Also, if there are a lot of x's in the lower left hand corner it is probably a love-letter.

There are different ways. Here is one I read about recently:

He had his little speech all written out for several days beforehand and it ran thus:

"I have called, Mr. Wealthyman, to tell you frankly that I love your daughter and I have her assurance that my affection is returned and I hope you will give your consent for her to become my wife. I am not a rich man, but we are young and strong and are willing to fight the battle of life together, and –"

There was a great deal more to it and he could say it all glibly before he left home. When he stood in the presence of Papa Wealthyman this is what he said:

"I – I – that is – Mr. Wealthyman – I tell you frankly that – that – I – your daughter loves me – and – and – I have called – to – to – to – to – frankly ask you to – to – be my wife – that is – I – we – she – no – we are willing to fight – that is – we – we are young and can fight – er – no – I hope you understand me?"

I hope he did, too, don't you? What is the moral of this? Oh, there isn't any.

[Seeing and Perceiving]

Monday, 27 January 1902

NOWADAYS FOLKS ARE DOING THINGS FOR WHICH, HAD they done or tried to do them a couple of hundred years ago, they would have been sent to Heaven in the shape of smoke. Marconi[167] would probably have been regarded as the very archfiend himself and instead of travelling comfortably around Cape Breton and Newfoundland and being feted and honored everywhere he goes he would have been treated to the rack and thumb screws and finally have made his exit from the stage of life as the "star" in an auto-da-fe performance.[168] I really believe that the world is getting a little more sensible as it grows older. Nowadays it does honor to its wizards instead of burning them.

But really all this wireless telegraphy business makes me ask what are we coming to? I read an article recently wherein it said that before long a thought-reading process would be perfected by which we could all read – and be read by – our friends as easily as the latest book. Whereat I murmured softly and devoutly to Theodosia:

"May the present scribe be dead."[169]

I am very thankful to reflect that the thought-reader will not be perfected in my time. But when it is we can imagine something like this taking place:

Mrs. A., armed with a concealed thought-reader, calls upon Mrs. B. Mrs. B. receives her enthusiastically and exclaims:

"You dear thing! I'm so glad to see you. It seems a perfect age since you've been in."

Mrs. A. smiles grimly. She knows that Mrs. B. is thinking,

"Bothersome old thing! What ever made her come today. She's always gadding about somewhere."

Then the conversation, on Mrs. B.'s part, proceeds as follows, all perfectly intelligible to Mrs. A.

"It's a perfect day, isn't it? (Mercy! what a hat! Doesn't the woman know she's making a fright of herself.) Oh, yes we are all well. How is your little boy? I hope he is recovering nicely from the measles. (It's to be hoped they've taken some of the wickedness out of him. Of all the ill-bred little cubs I know Bobby A. is the worst.) Have you been vaccinated yet? (Catch her! She's too mean to pay the fee.) Oh, how did you like the Burns concert? I saw you there. (In a dress that she couldn't possibly have paid for.) Your daughter sang that Scotch song so beautifully. It just brought tears to my eyes. (Kitty A.'s voice is as thin as paper and she is simply too funny for anything when she tries to sing Scotch songs.) How did you like the sermon Sunday? Lovely, wasn't it. Mr. Goodman is so spiritual. They say he is engaged to a lovely girl in St. John. (There, see her wince. She's been throwing Kitty at his head ever since he came, poor man.) Oh, yes, Mrs. C. was at Mrs. D.'s afternoon tea. She looked perfectly lovely. She has such perfect taste in dress. (She hates Mrs. C. and can't bear to have her praised. Her face looks actually green.) Do you go to the rink much this winter. You are such an enthusiastic skater I don't wonder you enjoy it. (A big clumsy woman like her skating! What a sight she must be! She does try so desperately to appear young, poor soul.) What, you're not going already. (I'm sure I wish she would go. She is such a bore.) Well, if you must. Now don't be so long coming back. (I wish there was any chance of it.) The church social Friday night? Oh, yes. I'll be there in good time. (She needn't think she's going to be let run it all her own way this time as she was the last.) Well, good-bye. (Thank goodness, she's off at last.)"

Life may be very piquant when thought-reading comes in, but somehow I don't believe it will be very comfortable.

A few days ago there appeared in the *Echo* a paragraph dealing with the comparative charm of words. It showed that the beauty of a word does not, as commonly supposed, consist in a musical combination of sounds, but rather in the ideas connected with the words. This suggested to me another fact I have frequently noticed in my own experience and have also heard others mention it. This is that the beauty of a word – especially a name – is to me very dependent on the way it is spelled. Have you ever noticed this in yourself? For instance the name, Sarah, when spelled with an h I can not abide; but when spelled Sara I think it is beautiful. Catherine, spelled with a C, jars on me; spelled with a K, it is one of my favorite names.[170]

The foregoing also reminds me of an interesting little exercise our teacher of philosophy at college gave us. It was in regard to "number forms." A number form is the arrangement in which the figures, from one to a hundred, present themselves to your mind's eye. Each member of the class was requested to draw a diagram of her number form on a sheet of paper and compare it with the others.

The result was decidedly interesting. Scarcely two of the forms were alike. One girl saw the figures stretching out in a straight line on a plane before her. Another saw them in circles of tens – that is, the figures from 1 to 10 were in a circle, then from 10 to 20 and so on. A third saw them in one huge circle of concentric circles with 1 in the centre. Some saw them in squares. Some in two parallel lines of 50's, or four lines of 25's. My own number form, when I came to write it out, was so weird and unlike any of the others that I almost felt ashamed of it. There seemed, I thought, something abnormal about it. The other day I came across an old exercise book in which the various "number forms" of my class were copied. The result was a revival of interest in it, and I have been persecuting everybody I have since met with the question, "How do you see figures?"

We are always being told that the world would be brighter and life more cheerful if we looked for the saving humor in everything. This is undoubtedly true, although from much repetition it has become trite to our ears. There is humor in almost everything, even life's tragedies, and its saving grace, if we can see it, will do much to lighten the load of too much seriousness.

Some fortunate people are born with this faculty. But it can be cultivated even in those not naturally so gifted. Of course, it is always easy to see the funny side of other people's troubles and worries and mistakes. It is not so easy to learn to see it in our own. But it can be done, and the faculty, when once acquired, is invaluable.

However, one should be careful not to go to the other extreme and turn everything into ridicule. Life would then become a farce. Humor is the spiciest condiment in the feast of existence, but too much of it, like too much pepper and salt, will destroy the flavor of the viands. Keep a little on hand – laugh at your mistakes but learn from them, joke over your troubles but gather strength from them, make a jest of your difficulties but overcome them – and life will be worth living.[171]

As I said a few paragraphs back the world is certainly not so cruel as it need to be. Recently I read in a newspaper a recipe for crab soup, which Martha Washington used to use, and which she wrote down herself in an old manuscript book which has come down from her descendants.[172] The first thing she did was to throw fifteen crabs into boiling water – alive!

Surely crab soup is not made in that way nowadays. To be sure, lobsters are still boiled alive. But we don't see it done. They're dead enough when we buy them.

Polly went to a party the other night and came home raving about the girdle Gwennie had worn to it.

"It was perfectly sweet," said Polly, rapturously. "I mean to get one something the same the minute father pays me my monthly allowance. I spent so much at the whitewear sale the other day that I haven't a penny to bless myself with now.[173] The girdle? Oh, yes! It was of pink panne,[174] folded twice around the waist and knotted at the left side into an upstanding bow, with two long ends. These ends were joined together and had as a pendant three roses and their foliage. The centre of the bow was also composed of three roses bunched together. These were jewelled with tiny rhinestone drops."

By the way:

How much do you gain by growling?

Isn't nonsense just as good as sense at times?

Is it fair to have to pay as much for a dozen little eggs as for a dozen big ones?

Is it any use to expect something for nothing?

Are there not two kinds of gossip?

Why don't reformers reform themselves?

Is there anything easier to do than ask questions?

[Garrets and Cheerful People]

Monday, 3 February 1902

HALIGONIANS[175] HAVE GONE ABOUT THE STREETS OF our city this week humming "From Greenland's Icy Mountains"[176] under their breath and gazing with wistful eyes at the airy spring muslins displayed in some of the shop windows. They do seem satirical, those muslins! But spring is certainly coming sometime, and meanwhile a little frost is healthy, and will teach us to count our blessings. This is what I tell Polly and Theodosia when I hear them growling about the cold snap.

Very, very often you read in those papers that are so full of good advice, which nobody ever takes, that "we should be always cheerful" – or, if we can't feel really and truly cheerful, we should at least pretend that we are, and thus by assuming a virtue, although we have it not, contribute largely to the sum total of cheerfulness in the world.

"Now," said Theodosia the other evening, as we sat around the table at our fancy work, "I don't altogether believe in that doctrine, don't you know. Of course I like cheerfulness when it is genuine, but I don't like spurious cheerfulness. And I'm not sure that I like people who are always and at every time cheerful either. Sometimes I get into an interesting melancholy mood, and then those professionally cheerful folks jar on it. I'd really like them to be a little bit subdued and sorrowful to harmonize with it. And when I'm 'way 'way down in the depths of the blues and just revelling in despair it never makes me feel any better to have somebody grin cheerfully and tell me to brighten up because things will come out all right some day. I'd sooner have them pat me on the head and say mournfully, 'You poor little girl; it is a hard old world for us all by spells, isn't it?' Why, the Bible says we ought to weep with those who weep.[177] That doesn't sound as if we had to be cheerful all the time, does it? No, I shall never pretend to be cheerful when I don't really feel so. I have the right to indulge in a luxury of the dismal dumps now and then. Now, Cynthia, don't you go and put this in the *Echo* next week."

Not long ago I read an article in some magazine entitled "The Passing of the Garret." It stated that the old-fashioned garret was rarely to be found nowadays, except perhaps in some equally old-fashioned houses. In up-to-date city houses the garret is now a "sky parlor," and is as elaborately fitted up as any room in the house.

That article made me sorry for the children of the next generation. What is childhood without a garret – a great big dusty, shadowy garret, full of cobwebby corners, where ghosts and Indians lurked in a perpetual twilight, with boxes and trunks of cast-off garments to "play grown-up" in, and a perfect treasure trove of old cracked, broken, rusty, moth-eaten odds and ends in every nook?

I have some very delightful memories of just such a garret in a big country farmhouse, where Polly and Theodosia and I used to spend our vacations. It was a glorious place, that garret! I don't know that I would enjoy rummaging around in it now, for I remember that it was haunted by spiders and mice – yes, mice! Incredible as it may seem, I was not afraid of mice in those brave old days.

It was long and roomy – an ideal spot for blindman's buff, which we played uproariously, first having stationed one of our number at the head of the stairs to warn the blindman if he ventured too near. We could make all the noise we wanted to, and nobody ever said a word. Aunty used to say that if she had not been accustomed to children all her life she would have been frightened to death at the shrieks and screams that used to come echoing down the old garret stairs.

We loved best to dress up in the cast-off fineries we found up there in boxes and trunks – old dresses and bonnets, and queer old garments long out of fashion. In these we would parade up and down the garret, admiring ourselves in a cracked mirror, with a tarnished gilt frame, that hung on the wall.

Once Ted found an old high-crowned beaver hat that had been grandfather's. He put it on, and pulled it right down over his face. After we had laughed enough at it we tried to take it off. It wouldn't come off. In vain we pulled and tugged and grew tearful. The hat would not budge.

Ted must have got it off sometime, of course, but I cannot remember how or when or why he has not had to wear it to this day.

We liked to play Indian there, too. The dark corners behind the trunks made such splendid ambushes – also very good pirate caves. But the garret, while a capital spot in daytime, was not so pleasant when twilight came on. How eerie and spookish it grew then in the dim light! The dried bunches of summer savory and sweet marjoram and thyme that dangled from the rafters filled us with terror. Aunt Harriet's bags of wool and bundles of rags looked like suspended criminals. The old mirror reflected a strange dim room peopled with phantoms. The mice scurried and squeaked among the boxes. In a chill fear we all crept down the garret stairs and left it behind us until in the cheerful morning sunshine it resumed its normal aspect.

But the children of the future will have no garret. There will be only a "sky parlor," and there cannot be Indians and pirates and ghosts, or any of those delightful things, in a "sky parlor." The future is to be a wonderful age, no doubt. But somehow I'm glad that I was a child before the passing of the garret.

When Theodosia and I went to the Orpheus concert[178] the other evening Polly stayed home and made sachets to perfume her new gown. Polly has a weakness for delicate, elusive scents in all her belongings – just a whiff of sweetness now and then like a hint of a rose garden or a wandering wind from a bank of spring violets.

Just now she has a new fad, and while Theodosia and I were drinking in the airy fairy[179] sounds at the Orpheus Polly was sewing diligently on six neat little squares of silk, making six small bags of them. These she was filling with violet sachet powder when Theo and I got home with our blue noses.

"I am going to sew a bit of baby ribbon to each," she explained, "and fasten them all to one long strip of ribbon. This is sown to the skirt band, and the six tiny sachets hang down under the folds of the gown and shake forth their stored-up sweetness at every movement."

[A Walk in the Woods]

Monday, 10 February 1902

DID YOU EVER WALK THROUGH THE WOODS IN WINTER when a slow twilight was filling them? And if you did, didn't you admit to yourself that of all the airy fairy places full of weird, elfin grace that you had ever been in, the winter woods at twilight were the most beautiful?

Theodosia and Polly and I spent a couple of days in a country farmhouse last week and one evening Theodosia and I started out for a woodsy walk. Polly wouldn't go although we asked her very politely. She said that in the first place she didn't believe we really wanted her; and in the second she greatly preferred a cosy seat in the ingle nook, a new novel and a plate of our hostess' delicious home-made "butter scotch," to wading around lonesome woods in snow to her neck and pretending to enthuse over Rembrandtesque shadows and gloomy copses.[180]

So Theodosia and I went alone and a delightful walk we had, despite Polly's dismal prophecies. We did not have to do any wading around for we were fortunate enough to strike a well-beaten wood-road and we wandered along it and drank in the delicate, elusive beauty around us as from a cup filled with divine enchantment.

The air was as clear and exhilarating as wine, brimmed here under the spruces with purple gloom and there, where the trees broke away to let in a glimpse of sunset sky, threaded with wonderful tones of cold rose and ethereal crocus and faint apple-green. It was so calm, too, that all the far eventide sounds drifted clearly through it – laughter so distant that it seemed like the mirth of wood-elves, human voices floating up from valleys where home-lights were twinkling out like earth stars, and the fairy-like chime of sleigh-bells in far-off snowy fields.

In the woods, too, were strange, half-heard sounds – the moan of two crossed branches, the murmurs of the pines, the soft splash of snow that slipped from laden boughs, the indistinct gurgle of a hidden brook, the scamper of some wild creature through the copses and the crisp crunch of the snow beneath our feet. How solemn and duskly beautiful the long forest avenues looked, with their white, untrodden pavements and the high-springing Gothic arch of the trees above. And what wonderful veils of white lace were draped over the shrubs and twigs of the undergrowth!

Theodosia and I saw nothing living but each other in that stretch of glimmering woods, but here, there and everywhere we saw the traces of wood denizens – the thread-like trail of scampering squirrels, the many tracks of rabbits, and the larger pads of some marauding fox. Perhaps the shy wood-creatures were peeping at us from the shelter of copse and undergrowth, but we could not see them.

How we enjoyed that walk! And how much good it did us! The blood tingled in our veins; our little private worries drifted from our minds and hearts; life seemed richly worth living. Theodosia looked up at the evening star, glimmering whitely through the boughs of an old pine, and quoted softly:

> "And so in mountain solitudes o'ertaken!
> As by some spell divine,
> Their cares drop from them like the needles shaken
> From out the gusty pine."[181]

When we got home we found that Polly had finished her novel, eaten all the butter scotch and fallen fast asleep, rosy and sweet, in the cosy corner. But we did not envy her – no, indeed. We had been roaming in fairyland and its spell was potent over us still.

Next day we both had colds.

One day recently Polly laid down the *Echo* with a sigh of despair and turned a glance of reproach on me.

"I do think it's just too mean of you, Cynthia," she said, mournfully.

"Oh, what – what – have I been doing now?" I asked anxiously.

"Why, you have something about me every week in the *Echo*, and – and – it's always horrid. People will think that I am a cross between an idiot and a b-baby. (Sob). You make me out a f-frivolous, silly c-creature (sob) who thinks of nothing but dress, and – and – flirtation – and all that sort of thing. You do give credit to Theodosia for a little sense now and again, b-but me, never. (Sob). People will think that I n-never had a serious thought in my l-life – and it's too bad of you, Cynthia."

Polly sobbed again. Polly is one of those girls, few and far between, who can look teary and pretty at the same time. Also, she knows it.

"Don't let that worry you, my child," I said, maternally. "In the first place, you're exaggerating. I never paint you quite so black as all that. And in the second place, people like you ever so much better than if you were a severe, sensible creature – like Theodosia or myself, for instance. You mustn't mind if I use you as a peg to hang a few morals on once in a while. You are the dainty, feminine little lass who is always popular with everybody. Your little frivolities are harmless and lovable. If you didn't think a good deal about dress you wouldn't be half such a pleasure to folks who like to see pretty things. It would be a terrible world, Polly, if everybody were intellectual and serious and in deep deadly earnest. We need people like that – but we need your kind, too, to humanize us. And you have the best of it, too. The other kind exists to think out your problems and fight your battles for you. Your mission is, as Josiah Allen says, 'to charm and to allure'[182] – and to brighten up every corner of the world in which you find yourselves. So don't cry any more, Polly. It becomes you, but it will produce crow's-feet if indulged in too often. You're a dear little soul, Polly, and I couldn't get along without you."

So Polly allowed herself to be cheered up.

The foregoing reminds me of an anecdote of Sam Jones I read somewhere recently.[183] The noted evangelist was once taking women to task for spending more time in prinking than praying.[184]

"If there is one woman in this audience," he said finally, "who prays more than she prinks, let her stand up."

One poor faded specimen of femininity, in the sorriest, shabbiest of clothes, arose.

The preacher looked at her.

"You spend more time praying than prinking?" he asked her.

She said she did – that she prayed a great deal and never prinked at all.

"Madam," said Sam Jones, solemnly, "you go right straight home and put half your praying time on your prinking."

[Double Standards]

Monday, 17 February 1902

St. Valentine's day has come and gone. Did you get any valentines? Polly got a comic one and she is furious. It was a broad slap at her flirtation tendencies and that is what vexes her. Nothing on earth can convince Polly that she ever flirts – even the least wee bit, you know. It seems to be inherent in human nature that we should be blindest to the very faults in ourselves that are most patent to other people. This must be why the cap of a comic valentine never seems to fit the recipient's head.[185] We have lots of other faults, of course, but this particular one, not at all.

We have started an anti-slang society around the table. Every time one of us catches herself or himself using a slang word or expression he or she has straightway to deposit a cent in a bank which Ted has purchased for the purpose and placed on the sitting room mantel.

At first we thought we would make the fine five cents. But Polly protested. She said her allowance was only so much per quarter and a five cent fine would bankrupt her in a week, so we put it at one cent. The money is to go towards Miss Stone's ransom.[186]

Ever since the heap of pennies in the bank has been increasing steadily. We never realized how strong a hold the slang habit had on us until we tried to break it. If you had asked me I would have said that I used very few slang words in my daily walk and conversation, and such would have been my honest belief. But I must candidly admit that my pennies have disappeared most rapidly and unaccountably since the institution of our anti-slang society.

We have had no end of fights over it. We can't always agree on what is slang and what isn't. Polly and Ted argue some disputed question every day and get excited and sarcastic over it. Aunt Janet sighs patiently and says that for her part she wouldn't mind our slang half as much as our quarrels. She thinks our organization should be called an anti-peace society.

Theodosia thinks we ought to make a distinction between slang that is "vulgar" and slang that isn't.

"You can't deny," she says, "that some slang expressions are rather 'cute' and hit off" – here Ted interposed with "a penny, if you please, Theo." Theo paid the penny and returned to her mutton[187] – "one's meaning much more aptly than if expressed in classical English. When you say that a person is 'talking through his hat' you express in a sentence what it would take a whole paragraph to elaborate. 'Not in it' is useful at a pinch and I could enumerate many more that are very pat. What's that, Ted – another cent? You mean wretch! Well, I'm not the only peb– I mean, there are oth– no, I don't. I'm not going to say another word today or I shall be dead broke."

And amid peals of laughter Theodosia put four cents into the ransom fund.

But there is something in Theodosia's argument after all. Some slang words and phrases are undeniably rather expressive and piquant. In due time they will be admitted to the good society of English undefiled and their lack of ancestry will be forgotten and forgiven. On the other hand, the use of slang is a habit that grows upon one to an alarming extent and as everyone has not the power to discriminate between "vulgar" and non-vulgar slang it is perhaps best not to indulge in it at all – except, of course, under provocation.

It has been the custom from immemorial ages for men to accuse women of killing other women's chances of social success by "faint phrase"[188] – that most effective weapon of warfare in skilful hands.

Well, perhaps we do, we must have some weapon of offence and defence. But what I want to know is this – isn't our delicate, unobtrusive way of doing it better than the brutal, outspoken criticism some men – to be just, not all. Oh, there are a few blessed exceptions, and any man who chances to read this will fondly number himself among them – inflict on their sisters, cousins and aunts. Even Ted comes out quite strong at times. When he heard of Gwennie's engagement the other evening he remarked, gently:

"So she's given up at last, has she. I know she never accepted Jim until all hope of getting anybody else had gone."

If Polly or Theodosia or I had said this Ted would never cease commenting caustically on our feminine spite and pique; but of course it was all right when a masculine creature said it.

I heard an acquaintance of mine say recently that a woman who wore one of the present fashionable long loose coats did so to conceal her bad figure; and another followed it up by saying that a certain girl he knew "was trying to hide her wrinkles." As the girl in question is only about twenty one would suppose she could not have many wrinkles to hide. But this charitable man chose to believe and state his belief that her rosy complexion was taken off and put on at will.

Now, if the men want to say these things, let them. I am not trying to curtail their privileges at all. What I do protest against is the injustice of their sneering at women for saying the same things. If it is just feminine spite and pique in women what, in the name of common sense, is it to be called in men? Never let the men worry themselves about our voting. Let them simply be just to us in this particular and they can run politics all by themselves.

Oh, no, indeed, gossip is not feminine gender. Don't think it for a moment.

I hope the girls at the Halifax "Central" are not as hard driven as the telephone girl in this story.

A nervous looking girl consulted a doctor, who asked her what she was suffering from. She said:

"I'm a telephone girl, doctor, and the work is a terrible strain on my nerves. The monotony of having a receiver constantly at my ears and saying 'Hello' tells upon them. When I'm off duty 'Hello' is always ringing in my ears and I am constantly saying it. When I wake up in the morning I say 'Hello.' And even when I kneel down to say my prayers I instinctively say 'Hello' before I commence them."

[Tall Tales and Close Calls]

Monday, 24 February 1902

HOW OFTEN DID YOU FALL ON A SLIPPERY STREET THIS winter?

I have seen some very comical tumbles of late. It's one of the funniest sights in the world to see somebody who is strutting along in front of you slip, gyrate wildly for a minute and then go neatly down. I never can help laughing when I see it.

It's so funny to see other people fall down. It isn't a bit funny when I fall myself. I don't know why but it isn't.

Did you ever know of people hurting themselves when they fall on the street? They never do because they always say, "Oh, no, I didn't hurt myself at all," and of course they are to be believed. They certainly ought to know.

A man of my acquaintance says that Theodosia is the most extraordinary girl he ever met. He was walking down Prince street with her the other day, and she suddenly slipped and fell. He picked her up and asked her if she had hurt herself. She frankly admitted that she had. He says he hasn't recovered from the shock of surprise yet.

The people who know everything – and, oh, there are so many of them – say that the age of fairy tales is past – that the children of nowadays don't like them and won't read them.

I don't believe that is true; and I don't believe that it is only children who like fairy tales. I've been grown-up for some time and I revel in fairy-tales still.

I wonder if the same old stories are told in child-land still that were current when I sojourned in that magical country. If not I'm sorry for the children who miss hearing those old classics. There was a never-fading charm and interest about them. And they stood telling so well, too. The hundredth time of relation they were just as fresh and unhackneyed and thrilling as the first. Mother always told them to us at twilight. We listened breathlessly and woe betide her if she left out any part or made any alteration. We would not tolerate this for a moment.

"No," we would say, "you've forgotten to tell us how the wolf just glared at Little Red Riding Hood and said: 'They are to eat you with.' And then he gobbled her right down," we would add with a thrill of delicious horror.[189]

Red Riding Hood was our favorite story because of its horrors and tragical end. There was a big spruce wood behind our house and we always thought that was the wood she went through in her little scarlet hood and cloak. She and her grandmother and that beautiful wolf were real folk to us.

A story that ran Red Riding Hood hard in popularity was that of the little boy and the three brown bears who lived in a little brown house in a wood.[190] The little boy went there one day, found the bears out, ate up all their porridge and played a good many more tricks on the poor bears. Then he got into the little bear's bed and went to sleep. The bears came home and found him there. (How we shivered with delight at this point!) They were going to eat him up. I forget just how he managed it but I know he succeeded in nailing the bears to their chairs by their tails and so made his escape. It was a continual source of speculation among us how the bears freed themselves or if they ever did.

Then there was the story about the old woman and her pig who wouldn't go and the stick that wouldn't beat it and the grease that wouldn't grease the stick and so on.[191] And Jack and the Beanstalk, of course, with its weird "fee fo fum, I smell the blood of an Englishman," and Bluebeard and Cinderella and the Sleeping Beauty, and Puss in Boots.[192] Oh, why don't people write stories like that nowadays!

Did you ever get on a street car and then discover that you hadn't any money with you to pay your fare?[193]

I did the other night. And I know now just how a condemned criminal feels.

I had a five cent piece with me when I got on the car. I thought it was in the left pocket of my coat. When I got settled comfortably down I felt for it. It wasn't there. I had a cold chill. I felt in the other pocket. Not there. I had another chill. Then I felt in a little inside pocket. All in vain. I had two chills at once.

I took off my gloves, laid them on the seat and went over all my pockets again. It was not there. I stood up and shook myself and then looked on the floor. The car was full of people, who were going home from the Academy of Music and they all stared at me, but I was past caring for a little thing like that.

But I could not find my fare. I concluded that I must have put it in my mouth and swallowed it inadvertently.

I didn't know what to do. Would the conductor, I wondered, stop the car and put me off in ignominy and shame? Was it possible that I could convince him that I was merely the victim of my own absent-mindedness and not an unprincipled creature trying to obtain a ride under false pretences. I was so glad I had on my Sunday-go-to-meeting clothes. I thought the conductor would be more likely to believe that I had once possessed a five-cent piece, although I no longer had it, than if I had had on only my second best. I tried to frame some sentences of explanation in my mind, but I forgot the first part while I was thinking out the last and anyway I knew when it came to the critical moment I would blush and stammer and look as if nobody had ever trusted me with a red cent in my life. I felt that there was nothing to do but trust to Providence. And for all the comfort that gave me I might as well have been the lady who, when told by the captain during a storm at sea that she must put her trust in the Almighty, exclaimed: "Oh, captain, is it as bad as that?"[194]

Just at the conventional moment when all hope had fled and the conductor was before me holding out his box I suddenly remembered where I had put that wretched coin of the realm. I had not swallowed it after all.

I meekly fished it out of the index finger of my glove and poked it in the box. I smiled at everybody and felt that it was a beautiful world.

From a perusal of the "funny" papers wouldn't you think

That nobody ever paid his debts.

That women spend all their time saying uncharitable things about each other and

That men spend all theirs trying to borrow a five from each other.

That every old maid in the world does nothing but lay snares for every single man she knows, and

That all the married people wish they were single again.

That there never was a widow whose husband hadn't a happy release.

That there never was a nice mother-in-law.

That there is something funny in a man's coming home at night dead drunk.

That the church deacons always gamble at races.

That a woman can't pass a milliner's window without stopping to look in.

That no young wife could ever cook anything fit to eat.

That all people in love make fools of themselves.

That all spring poets starve.

That a woman never tells her real age.

But what a comfort it is to reflect that there are quite a few decent people in the world for all, despite the funny papers.

[Graves of the Past]

Monday, 3 March 1902

FEBRUARY HAS TO HAVE A THAW. "OLD INHABITANTS" will tell you that "Febooary" never goes out without a thaw.

On some rare occasions they have known it to almost do so, but the thaw would begin at five minutes to twelve on the night of the 28th and so save the tradition. Well, there was no such close shave this year. February redeemed its reputation triumphantly before its departure.

Ted is one of those unlucky – or lucky, just as you choose to regard it – individuals who were born on the 29th of February. Consequently he has been cheated out of his proper share of birthdays and it is a sore point with him. Just now, of course he is worse off than ever, because eight years must elapse between his last birthday and his next.[195]

That pouring rainy night last week Polly and Ted and Aunt Janet went to the Academy of Music and Theodosia and I found ourselves spending the evening alone. I was curled up snugly in the cosy corner, nibbling some chocolate caramels and gazing dreamily – dreamily is the proper word, isn't it – into the glowing coal fire, which was snapping and spluttering away to itself in the nice companionable way such fires have; presently Theodosia came in and curled herself up on the big bear rug before the fire – a real silver tip,[196] by the way, that Ted shot when he was out in British Columbia last winter. The silver tip nearly ate our Teddy up, too, and – but where was I at?

Oh yes! Theodosia came in and sat down on the coat of the defunct silver tip with a queer little old box on her lap. You know the kind. Most of us have one of the same species stowed away somewhere full of curious old trash that all the gold of Ophir couldn't buy from us.[197] Not that anybody would offer it. The contents of such boxes are worthless to all except the owners.

The boxes may differ externally, but they have a faded, cherished air, as of a box that has seen better days. Theodosia's is of polished wood and has a checker board inlaid on the cover. It is locked by a curious little silver key with a dragon's head for a handle. Theo turned the key solemnly, with the air of one who is opening a grave of the past. There was a dreamy smile on her face.

"Poor Dick! He gave me this box years ago when we were children together, for a birthday present. I've always kept my treasures in it. I wonder where Dick is now. He married some girl in St. John and went to the States."

Theodosia shook her head sadly. Evidently she thought Dick's fate a gloomy one. I looked on with interest. I love old boxes and Theodosia's looked interesting. I had never seen her treasures before and I was sure there was a round dozen of romances locked up in that little inlaid box.

The first thing Theodosia fished out was a queer little gold ring, of the kind that used to be known as a "friendship ring" – two hands clasping each other. It was somewhat bent and battered and had, it must be confessed, a rather brassy appearance.

"My first sweetheart gave me this," said Theodosia, as she slipped it on sentimentally. "We were both ten years old. He earned the money for it picking berries for a cross old woman who lived near us. He was such a dear little chap, with big blue eyes and yellow curls and freckles. There ought to be a letter from him somewhere here, too. Ah, here it is," – picking up a little square pink envelope from which she extracted a sheet of pink paper scrawled over in a very big boyish hand – "he slipped this into my spelling book one day and I thought I had never read anything so delightful. I think so still. What's that, Cynthia? Let you read it? No, indeed. How badly spelled it is! And how ungrammatical! Strange I never noticed those faults at the time."

"Here's a photo of my graduating class. Twelve girls of us all in new dresses. How very prim we look. What a dumpling I was then. Dear me! three of those girls are dead, four are married and the rest are scattered far and wide. It makes me blue to look at it!

"Here's a picture of myself when I was a baby. Do you think I ever looked like that, Cynthia? Well, I was a pretty baby anyhow. Aunt Debby always tells me that," and then remarks with a sigh, "Strange how people do change when they grow up. Look at my mouth – wide open as if I were going to bawl. Cynthia, you may count yourself happy. You haven't any picture of yourself when a baby to darken your maturer days."

"These," continued Theodosia, picking up a chubby bundle of

pale blue envelopes tied together with pink ribbon, "are not, as you might imagine, billet-doux.[198] They are the letters written to me by my school chum at the most sentimental stage of our careers. They are full of vows of eternal friendship and protestations of undying affection. We never speak as we pass by now. I wonder if she has my old letters still. They were written on pale pink paper. I think I must burn these.

"Here's a letter from myself at twelve to myself at sixteen. No, I won't let you see it either. You might print it in the *Echo*. It's a curiosity of literature.

"Dear me, what are all these buttons – four of them and all different?"

"They have a masculine look," I said maliciously. "I should say they had come off somebody's coat."

Theo brightened up.

"Oh, yes, to be sure. How stupid of me. That big spotty one came off Harold's coat. And that black one was Jim's. I forget whose the other two were. Here's a lot of verses Harry wrote to me before we quarreled. They're very sentimental and the rhymes don't stand squarely on their feet. Still I thought them very fine at the time. Here's a piece of Kitty Scott's wedding dress, and here's my first ball programme. What a jolly time I did have. Just look. Tom's name is in six places.[199] Wasn't that dreadful. I wore pale yellow and everybody said I looked heavenly. Dear me, whose hair is this? It must be Howard's. He is the only one I remember having curly black hair like that. This envelope has a lot of faded roses in it. I wore them at the dance before Jerry went away. Look at these old school compositions – and an old New Year list of resolutions – and here's another bundle of old letters."

Theodosia became absorbed in reading them, and I lazily reflected what fools we mortals be[200] and wondered if I had as much rubbish as that in my box up in the garret. If I have I must hunt it out some day and burn it … if I have the heart to do so. We prize some of the things in those old boxes very dearly, don't we?

"That Miss B. we met at the M———s has an imaginative temperament," said Marian the other evening. "She is affectionate and demonstrative but obstinate to a fault."

"How do you know?" I queried.

"She uses lily-of-the-valley perfume," returned Marian. "You can tell people's characters by their favorite perfume just as well as by their walk. Dorothy A—— is warm-hearted and imaginative, and inclined to extravagance and treats life flippantly – she likes rose perfume. Heliotrope is Gwennie's pet: even if I didn't know her I could tell that she was dainty, neat, and demure, hating fuss or notoriety. Constance B—— is religious, affectionate and peace-loving. Connie always keeps Lent strictly.[201] She affects violet perfume. Yes, I always judge people by the perfume they use."

I was silent from horror. Before coming downstairs I had by mistake scented my hanky with some certain "loud" perfume that Ted keeps to look at. What on earth would Marian think of me?

"Mr. A.," said Polly the other evening, "guess how much I paid for these new furs."

Mr. A. looked wise. He was probably thinking something like this:

"No doubt she has purchased them at some wrecked goods sale for a mere song so, though I don't know a thing about furs I'll make it low enough to get the credit of being a good guesser."

"Forty dollars," he said.

"Mr. B.," said Polly calmly, "it's your turn to guess."

Mr. B. is a young man wise in his generation. I knew perfectly well that he had no idea whether Polly's furs were muskrat or Russian sable, but he said, without turning a hair:

"Five hundred dollars."

"That's a better guess than Mr. A.'s anyhow," said Polly looking resentfully at poor A. "They cost seventy-five dollars."

[Spring and Smiles and Old Maids]

Monday, 10 March 1902

SOMEWHERE OR OTHER SPRING IS ON HER WAY TO US. WE had a few days last week that were her heralds and were they not charming? The staleness and monotony of the dull winter days seemed blotted from our recollection in the exhilarating breath of the coming spring – the golden days of the world's renewed youth.

To be sure, there are cold days and tingling fingers and perhaps snow flurries before us yet. But we know that the sceptre of winter is broken and that it is merely a question of a few weeks before the buds on the trees will be swelling, moist with promise of leaf and blossom, and the grasses and ferns poking up their dear green heads along the driveways in the Park.

Some people complain of our long, lingering northern springs, but for me there is an inexpressible charm in the slow, gradual awakening of all the world beneath the sunlight. I like to watch the trees turning from their silvery gray to misty purple and then to tender green. I like to watch the long snow wreaths dwindling along the edges of the woods from day to day, the mellow tones creeping into the pearly horizons, and the grass growing ever greener and greener in sheltered places. There will always be something worth living for as long as there are springs.

To be sure, there is mud – and housecleaning! But what would you? The first Eden of all had its serpent.

A saunter down Barrington street would tell you that spring was coming if nothing else did. How the shops are blossoming out in "spring goods" – muslins and laces and silks galore. The millinery windows are abloom with hats especially the ever-useful and perennial "sailors." And, if every other sign failed, I would still know that spring was a-near, because Polly is up to her eyes already in patterns. There will be no peace or rest in our household from now until her spring outfit is completed.

But isn't it jolly when you discard furs and winter garments for the first time and sally forth in spring attire? Don't you feel as if you had been made over new?

"I liked her smile," said Ted, one day, apropos of a new acquaintance we were discussing.

His remark set me thinking about the different kinds of smiles there are in the world. There are smiles and smiles. Can't you classify all your friends by their own particular and private smiles?

I have in mind a friend who has the most delightful smile in the world. It always puts me in good humor just to see it. There are dimples in it and lots of other things that go to make smiles beautiful, but it is not on their account I like it. It is because of the real friendliness it expresses. You feel that she is smiling at you because she likes you and not because she just thinks it is her duty to do so. It is not too broad a smile – it lingers round her lips and peeps out of her eyes and irradiates her whole face. I always feel good for hours after I've met her.

Then there is the sarcastic smile. Isn't it terrible? I can endure sarcastic tones and even bear up bravely under sarcastic words. But the sarcastic smile shrivels me right up, mentally and physically. There is the "made-to-order" smile which is awful. People put it on when they think they ought to be glad to see you but are not. It always makes me think they must have the toothache. There is the "nervous" smile, which folks assume to hide their nervousness. That one always wants to make me scream. There is the condescending smile that makes your very soul creep. There is the sympathetic smile that warms the cockles of your heart. There is the jolly, comradey smile that brightens the world up for you.[202] And there are dozens of others.

The Kaiser has instituted a campaign against rats.[203] Nice man! Now, if he or some other of the powers that be would only exterminate mice the thanks of grateful womanhood would be his forever.

Just think. A world without any mice in it! Why, life would be worth living.

Do you know that the amount of clover grown in any place is in direct proportion to the number of old maids living there? Well, it's true; no less a person than Darwin proves it.[204] Listen. The clover crop depends on the number of bumble bees that visit it, they being the only insects whose tongues can reach down into the clover blossoms and so fertilize them. But field mice eat bumble bees. Cats eat field mice. Old maids keep cats. So, the more old maids the more cats, the more cats the fewer field mice, the fewer field mice the more bumble bees, the more bumble bees the better clover crop. Isn't logic a beautiful thing?

"It was dreadfully pretty," sighed Polly. She was referring to a muslin shirtwaist she had seen in an uptown store.

Ted reached across the table and coughed.

"The mud on the streets today was divinely abominable," he remarked calmly.

Polly looked queer and Theodosia queerer. Ted remained calm. I bent towards him anxiously.

"You don't think the recent sudden changes in temperature have affected your brain, do you, Teddy-boy?" I asked sympathetically.

"Oh, no," said Ted, cheerfully. "I'm feeling a little weary, that's all. This has been such a superbly tiresome day."

Polly colored and looked out of the corner of her eyes at Theo and me to see how we were taking it.

"Tired as I am," went on Ted, "I suppose I must go and hear Captain Bernier lecture on the Pole tonight.[205] They say it's horribly interesting. Cynthia, pass me the cheese, please. This meat is so exquisitely tough that I really can't eat it."

I passed the cheese and, like Brer Rabbit of immortal fame, "laid low and said nothing."[206] Polly looked cross and Theodosia seemed bursting with some suppressed amusement. Ted hasn't had an outbreak since. But what do you suppose he meant?

[Old Houses and Parlour Games]

Monday, 17 March 1902

You should hear Polly groaning over what she calls her "March complexion." As a rule, Polly has a very good complexion, clear and creamy with a dash of ripe tinting in the cheeks when the blood shows through. But nowadays when she comes in from an outdoor walk she does look funny.

Her face is spotted with red and there are patches of color on her forehead that look as if they had rusted there. They make our Polly look as if she had the jaundice.

Everybody who has ever studied the second primer[207] knows that the March winds do blow.[208] And very trying to the soul of femininity are those same stinging, unkind winds. Polly is wasting her substance on cold creams and Theodosia and I are trying to look as if we didn't mind a little thing like that – but deep down in our souls we do!

The last time Theo and I were out in the country we came across a deserted old house in our rambles. I improved the occasion to moralize a bit. An old deserted house always makes me feel that way. There is always something so mournful and pathetic about it as if it were grieving for its lost joys and long-silent songs.

Everything about this old house seemed written over by the fingers of the past. It was the ghost of a dead home staring out of its broken windows hollowly and sadly. The rooms were empty and desolate, tenanted only by scampering squirrels or fugitive mice where once children's feet had pattered and childish laughter had echoed. Once those lonely dim old rooms had known life. There had been wooings and weddings, births and deaths, partings and reunions there. Scores of feet had passed over its crumbling threshold, some strong and eager, some feeble and halting. Song and laughter had echoed through it.

Now it was worn-out and deserted. The father and mother were sleeping in the little hillside burying ground and the children were all far away, busy men and women of the working world. An old lilac tree, purple with blossom, swung before the empty parlor window. A red rose, planted by dead hands, bloomed at the mossy sagging doorstep. The wind sighed and moaned softly in the gnarled old apple trees around it.

"Oh, come away, Cynthia," said Theodosia with a shiver. "It's like something dead – it's a ghost."

I have great love for old homesteads – old houses which have sheltered three or four generations and cradled joy and sorrow until one has a fancy that their very walls must be permeated with the essences of the lives and loves that have glowed between them, and give it out again as a benediction on their inmates. An old homestead, ripened and mellowed by humanity for over half a century, is a truly beautiful thing.

The other evening Polly was invited to a party given by Master Algie B—— to his young friends. He wanted Polly to help him entertain.

"You're so jolly," he said, frankly, "and always have some good ideas for fun and – and – keep things stirred up, you know."

From the various accounts I have heard of that party and the reckless hilarity which reigned in the house of B—— while it was in progress I should judge that Polly fully succeeded in "keeping things stirred up."

This is one of her fun-raising devices:

All the boys were lined up in a row, each holding his left foot behind his back in his right hand and grasping his right ear with his left hand. Polly then spread newspapers on boxes about six inches from the floor at the other side of the room. The boys had to hop towards them and endeavor to lift them with their teeth. Properly performed this is guaranteed to be productive of something funny.

At our house the other night we were playing the old game of "mental photographs." Several of our friends were in and we got considerable amusement out of it. A list of questions is drawn up and are supposed to be answered truthfully – or at least as truthfully as your conscience will permit.

Out of the lot Ted's and Polly's were the most amusing, Ted's because he made it so of malice aforethought, Polly's because it was so naive and jumbled up. Here they both are, Polly's first as due to courtesy:

Who are your favorite prose authors?

The Duchess and Sienkiewicz.[209]

Favorite painters? Rembrandt and Millais.[210]

Composers? Wagner and Sousa.[211]

Book? Anderson's Fairy Tales.[212]

Play? Merchant of Venice.[213]

Your favorite heroes of fiction? Ivanhoe and Lancelot.[214]

Your favorite heroine? Little Eva and Becky Sharp.[215]

Your favorite hero in real life? Lord Roberts.[216]

Your favorite heroine in real life? Clara Barton.[217]

What do you enjoy most? Eating caramels.

What do you detest most? Getting the skirt of my dress muddy.

At what historic event would you most like to have been present? The execution of Mary Queen of Scots.[218]

What quality in men do you admire most? Their admiration.

What quality in women? Gumption.

Where would you like to live? In Halifax of course.

What is your ideal state of happiness? A new novel, a cosy corner and chocolate caramels.

What is your favorite occupation? Fancy work.

What gift of nature do you desire most? A straight nose.

What is your motto? Have a good time as you go along.

Ted's is, I regret to say, flippant. Here it is:

Favorite prose author? Old Subscriber and Vox Populi.[219]

Poets? Anon. and Ibid.[220]

Painters? I don't like to give the ladies' names.

Composer – Cynthia's cat.

Favorite Book? The dictionary.

Favorite Play? The V trick.[221]

Favorite hero of fiction? Santa Claus.

Favorite heroine of fiction? Betsy Prig.[222]

Favorite hero of real life? Hobson.[223]

Favorite heroine of real life? A good cook.

What I enjoy most? Getting photographed.

What I detest most? Looking at the results.

The historic event at which I would have liked to be present? The interview of Eve with the serpent.

Quality in men I admire most? Ability to sit opposite a mirror at dinner and not look in it.

Quality in women? Sense of humor.

Where I would like to live? Wherever she is.

Ideal state of happiness? A cold night, a hot fire and taters in the ashes.

Favorite occupation? Watching someone else work.

Gift of nature I most desire? The gift of the gab.

Motto? Remember there are others.

[The Virtues of Laziness]

Monday, 24 March 1902

OH, I SHALL NEVER AGAIN SAY I LIKE A RAINY DAY! Wasn't last week horrible? Gr-r-r-u! I had been dreaming such sweet little dreams of spring blossoms and birds and songs – and I was rudely awakened to the bitter realization that I must wade around in overshoes and raincloak and carry an umbrella in the teeth of a furious wind.

By the way, isn't it harrowing to have your umbrella turn inside out? That is one of the times I feel convinced of the total depravity of inanimate things.[224]

But this is not an argument against a bit of day-dreaming. It's a good thing after all, if indulged in with moderation. It lifts us out of our little everyday ruts and gives us a jaunt through the realms of fairyland and our castles in Spain.[225] We can escape from ourselves in it and that is also wise, now and then. Yes, I shall go on dreaming. But I will also get my umbrella mended and invest in a rainy-day skirt.

Next Sunday is Easter. Have you got your new hat. Polly has – she discovered it at one of the millinery openings last week and declares that it is a "dream" and a "vision" and "perfectly divine." I feel that it is my duty to lecture her on her frivolity and tell her that she should think more of the real meaning of the Eastertide and less of the pomps and vanities of the world,[226] as symbolized by new hats.

But there! I might as well talk to empty air.

All the time my little preachment is going on Polly is looking at her hat from fifteen different points of view in the mirror and at the end she turns to me and demands anxiously:

"Cynthia, don't you think it is more becoming when I wear it tilted just a little bit over my left eye – so?"

Theodosia is freckling over the bridge of her nose. She is wild about it. She laughed at Polly's windburn last week and this is her punishment. I told her never to mind, freckles were only "the kisses of Apollo,"[227] and "beauty-spots," but Theo acridly retorted that she never liked being kissed on the nose and that they jested at scars who never felt a wound.[228] So I stopped trying to cheer her up – why is it people always resent being cheered up? – and advised lemon juice.

Some day I'm going to write a treatise on the virtues of laziness. I like lazy people. They rest me.

Hands will go up in horror over this and there will be *sotto voce* remarks about birds of a feather.[229] But that cap doesn't fit so I won't wear it.[230]

There is wisdom in laziness – up to a certain degree. What is the use, as we used to say at school, of killing yourself to keep yourself alive? A delightful condition of leisurely contentment conduces to longevity. It's all nonsense to insist that one must always be doing something. They used to tell us when we were small that Satan always found some mischief still for idle hands to do and frightened us into being industrious that way.[231] But there are always two sides to every question.

It's wise to rest well and thoroughly sometimes – to give over being fussily energetic and dream dreams. It's never wise to fritter away one's strength by "doing something" every minute. Time may be saved, but vitality will be wasted.

I remember when I was a child people used to tell me that the early bird captured the worm.[232] I used sometimes to want to ask them – what about the worm? I never did; but to this day I firmly believe that if the worm were not out so early he might not be caught – and gobbled down without grace.

"Strenuous" is the fashionable word just now. We hurry and scurry and forget altogether what rest really means. We forget that while it is a good thing to do it is sometimes just as desirable simply to be. "The world is too much with us."[233]

When I propounded these statements around the table the other night Polly sighed and said she was glad she was justified at last and that the next time I tried to hustle her out of bed early in the morning she would know what to say to me.

Theodosia is going to give a photographic party next week. She expects to get a lot of fun out of it.[234]

Each guest is expected to bring a photograph of him or herself in infancy – the earliest that can be procured – and the entertainment is to be derived from the efforts of the company to identify the likenesses. All the photos will be pinned on a large square board and numbered. Each guest will be given a list to fill up and the one who has the largest number of correct guesses will win a prize. There will be a fine for making a mistake in regard to the sex.

"Isn't it lovely!" sighed Polly rapturously. We were at one of the Symphony concerts and she referred to a chorus. I agreed with her: it was lovely.

The other night at the Academy of Music Polly gazed with fascinated eyes at the clever antics of "Foxie." "Isn't he lovely?" she whispered to me radiantly.

Last Sunday we took a walk in the Park. The blue waters of the harbor sparkled and shimmered in the sunshine. The wind purred softly among the crests of the pines and sent resinous whiffs down the long dreamy avenues. "Isn't it lovely?" said Polly, with a deep-drawn breath of delight.

When we went home I picked up a number of *Ainslie's Magazine*[235] and opened it at the full page picture of a rhinoceros' head – the most uniquely ugly thing I ever put my eyes on. Polly looked over my shoulder. "Oh, isn't he lovely?" she demanded admiringly.

[How Kissing Was Discovered]

Monday, 31 March 1902

EASTER IS OVER. THEO AND I USED TO ROAM AROUND town last week enjoying the display of Easter flowers in the shop windows. What lovely things flowers are, anyway! They are one of the few blessings that escaped unharmed from Eden.

Speaking of Easter flowers reminds me of a pretty legend I heard the other day concerning the origin of the Easter lily. A lily, blood-red in hue, grew at the entrance to the tomb where the Christ was buried.[236] So great was its sorrow for him that its red petals blanched with its grieving through the long hours in which

He lay entombed and on the morning of the resurrection it was as white as snow.

When the angels rolled the stone away and the Christ came forth his first wonderful smile fell upon the drooping white lily at His feet and instantly it was invested with a grace and beauty no lily had ever possessed before. That was the first Easter lily and ever since it has been the symbol of the resurrection.

In reading – or, rather, re-reading, for it is one of my book-loves – Oliver Wendell Holmes' "Professor" the other day, I came across a piquant phrase in which he speaks of a person who "had an east-wind in his soul."[237] I at once shut the book and ruminated awhile. I knew I had found out what was the matter with some folks of my acquaintance. I had often wondered what their complaint might be called – and here it was diagnosed for me – "east wind in the soul."

We all know them – those people with east wind in their souls. There is a chill in their presence – you can feel it when they are coming towards you a block away. Somehow, they seem to throw a blight over everything. Uncomfortable themselves, they want to make everybody else uncomfortable too. They are growly and discontented. If they see you enjoying yourself innocently they can't rest until they have poisoned your enjoyment by a sneer or a gloomy prediction. They look chronically on the dark side of things and try to make everybody else do likewise.

Oh, they are very uncomfortable kind of folks to have around. It's bad enough to have the east-wind get in your bones and it's worse still to have it get on your nerves. But it's worst of all to have it get in your soul. If you feel any premonitory symptoms hasten to get rid of it before it gets chronic. If you don't there is no hope for you – in this world at any rate.

Last week an article appeared in the *Echo* on the "History of Kissing." It fell short, however, in that it told us nothing of the origin of kissing. Here is the story. I don't vouch for it, remember – I wasn't around at the time. "I tell the tale as 'twas told to me."[238]

Kissing was invented in Greece, where so many good things have been discovered. Kisthenes was a young shepherd who daily tended his flocks on old Mount Pelion and his sweetheart Aglaia, who lived in the little village at its foot, used to go up the mountain every day to chat with him.

One day she came to a brook and saw something sparkling among its pebbles. She picked it up and it was a very beautiful stone, shimmering with all the colors of the rainbow.

"What a nice present this will be for my Kisthenes," said Aglaia.

Just then she heard a noise and looking around saw the god Pan peering at her from a thicket of laurels. Pan was very angry. This brook was under his special protection and all gems found in it were his. So he demanded the stone from Aglaia.

Aglaia promptly ran and Pan ran after her up the slope of the mountain. Aglaia was a very fleet-footed maiden, so she managed to keep ahead of him and came upon Kisthenes just as Pan had very nearly captured her. She flung herself breathlessly into her lover's stout arms and Kisthenes implored Pan to go away like a good soul and leave them in peace.

Pan was the god of shepherds, so, though he didn't want to at all, he had to grant the prayer of Kisthenes. He clattered off in a shocking temper and Kisthenes tried to soothe Aglaia, whose nerves were badly upset by her scamper up the mountain.

"Where is the pebble?" asked Kisthenes when she had faltered out her story. "I suppose you dropped it in your flight."

Not so. Aglaia had, with commendable presence of mind, clapped the gem into her rosy mouth. There it still was safe and sound; and now the question was, how could she give it to Kisthenes?

Her arms were pinioned to her sides by Kisthenes' clasp and if he let her go or loosened one of his arms to take the pebble Aglaia would fall to the ground, so weak and trembling was she. Aglaia solved the puzzle. She poked the gem out between her pretty lips and told Kisthenes to take it with his.

Kisthenes stooped to do so and in a trice he forgot all about the gem – in fact, it was never heard of again – for as his lips touched Aglaia's such thrills and trills and semi-demi-quavers chased each other all over him that he could think of nothing else. Kissing was discovered.

Kisthenes and Aglaia, after several experiments, decided that they would keep it all to themselves – which was very selfish of them, but lovers are proverbially like that. However, Aglaia had a very dear school friend down in the village and, under solemn promise of secrecy, she told her friend about this new thing which, in honor of Kisthenes, she named "kissing." Her friend had a young man of her own and she told him about it. He – being a sad flirt – had two other girls over in another village on Mount Ossa, and he told them about it. And so it spread. All authorities agree that this is the most reliable account of the origin of kissing.

[Charms and Superstitions, Tricks and Surprises]

Monday, 7 April 1902

Did you get April fooled last week? At our house we all arose on April's birth morning with a grim determination not to believe a word that our best friends said to us or tamper with anything that looked suspicious the whole day through. And yet, the sorrowful fact remains that – I blush to admit it – I fell into the very first trap with grace and agility.

When I went downstairs Ted was in the hall looking over a morning paper with a very shocked face.

"Cynthia," he said, with a shudder – oh, it was very well done. In justice to myself I must say that – "this is frightful. There has been a terrible accident up at the north end – nine lives lost."

"Oh," I gasped, feeling a dozen thrills of horror. "Oh, Ted, what happened?"

"A street car ran over a cat," said Ted solemnly.

And there I was! If it had even been a new joke there would have been some excuse for me. But it is old – so old! Why, it has been going the rounds of the funny columns for years.

Well, I tried to take it meekly and all through breakfast I brooded over my revenge. When Ted started to go down town I called to him and asked him if he would mind doing an errand for me. He said no, of course not. So I wrote out a memorandum and told him to get me three yards of sparrowbill purple ribbon.

"Be very careful to get sparrowbill," I said. "No other shade of purple will do. I want it to match my new suit. I daresay they won't have it at all the stores. It's a new shade."

"I'll hunt around until I get it," said Ted so obligingly that I felt a slight pang of remorse – until I remembered that hideous joke.

When Ted came home at night he looked as if he were suffering from that tired feeling.

"I couldn't get that fiendish shade of ribbon you wanted, Cynthia," he said wearily. "I've been to every dry goods store in Halifax and the clerks all looked at me as if they thought I was crazy. Said they'd never heard of sparrowbill purple."

"No more did I," I said maliciously. "You shouldn't go gunning for new shades on the first of April, Teddy-boy."

Ted, not being dull of comprehension, understood. He grinned.

"Guess we are square," he said frankly.

Gertrude and Phil came to visit us last week and brought along their baby. It is the most wonderful baby that was ever born. It is about the only baby of any account in the world. At least, this is the way Gertrude and Phil seem to regard it. To me it looked just like any other baby, but, of course, as Gertrude said scornfully, I'm no judge. To me all babies as new as this one look so much alike as so many peas.

To be sure, Gertrude's baby must have a very good constitution or it would never have lived through all the petting and pulling about it has got at our house since it came. Polly and Theo fight regularly as to who shall hold it and even Ted sneaks in whenever he gets a chance to look at it lying asleep in its cradle.

One evening, when Gertrude was sitting with her baby in her lap and the rest of us were all disposed around her in a circle, like an admiring court around its queen, we began talking about the various superstitions about babies.

"I hope the baby was carried upstairs before it was carried down, Gertrude," said Aunt Janet. "If it wasn't it will never have any luck in life."

"Do you keep a cat?" said Theodosia. "I've heard somewhere that a baby and a kitten cannot thrive in the same house. One of them will pine away."

"When you have a baby christened," said Ted, "if it does not cry a little it will have bad luck all its life. You'd better pinch the baby, Gertie, to make sure."

"If you cut or trim its nails the first year of its life it will be light fingered," said Polly, "and you must not let it look into a mirror until it is a year old; it will grow up proud and vain."

"Never rock the cradle when the baby isn't in it," said Marion. "To do so will bring disease or misfortune on it."

"You should never walk entirely around a baby," said Gertrude. "That brings ill-luck, too."

"If a baby is born at new moon time it will be blessed with a well-hung tongue," said Aunt Debby, "and if born during the last quarter it will have a keen reason."

Everybody had said something but myself, so, not to be behind hand, I quoted the old rhyme:

"Monday's child is fair of face,
Tuesday's child is blessed with grace,
Wednesday's child is born for woe,
Thursday's child has far to go,
Friday's child is loving and giving,
Saturday's child must work for his living,
But the child that is born on the Sabbath day
Is bonny and blithe and good and gay."[239]

"Surprises," said Theodosia crossly, "are dangerous – deadly – positively immoral. I never feel more wicked than I do just after I've been surprised."

"Some surprises are nice," said Polly dubiously.

"Very few," I chimed in. "I agree with Theodosia.[240] The right kind of surprises is rare and when they do come they come at the wrong time. I hate to be surprised."

A surprise, even an agreeable surprise, is more or less of a shock. Few of us are at our best when taken by surprise. We are at a disadvantage and we feel that isn't fair. Sometimes you'll hear folks saying,

"Oh, we never let Kitty know when we're coming. She's always glad to see us and it is so pleasant to give her a little surprise."

It may be pleasant for them. I'm very sure it isn't for Kitty no matter how well she may disguise it. Doubtless, she has a dozen plans that are all wrecked by the sudden appearance of even welcome guests. And, if the guests happen not to be welcome – well, that is adding insult to injury.

Oh, I wish all my friends and relatives would break themselves of the surprise habit. But I suppose that is too much to expect in this world.

Polly believes – or pretends to believe – in charms, so at Easter we all gave her one. Ted gave her an enamel four-leaved clover – for good luck, of course. I gave her an ancient coin which insures good fortune at games – Polly has won every game of ping-pong she has played since. Theodosia gave her a silver pine cone which preserves from sickness, and Gwennie gave her hazelnut, which is said to bring great length of days.

[Smiles and Tears]

Monday, 14 April 1902

APRIL HAS SO FAR WELL SUSTAINED HER REPUTATION AS a month of smiles and tears, hasn't she? Only it really seems to me that so far we have had a great many more tears than smiles. Theodosia dislikes April's teary side because she cannot keep her hair in curl. Polly hates it because she cannot wear her new hat and Ted and I growl at it on general principles. But Aunt Janet, bless her, smiles placidly and says:

"Never mind, dears. You know it's bound to clear up sometime."

There is a great deal of sound philosophy in that remark of Aunt Janet's, not only as regards April weather but all the other cares and troubles of life under the present dispensation. What a comfort it is, when things are going badly and there are big black clouds in our skies and a Scotch mist over all our plans and hopes, to remember that it's bound to clear up sometime – that sometime the sun will shine out over the clouds and the mists will loop themselves up into curtains of glory on the hills and then fade away altogether, and that our worries will straighten themselves out in the long run.

Somebody has said that April is like a woman because of her smiles and tears.[241] Polly looks upon that as a slander on our sex but I don't. Sometimes tears are just as good as smiles and if a woman doesn't indulge in both pretty often you may depend that there is something wrong in her make-up.

A good, comfortable cry is the most nerve-soothing thing in the world – if you pick a good time for it. You don't want to be seen, of course, for some time after you've indulged in it. The other day I had one. It was pouring cats and dogs out of doors and my plans were all spoiled and I had fought with Polly, and Theo was away and I was horribly lonesome. I crawled away to a corner and buried my nose in a cushion and had a lovely howl. I thought of all the mistakes I'd made and raked up all my old, forgotten troubles and oh, I was deliciously miserable and it did me such heaps of good, that luxurious cry did. I felt all right and happy and cheerful when I had got through.

The other day Polly "straightened out" her top bureau drawer.

That top bureau drawer of Polly's is one of our standing family jokes. When we want to express terrible confusion we never think of comparing it to original chaos. Oh, no! We say it is as bad as Polly's top bureau drawer.

Polly "straightens" it out about once every month and when she finishes she says with a little purr of self-congratulation:

"There, now! That's all nice and neat and I'm going to keep it so. What are you grinning at, Cynthia?"

I never grin. That is only Polly's way of putting it, you know. But I do smile when I hear Polly make that remark.

I know that at the end of twenty-four hours that bureau drawer's last state will be worse than its first – one awful tangle of ribbons and gloves and ties and hankys, seeming to have no beginning or ending, and when Polly wants to find anything she has to claw it all over wildly half a dozen times before she finds it.

I think it would be a splendid idea to have top bureau drawers fitted out with handy sets of pigeon-holes which would keep the little trifles in place and prevent laces from getting mixed up with ribbons and belts and ties from becoming interlaced. Things keep fresh and smart so much longer when they are kept neatly folded among their own kind.

As the folks who build bureau drawers have not as yet awakened to this long felt want, however, Theodosia has substituted a system of boxes. Her top bureau drawer is a model of neatness.

It is filled with a layer of card-board boxes of all shapes and sizes from the long oblong one where her veils are folded to the tiny round pill box in which she keeps odd buttons and hooks and eyes. Everything is kept in its own place and this is not difficult since its place is always there ready for it and is never usurped by anything else.

I have tried to coax Polly to adopt this plan. But there are some people you can't reform!

Laura was visiting us last week and the first morning we had eggs for breakfast. After she had eaten hers she made a tiny hole in the bottom of the shell. When I asked her why she said she really didn't know; she always did it, that was all.

Ted rose to the occasion. Once in a while Ted shows himself to be possessed of any amount of queer odds and ends of knowledge. You'd be surprised.

"That," he said, "is really a superstitious custom which the old Romans carefully observed. People used to believe that if a witch found an empty egg-shell lying about she would make use of it as a boat and cause terrible storms and shipwrecks. If you punch a hole in it of course you render it unseaworthy.

"The Japanese never leave egg-shells lying around because they believe that anyone who steps over them will go insane. In some parts of England there is a belief that if you burn egg-shells the hens will stop laying. It is also very unlucky to dream about eggs."

One of the latest fads in smart society is a gold and pearl net for the hair. These are very beautiful with my lady's glossy curls gleaming through their meshes. The idea is an old one, for centuries ago high born Spanish dames confined their locks under jewelled nets.

They are both becoming and effective. One very pretty one has fine threads of gold woven in a diamond shaped mesh over softly puffed golden hair. Polly has one of small pearl beads and it is very fetching.

[The Great Art of Letter-Writing]

Monday, 21 April 1902

WHAT WITH DANCES, OPERAS AND CONCERTS HALIFAX has been quite gay recently. And when the fine days did come after all the rain weren't they hugely appreciated? We are creatures of the sun, we men and women, and come to our best only in his smiles. But this is enough to say about the weather. I'm in duty bound to mention it, you know. There is no luck for anyone who flies in the face of old traditions too openly.

The other evening around the table we amused ourselves by telling stories about the "funny sayings" of children. We each had to tell one story that we had heard, read or invented – it didn't make any difference which. But if it were the last it had to be good enough to be – like beauty – its own excuse for being.[242]

Ted led off with a story he had heard somewhere. A new baby had arrived at a certain household and the older brother was looking at it gravely. "Where did it come from, Aunty?" he asked. "God sent it," replied Aunty gently. "I don't believe God did," said the older brother gravely. "I think the milkman brought it." "Why the milkman?" queried Aunty. "Because," said the child, "it says on his cart 'Families supplied.'"

Polly followed this up with a gruesome anecdote about two little lads who were discussing their love for their father and mother. One couldn't live without "muvver." If she died he would go and dig her up. But the other had a better plan. "If favver dies I'll have him stuffed."

Theodosia told of a prayer she had once heard a little girl say reverently. "Oh, please, dear God, make me pure, absolutely pure as Epps' cocoa."[243]

This reminded me of another story I had heard about a little boy whose father had gone to the city, promising to bring him a toy train when he came home. Very sincere was the small chap's prayer. "God bless papa and bring him home safely – and – and – his luggage."

Aunt Janet finished up by telling of a little six-year-old cousin of hers who used to pray "God bless grandmamma and help her to speak the truth," when he wanted a special blessing for his saintly grandmother.

Theo flung down a letter the other day with a rather disgusted expression upon her face.

"I sometimes wonder why Gertie writes letters at all," she said. "She puts so little in them. I don't see how it is. Personally Gertie is one of the brightest and most entertaining girls I know and yet her letters are dry as chips."

Letters very often fall short of what they ought to be and indeed, of what they might be if the writers took a little more trouble over them. We have all got letters that were disappointing in their brevity and dullness. And again we have had letters that for interest and brightness were the wells of water in a thirsty ground.[244]

It is a good plan when writing a letter to keep strictly in mind, as far as you can, what will interest your friend and not simply what interests you.[245] Don't fill up your letter with scraps of news about people and places unknown to her unless they are entertaining apart from their personal interest. Write to her as you would talk to her. Tell her all the harmless gossip – there is such a thing, you know – she would like to hear and don't write anything that you think might hurt or worry her in any way, unless it is really necessary. Don't gush – that is if you are over eighteen. If you are under that age it is no use telling you not to. School girls have to gush and write sentimental letters to their darling chums vowing eternal friendship and all that sort of thing. It's a phase they have to pass through. And how silly those soul outpourings do read, years afterward, when you read them over in cold blood.

Again, never write a letter when you are angry. Or if you do, don't mail it for twenty-four hours. Then read it over and put it in the waste basket. It may save you a heartache in after years. Remember that "written words remain."[246]

Above all bear in mind Sam Weller's immortal dictum:

"She'll vish there was more and that's the great art of letter-writing."[247]

Nowadays when real lace is so extensively worn it is well to be up in lace lore. Here are a few points I have gleaned here and there. All "real" lace is hand-made, of course, and is easily detected from the machine woven imitation because the meshes in real lace are generally irregular while the machine made is uniform in weave.

There are only two kinds of real lace – "pillow" lace, which is made with pins and bobbins, and "needle" lace with which we are all familiar. Needle lace has a more distinctive outline than pillow lace, which has a flat pattern and a soft, smooth outline. Some of these pillow laces are exquisitely beautiful.

Almost fabulous prices have been paid for laces. Forty pounds an ounce is the largest sum ever given for lace. The art of lace making is very old and has a glamor of romance about it. It is an essentially feminine art and it is a rare woman who does not love the making of it as well as the wearing.

Nowadays the voice of the housecleaner is heard in the land.[248] I have heard men saying that there is no real need of this periodical overturning – that it was just a notion the women have. When the men talk about anything they don't understand they are too funny for words. Polly and Theo and Aunt Janet and I have to sit on Ted systematically every spring or there would be no living with him at all.

It's a relief to dig out old corners and weed out the accumulated rubbish of months. You're sure to find a lot of things you've looked for high and low and given up as lost. And there's fun in shifting the furniture about and figuring out new ways to hide old holes in the carpets. Of course there are drawbacks – but isn't the same to be said about most mundane things?

[The Great Art of Packing a Trunk]

Monday, 28 April 1902

MARIAN DROPPED IN THE OTHER EVENING TO TELL US a harrowing tale of her recent "flitting" from one boarding house to another.[249]

"I'm tired to death," she said pathetically. "For the past three days I have felt like the man without a country – or was it without a shadow? I forget which.[250]

"First thing I had to pack up. I hate packing. But this time I was determined to be systematic and thorough. I hunted out a newspaper article on packing a trunk and started to follow its instructions. The first thing, it said, was to carefully sort out all your belongings into piles and put like with like. Well, I did this. The bed was the only place I had to put them and I piled them there. I meant to keep the piles separate, but when I got through everything seemed to be mixed up together and the things that I wanted to pack first were at the very bottom of the pile.

"I discarded the newspaper clipping in despair and went at the job in my own old abandoned way. I got it done in time – after a fashion. Then I called Winnie and Mab in and they sat on the trunk while I locked it.

"Of course, as soon as this was done – and I hope you'll never be as tired and dusty as I was, Cynthia – I began to discover that I had packed a lot of things that I needed at the very bottom of the trunk – my brush and comb, for instance, and my dressing jacket. Also, I couldn't find my soap. I had to unlock the old thing and poke and dive into it for half an hour before I found all I wanted. I would get hold of something that felt like what I was looking for and pull it up and it would be something else. No, Ted, I did *not* swear. You know I would not do such a thing. But Mab said my looks were profane.

"Anyhow I lived through it and got moved. Then came the unpacking. Girls!!! You'd have thought I'd begun at the top of that trunk and packed down.

"My oil stove was on top of my second best hat. To save space I had put all my handkerchiefs in a little saucepan I use for making candy in and I rolled an organdy shirt waist round it. But I had forgotten that the bottom of it was all smoky and that shirt waist is ruined. Then I'd packed a bottle of shoe polish upside down and it leaked all through my very spiffiest whitewear. It's no wonder I look like a wreck. My mind won't recover its tone for a month."

Although Marian made such a poor use of her newspaper article perhaps others will do better. So here are a few new-old hints for the use and behoof of those who are about to "flit."

It is best to begin with boots, stockings and heavy underwear which should be laid at the bottom of the trunk. The golden rule in packing is "Take care of the corners and the centre will take care of itself."[251] Cuffs, collars, gloves, ties and hankys should all be packed together and the trays are the best place for them. All sleeves and bows of dresses should be stuffed with tissue paper or – if you are stinted for space – you can use rolls of fine underwear for stuffing the sleeves. In packing skirts fold them three or four times from the centre to the front. Generally it will be necessary to turn up the skirt at the bottom which should be done after the lengthwise folds are made. Even if you are travelling only a short distance do not leave your handbag out of calculation. It ought to contain soap and a towel, a wash cloth, nail brush, comb and hair brush, clothes and tooth brush, pins, needles, thread, thimble and scissors, two or three handkerchiefs and collars. So fortified you could live for a few days in comparative comfort even if your trunk mistrysted. If you take more than one trunk it is a good plan to list all the articles in each and tack the list inside the cover.

We hear a good deal from time to time about the miserable condition of women in China, especially in regard to their subservience to their husbands. Well, doubtless they have grievances; but I suspect that the theoretical authority of the Chinese husband is sometimes much greater than the practical authority. Even in Canada – nay, right here in Halifax – brides vow at the altar to obey their husbands.[252] But do they always do it? Place aux hommes![253]

Apropos of China, here is a story I read the other day which is a favorite "joke" in the flowery kingdom.

Ten henpecked husbands resolved to form a society to resist the impositions of their wives. The ten wives heard of the plan and while the meeting for organization was in progress entered in a body. Nine of the rebellious husbands incontinently bolted, but the tenth one retained his place quite unmoved by the frightful apparition. The ten ladies, merely smiling contemptuously on the one man left behind, returned to their homes satisfied with the success of their raid.[254] The nine husbands thereupon returned and resolved to make the heroic tenth the president of the society. When they went, however, to inform him of the honor it was found that he had died on the spot of fright.

Lives there a woman who doesn't love jewels? If there be such a weird, unfeminine creature, out on her!

Theo had an opal ring given her the other day as a birthday gift. We all told her that opals are unlucky, but Theo flouts all such superstition disdainfully and wears her opals gaily.

There is another superstition connected with the opal. It is said that it glows bright when the love of the giver for the wearer remains constant and true and grows dim when it falters or fails.

To my thinking, opals are the most beautiful jewels in the world. They are pearls with souls.

Legend says that pearls are the crystallized tears of sea-nymphs. Hence the superstition that they bring sorrow to their wearers. This legend, like many others, is more poetical than true. Pearls are really the tombs of small marine worms known as "distomes." Ordinarily the pearls decay in a year's time releasing the encysted creature. But if the distome dies the pearl will go on enlarging until it is of great value. That an insignificant worm should have a coffin worth thousands of dollars is really as poetical an idea as the old one about the nymphs. Colored pearls are valuable for their rarity. Fabulous prices are paid for these, especially for the pale green.

A diamond is simply a "spark of pure carbon." We think of diamonds as colorless and transparent, but they occur frequently in many colors, and there are black diamonds which are very valuable. The diamond is emblematic of innocence and is the birth-stone of April.

The turquoise is for December. An old legend relates that it fades when its wearer is ill and dies when he is attacked by an incurable malady. If your birthday is in December wear a turquoise and you need never fear falling off a high place. It is also said to be a protection against contagion. This would be a pleasanter safeguard than vaccination, but I suspect its efficiency depends a good deal on the "faith" of the wearer.

[Jonah Days]

Monday, 5 May 1902

LAST WEEK THE VOICE OF THE GRADUATE WAS HEARD IN the land.[255] Polly and Theo and I took in all the convocations, of course. Theodosia is interested in the Higher Education of Women – spelt with capitals – and Polly had two or three of the graduates on her calling list. When we got home from the Academy of Music on Tuesday we talked it over.

"Didn't Jack look splendid," sighed Polly. "There's no use in talking, he is very handsome and distinguished-looking. And those bachelor gowns are really very becoming to girls. They almost make me wish I had gone in for an Arts course."

"I wonder if any of them know how to cook," said Ted – who has a habit of saying things like that.

"Why shouldn't they?" demanded Theodosia indignantly. "Is a knowledge of Greek going to prevent anybody from cooking? If so, what did the people who used to talk Greek live on? Did they eat things raw because the women knew Greek? A man can eat a dinner no matter how many dead languages he knows; why can't a woman cook it under the same circumstances. You men are always thinking about your stomachs."

"It ill becomes a man who once made a certain historic gingerbread in this household to rail at the possible culinary shortcomings of others," I said severely.

Ted looked at me with an "et tu, Brute," expression and said no more.[256] He might have stood out against Theodosia's broadly chopped logic, but my reference wilted him.

You see it happened this way. Ted used to think he knew all about cooking because, once upon a time, he made some pancakes and nobody died after eating them. On the strength of this he used to criticize the things Polly and Theo and I cooked with the lofty air of one who knows it all. We didn't mind much. You have to humor the men in some respects, you know. And after all, Ted is a good soul.

One day I made a gingerbread and it was more or less a failure – flat in the middle and hilly around the edges – you know the kind. Ted is fond of gingerbread and he was nasty about this. He made some sarcastic remarks that hurt my feelings and I retorted by telling him to make better gingerbread himself if he could.

Ted never took a dare in his life and next day he put on one of Aunt Janet's aprons and he made the gingerbread for tea. The joke of it was that he was real deft and knacky about it, too.

You'd have thought he had been cooking all his life. The cake came out of the oven as light and puffy as golden foam. Ted beamed and you've no idea how silly I felt.

"If you like, Cynthia, I'll give you a few lessons in the art of making good gingerbread," said Ted condescendingly.

But I had my revenge when we tried to eat that gingerbread. Ted had flavored it with a big spoonful of mustard instead of ginger!

He hasn't offered to give me lessons in cooking since. If you want to see Ted wither up and shrink visibly before your eyes just say "gingerbread" to him.

Polly made a queer mistake once. It was long ago and she is under the fond delusion that we have forgotten it. But nobody who tasted that cake ever could forget it.

We had company for tea that evening and Polly made a cake for them in a hurry. It looked very nice when she put it on the table – the golden slices tipped with icing, nestling among the flutes of a cobweb-like doily. Polly passed it around proudly, remarking – probably for the benefit of her particular young man pro tem,[257] who was present – that she had made it herself. We all took a piece and each took a big, brave bite.

Well, we are all living yet, so it did not prove fatal, but at the time I certainly thought Theo would choke to death. Theo has a delicate throat.

The truth was that Polly in her haste had iced that cake with saleratus[258] instead of confectioner's sugar.

While I am on the subject I may as well relate the story of the very queerest mistake I ever heard along this line. I often tell this story, but people never believe me. They think I'm romancing. But it really happened, "cross my heart solemn and true."

I was once visiting at a country Methodist parsonage, the charming little mistress of which was a friend of mine. One day a lot of unexpected company came when there wasn't a bit of cake in the house – company always does come at such a time, by the way. It's of a piece with the innate contrariness of things. However, Gwennie left me to talk to the visitors while she whisked into the kitchen and concocted a layer cake which came to the table in due time looking as nice and as innocent as you please.

I shall never to my dying day forget the taste of that cake – neither, I imagine, will Gwennie's guests. To be sure, one man among them ate every crumb of his section and never flinched. He was of the stuff of which heroes are made. I suppose he thought it was merely some new-fangled flavoring and that he must not hurt his hostess' feelings by failing to eat it. I read in a paper recently that that same man has been elected to a position of high honor and responsibility in the Methodist church and I don't wonder. He deserved it if ever a man did, and I am sure he will fulfil its duties with honor and conscientious fidelity.

To return to our mutton[259] – that is to say, to Gwennie's layer cake. Gwennie thought she had flavored it with a generous spoonful of vanilla. What she really had put into it was a certain anodyne liniment, widely known and advertised at the present time.

We found out afterwards that her husband had broken the liniment bottle and had poured what remained of its contents into an old empty vanilla bottle. It was just the same color as vanilla and Gwennie was in a hurry – hence her mistake.

Fortunately it wasn't poisonous or the Methodist ministry would have lost one of its bright and shining lights.[260]

"This has been a Jonah day for me,"[261] sighed Kitty, who dropped in the other evening.

"What is a Jonah day," I asked, for the expression was new to me.

"Oh, a day when everything goes wrong," returned Kitty dolefully. "You know when we were children they used to tell us on such a day that we got out on the wrong side of the bed in the morning.

"I felt cross and grumpy when I got up. It was pouring rain and things were at sixes and sevens all day. I quarrelled with Amy and a letter I expected didn't come and I tore a big cati-corner hole in my second best skirt, and I broke my hand-painted china hairpin plate and lost my tooth-brush. Oh, you needn't preach! It wasn't crankiness or carelessness. It was just the day. It was a Jonah day and things were bound to go wrong."

I don't see how Jonah days can come in spring, myself. I should think everything would go right in spite of itself in these splendid awakening days. What a freedom there is in the very air and what a glory on the hills. It warms the cockles of my heart to meander past Government House and see the big fat buds bursting on the trees and the green spears thrusting up out of the mellow earth.[262] It is the sweet o' the year[263] and let's all open our hearts and souls widely to it and drink in its delight – a delight which, thus stored up, will serve to tide us over the dark days that may come to us later.

[On Photography]

Monday, 12 May 1902

"NOW," SAID POLLY YESTERDAY WITH A DETERMINED expression, "housecleaning is over and likewise the woes of spring dressmaking. So I am going to get out my camera."

We all tried to look as resigned as possible. We knew what was in store for us. We knew that henceforth, no matter how harmlessly and inoffensively we deported ourselves we were liable to be "snapped" at any hour of the day, in any attitude. We knew that it would not be safe to throw out what seemed to be a dish of simple water because we would probably discover when too late that it was some weird mixture of Polly's called a "toning solution." We knew that we would risk the peace of the household if we opened a window without first examining all its ledges. Probably Polly would have a printing frame on it and the wretched thing would tumble down and break the plate. And, worst of all, we knew that we would have to listen to unintelligible jargon about "time exposures" and "hypo" and "frilling" and "negatives" and so on. But as Ted says, when for your sins you are condemned to have a camera fiend in the family, the only thing to do is to bear it philosophically and keep the fact as quiet as you can.

The most reliable test of friendship I know of is to take a snapshot of your friends. Then show it to them. If they forgive you and allow it to make no difference in their friendship then you may be sure that they are true-blue and can be trusted with life itself. There is no test so sure. It will separate the gold from the dross[264] every time and though by this heroic measure you will probably narrow your circle of friends down to a very small compass you will have the comfort of knowing that those can be depended upon.

Amateur photographers have to suffer a good deal of equally amateur joking, but when all is said and done there is really no "hobby" which has such a fascination or out of which more pleasure can be extracted.[265] Of course one must be in earnest about it and not be a mere dabbler. There is nothing beautiful about a weird snapshot of your friends or a slap-dash exposure where the houses come out canted at an angle that surpasses the leaning tower of Pisa.[266] But a really pretty bit of scenery, nicely furnished and properly mounted, reminiscent of a pleasant summer day's walk or outing is a thing of beauty and a joy forever. Several friends of mine have recently invested in cameras and have asked me for some advice regarding the use and abuse of them. So I will give a few pointers won from experience.

In amateur photography, even more than in anything else, the golden rule is "carefulness." You simply can't be careless if you would succeed in producing photos worth having. The most trifling oversight will sometimes spoil a good picture. If you make your exposures in a slap-dash style, if your dark room leaks light, if your hypo solution is not kept religiously apart from your developer, if you do or leave undone a hundred other things you will fail to obtain good results.

In starting out don't attempt too much at first and recklessly expose half a dozen plates before developing one. Make haste slowly.[267] A 4x5 camera is large enough for a beginner. Get all the supplies necessary, for, of course, you will not be content to be a "button pusher," but will do your own developing and finishing. Above all, get a good dark room lantern. Misplaced economy here will result in worry and disappointment. In spite of some opinions to the contrary, I think a beginner would do well to commence with a slow brand of plates. Indeed, I like the slow plates best at any time. I consider that they yield more artistic results.

In your dark room have a place for everything and keep

everything rigidly in its place.[268] Dust your plates before putting them in the holders. A camel's hair brush is used for this, but if some time you can't find it draw the palm of your hand softly over the plate, taking care that it – your hand – is quite dry. If you are ever where you cannot gain access to a dark room and yet want to change plates, here is a plan I have followed with success. Get into a windowless closet, sit on the floor and get somebody to put right over your head a heavy quilt – a red one if possible. Then have the door shut tightly and change your plate. If in summer this is a fearfully warm job, but it is better than getting your plates light-struck.

Choose your view carefully with an eye to light and shade effects. You will always get better results by using a tripod and taking time exposures, although of course this requires more skill. In regard to exposures no cut and dried formulas are of any use. The time is regulated by the strength of light and the kind of plates used. In this you must simply learn by making mistakes. Do not take pictures between eleven and three o'clock. The results are never so good.

In developing don't under-develop. A beginner is fatally apt to, getting alarmed when the picture begins to fade and whisking it out of the solution. Leave it until very dim and indistinct. Wash well before putting in hypo. I let my plates soak for ten minutes. Also leave them long enough in the hypo. The use of an alum solution will prevent "frilling" – which means that the film curls up around the edges of the plate. In cold weather you will have no trouble with this. After your plate is taken out of the hypo soak it in water for half an hour. If not in running water change the water six times. This is very important, as the least bit of hypo left on the film will eventually spoil it. Above all things, be thorough. Don't be content with "good enough." Aim at the best.

A pretty effect may sometimes be obtained in a landscape picture by cutting out of white paper a tiny new moon and pasting it properly on the glass side of the negative. The result is a "summer moonlight scene." You can take pictures by moonlight, by the way. The exposure calls for hours instead of seconds. Generally the result looks more or less like a foggy plate exposed in the usual way, but very beautiful effects have been obtained in this way. However I do not advise beginners to attempt it.

If you want to make a "winter moonlight scene," here is how you go about it. Take an ordinary negative of some landscape. Don't have leaf trees in it. Evergreen trees and an old farm house or so make the best picture for this. Place it in the printing frame, film upward. On top of this place a fresh plate, the two film sides together, and back them with a bit of black cloth for greater security. Then hold frame about 18 or 20 inches from gas jet and turn up gas quickly. Time of exposure will vary from 2 to 20 seconds, according to character of light, plate and negative used. After exposure develop the plate as usual. It is called a positive. Paste a full moon in proper position on its back and print off. The sky will come out black while ground and trees will white with – apparently – snow. The effect will be very pretty. I may add that your "positive" is also a magic lantern slide.

Sometimes your camera will play you very odd tricks. I have had some curious pictures result from accidentally exposing the same plate twice. This is how "ghost" pictures are made.[269] Once I took a picture of two girl friends of mine standing side by side. Later on I happened to re-expose the same plate on a landscape view. The latter came out very well. The girls were also there, wan, transparent figures with all the background clearly visible through them. It was apparently a perfect picture, which, of course, does not often result by chance.

Well, I hope you will all get a great deal of pleasure out of your cameras this summer. It will be your own fault if you don't, be sure of that.

[The Moral of May]

Monday, 19 May 1902

THE MORAL OF MAY SO FAR SEEMS TO BE "DON'T PACK your furs away too soon." Never mind! We may have showers of snow in May, but we don't have volcanic eruptions at any time of the year. As Ted – or is it Emerson? – says, "There are always compensations."[270]

When we were children the phrase "Happy as a queen" expressed for us the highest summit of human bliss. As we grew up we gradually realized that, after all, kings and queens were not a bit different from other people, unless, perhaps, it might be that they had less of a fair chance for ordinary happiness. Nobody, at least, would say "happy as a queen" when they thought of poor little Wilhelmina.[271]

At our house we have been so interested in her. And so, I think, has everybody. Somehow, she has always seemed such an attractive little bit of royalty and more "really truly" than any other crowned head in Europe – nearer to us, as it were, if only by reason of her youth and her girlishness, which seems to be pretty much the same as in girls not born to the purple. To me, at any-rate, there has always seemed more individuality about Holland's girl queen than about any other of Europe's rulers.

During her recent illness even lazy Polly got out of bed half an hour earlier in the mornings to run down and find out from the morning paper how "our little queen" was. And when we found that she was getting better we all felt as delighted as if it were somebody belonging to us. Poor little girl queen, whose short tenure of the sceptre has been filled with so much tragedy!

"I don't know that I ever really wished to be a queen," says Polly, "but if I ever did I'm cured of it now."

"Some day," said Annette plaintively, "I am going to write a treatise on 'The Trials of a Country Schoolma'am.'[272] It will be a harrowing bit of realism. It seems to be the prevailing impression that we live in clover[273] and have nothing to do but draw our quarter's salary. My treatise shall be devoted to the purpose of telling the truth about us."

Annette is teaching young ideas how to shoot in a certain Nova Scotian country district, which, for obvious reasons, shall be nameless.[274] She had come up to Halifax last week to spend Sunday with us and tell her woes to Polly and Theo and me.

"If a week should pass without somebody telling me that I am doing easy work for big pay," went on Annette, "I should conclude that I might as well order my ascension robe 'immediately and to onct.'[275]

"'Well, you get your money easy,' some ratepayer will tell me. 'All you have to do is sit there and hear lessons and keep the youngsters quiet.'

"I used to argue the matter at first, but I'm wiser now. Facts may be stubborn things, but they are not half so stubborn as fallacies.

"Why, to begin with, I have nine grades in my school and I have to teach a little of everything from investigating earthworms to the study of the solar system. In the wild effort to cram all sorts of research into a short six hours a day I don't wonder if the children feel like the little boy who was taken to see the biograph.[276] 'I have to look for what's coming next before I know what went last,' he said. I feel that way myself.

"Then I get such letters! Tommy's mother writes me that Tommy is not coming on in arithmetic as fast as she would like. She says he is only in simple reduction yet and Johnny Jones across the road is in fractions and Johnny isn't half as smart as her Tommy and she doesn't understand it. And Susy's father wants to know why Susy can't write a letter without mis-spelling half the words, and Dick's aunt wants me to change his seat because that bad Brown boy he is sitting with is teaching him to say naughty words.

"As to the financial part – but I will not begin on that because there is no end to it. Last year I saved sixty-five cents. And I don't think I was extravagant either. One cannot live by bread alone.[277] Those whom the gods wish to destroy they first make schoolma'ams."[278]

"But of course," went on Annette after she had eaten the greater part of a box of chocolates Ted had given her and so felt cheered up, "there are bright spots even in a country schoolma'am's existence. There are the compositions! They are as good as the funny papers. I always look forward to reading them as a positive treat. One day last week I told the fourth class to write a composition on 'Birds.' One boy started out with the sentence, 'Our cat catches birds.' Then he branched out and gave me the history, character and accomplishments not only of his private and particular cat, but of every other feline in the neighborhood. But not another word did he say about birds.[279]

"Another time I told them to write about ships. This same boy wrote 'A boat is a small ship. Sailing in a boat is pretty nice, but it is better not to do it, because if you go sailing you may be caught in a storm and drowned and then you will come home and lay the blame on the man who built the boat.'"

Annette has a neck chain which is a very pretty idea. I suspect her best young man gave it to her. Gems are set along it at wide intervals and their initials spell "Dearest." There is a diamond, an emerald, an amethyst, a ruby, another emerald, a sapphire and a topaz. A pet name might be worked out in this way and anyone not in the secret would never suspect it.

Everybody remembers the old-fashioned autograph album, specimens of which yet survive in out-of-the-way places. It is never heard of nowadays, but its place is taken by various fads and one of these is the "face" book. Get a well-bound sketch book and in it get each of your friends to draw a head of some sort – girl, man, child or animal. It does not matter if they cannot draw at all. They must do their best and the attempts of the non-artistic often prove the most amusing. They should, of course, sign their names to the pictures. The collection when finished is usually most interesting, exceedingly comic attempts being interspersed with the charming sketches of one's artistic friends.

[Delightful Days]

Monday, 26 May 1902

One afternoon last week Polly and Theo and I took a day off and went over to Dartmouth.[280] We had a delightful outing, too, although we had a hard time to keep Polly from doing crazy things. The spring seemed to have got into her blood and Theo and I took turns keeping an eye on her. We kept the other eye on the beautiful misty blue lakes, the shimmering young green tints on the trees and the velvet emerald of slopes that fronted the sun. We saw the purples on the far away hills and the glinting fir tops that seemed whispering to the sky. We found faintly perfumed blue violets nestling amid the grasses by old stone walls, and we felt as if we had discovered a gold mine when we came upon a green space dotted with dandelions, as if some spring fairy had shaken star-dust over this corner of the world. The ferns were poking their dear curly heads up in sunny corners, and here and there the wild plum hung out its reddish leaves and its lace-like feathery bloom.

Polly and I picked all the flowers we could lay our hands on, but Theodosia wouldn't. She said she felt so glad to be alive herself that she hadn't the heart to shorten the life of even a wild blossom. Perhaps she was right, when you come to think of it.

Nature has worked her yearly miracle the past week. She is a transfigured nature. And the miracle is none the less marvellous because it was expected or because we may have beheld it many times before. It always brings with it an unutterable sense of new birth and new life. For many weeks there have been hints of its coming. But through it all the real spirit of the spring slept. Now it has awakened. With a leap and a bound Nature passes to the full blossom of her spring, and the whole world, as we know it, is transformed.

We wait longer for it than the children of more southern lands. But what we lose in delay is recompensed by the glory of the realization.

The time is at hand when people begin to think of vacation. Short or long, it is the golden spot in the year for us. We want to make the most of it and have something of it to gladden the rest of the year after it is over. In connection with this let me tell you about the "vacation memory book" that Polly and I made last summer.

We spent several weeks together in the country, and this book was devoted to our vacation haunts. We took an ordinary scrapbook, and on the first page we pasted a snapshot of the house where we stayed, and underneath we wrote a lot of original verses, which were pretty good fun for us, even if poor poetry. Following on each page were snapshots of all the places in wood and hills and shore that we visited, with an appropriate quotation or a bit of nonsense rhyme reminiscent of our good times. We put other souvenirs in as well, such as nicely pressed flowers from some pet spot. Every page is a memory of some delightful day, and when we turn its pages over in the winter we live our vacation once more. We are going to make another this summer, and I am sure that anyone who tries this plan will find pleasure in it.

One day not long ago, when I was rummaging in the attic, I came across – guess what? Two bound volumes of *Godey's Lady's Book*, dated fifty years ago, when our grandmothers were young and our mothers were little girls.[281] I carried them downstairs, and we spent the evening looking over them and fairly shrieking with laughter.

Godey's Lady's Book was the fashionable magazine fifty years ago. Aunt Janet, to whose mother the book belonged, told us how eagerly its monthly visit was looked forward to – for, of course, in those days there were very few magazines – and how its pages of fashions and fancy work were conned and lingered over.

But those books were really "too funny for anything," especially the fashion-plates.

"Do you really suppose that the present day fashions will look as queer fifty years hence as these do today?" asked Polly.

Enormous hoop-skirts were in fashion then, multitudinous flounces, drooping mantillas,[282] and oh, such funny bonnets. And as for the head-dresses of lace and ribbon, I don't know how they ever managed to keep them on. Cork-screw curls were there, too, in odd little bunches on either side of placid, doll-like faces. They reminded me perfectly of the original illustrations in Thackeray's works.[283] The oddest hat of all was a broad-brimmed affair with a heavy flounce of lace dependent from the brim all round, and falling below the eyes. It made one think of a highwayman's mask somehow. As for the children's fashions you would think there were no children in those days at all – nothing but miniature men and women, for their clothes seemed to be a faithful copy of their elders' in all but size.

The reading matter was as quaint as the illustrations. Such lackadaisical poems, all breathing of heart break and daisies and blighted affections. And such quaint queries and equally quaint answers in the "letter box." We had an evening's solid enjoyment out of those books. What puzzled Ted most was how folks ever got "wooed and married and a'" in those days,[284] for he declared that with such hoopskirts he didn't know how a young man ever got close enough to a girl to see what she looked like, let alone proposing to her.

"Fancy standing five yards away from a girl on the outer-most edge of a hoopskirt, and trying to say pretty things to her," he said.

"I guess they managed it somehow," said Polly, serenely, "or else hoopskirts wouldn't have remained in fashion as long as they did."

And then we saw Aunt Janet laughing.

Cousin Rebecca came to our house last week. She is Aunt Janet's cousin, not ours, by the way, and she is a born reformer. Of course she tried her hand on us.

"I thought to myself," remarked Polly, apropos of an incident she was telling us.

"How else should you think, my dear?" said Cousin Rebecca, judicially. "If you thought aloud you would have to say so. Either you 'said to yourself' or you simply 'thought.'"

"I nodded my head," I remarked later on to Ted.

"Did you ever hear of anyone nodding her legs or her elbows?" asked Cousin Rebecca. "You may properly say 'I shook my head,' for you can shake other things. But in the present development of the language you can nod no other part of yourself or of creation than your head. It is enough to say, simply, 'I nodded!'"

I tried to look meek. Later on Ted caught it, too.

"I rose up," he said.

"Are people in the habit of rising down in Halifax, or is it possible for them to do so?" queried Cousin Rebecca, mildly. "If so, your use of 'up' is allowable – not otherwise."

No doubt Cousin Rebecca is right, and we are honestly trying to reform our English. But I don't know that we love her any the better for it.

(1901–1902)

Half an Hour with Canadian Mothers

This next piece – a blend of poetry, sketches, and child-rearing advice – appeared in the November 1901 issue of *The Ladies' Journal*, a Toronto magazine to which Montgomery had already contributed a number of short stories and poems, including her first published story, "A Baking of Gingersnaps," in 1895. The byline identifies the author as "Miss L.M. Montgomery" and announces her location as "Cavendish, N.S." – indicating perhaps that the editor of the periodical conflated her home town in Prince Edward Island with her current residence in Halifax. Some of the elements included in the piece would eventually be republished on their own: the sketch "One Mother's Opinion" in *The Standard* (Chicago) and *The Pacific* (Berkeley), the treatise "What to Teach Your Son" in at least three dozen North American newspapers under a variety of titles, and the poem "Mother's Mending Basket" in *The Ram's Horn* (Chicago).[1]

MOTHER'S MENDING BASKET

Now when the day's work is over and done
   Mother sits down by the door
In the soft light of the low setting sun
   Turning her basketful o'er.
So many worn little garments to mend,
   So many rents to repair –
Who but a mother has patience to spend
   So much of time and of care?

Wee Neddie's stockings are out at the knees –
  That is what marbles have done –
Bobby, his jacket has torn on the trees
  Which he was climbing "for fun."
Willie's new trousers, just worn once, and yet
  See, what a terrible tear!
Will with contrition avows his regret,
  But "doesn't know how it got there."

Kitty is out at the elbows and sleeves,
  Molly has tatters galore,
Bess is in fringes and Baby Nell grieves
  Over holes in her new pinafore.
Each one has something for mother to do,
  Deeming with consciences light,
No matter what may be wrong or askew,
  "Mother will fix it all right."

Swiftly the dear patient fingers must move,
  Swiftly the bright needle gleams,
As she sits there at her labor of love
  Dreaming her motherly dreams.
Smiling o'er memories happy and bright,
  Sighing o'er some that are sad,
Mother will breathe o'er her basket to-night
  A prayer for each lassie and lad.

THE CHILDREN'S GARDEN

"Come with me and see the children's garden,"[2] said a dear old lady, with lovely silvery puffs of hair and bright, dark eyes, to me once.

I knew that all her own children were long ago grown up and scattered from the Atlantic to the Pacific, and even further; but I also knew that she had many grandchildren who loved to spend the vacation days at the old homestead, and I went with her, expecting to see, perhaps, a little plot of ground, somewhat untidily cultivated by childish hands, with straggling beds of gay-hued annuals.

So that when I really found myself in the garden I stared.

"Is this it?" I said.

Mrs. Adair nodded.

"Don't dare to tell me you don't think it is a lovely place," she said.

It was a lovely place. Had it been in front of the house one might have called it a lawn; but, being where it was, it was just a garden – a lovely, quaint, unworldly old garden, where trees and flowers and shrubs grew at their own sweet will in orderly confusion.

Just inside the gate, which was arched over by twin lilac trees, were two huge clumps of tiger lilies, like gorgeously bedight sentinels on guard.[3] All around the enclosure – which was about two acres in extent – ran a double row of trees of all kinds – apples, pears and plums, mixed up with white birches, branching willows, tall poplars and even a big pine in one corner.

Trees were scattered here and there all over it, and between them ran winding paths, bordered by shrubs and old-fashioned perennials – peonies and hollyhocks, foxgloves and "bride's bouquet," sweet William and "bleeding hearts," and a score of others.[4]

It was like no garden I had ever seen before – it was quite the sweetest and most delightful, with all the charm and distinction of really lovely old, old things.

"It's a place one might dream of, or in," I said. "It has grown through the years – I hate brand new things. But a children's garden!"

Mrs. Adair smiled.

"You expected something different, didn't you? But this is really my children's garden. Let us sit down and I will tell you about it."

We found an old stone bench under a couple of big willows, where lilies of the valley crept about our feet, with their spikes of fragrant bells.

"You are quite right in thinking this a garden that has grown," said Mrs. Adair. "Forty-eight years ago my little first-born son was laid in my arms, and his father said:

"'I've just bought the two-acre lot from Moore, wifie. We

can have it for a garden, and I'll go out and stick a tree down in honor of the heir.'

"You see that magnificent willow across from us? That was Frank's birth tree, and the beginning of our garden. It just went on from that. For every baby that came to us a new tree was planted here. That big apple tree over there is Alma's tree.[5] The rowans on the slope are Allan's. The hedge of cherry trees on the west side were planted by his father on the day Rodney was born. Each of my ten children has a birth tree here.[6]

"Then, whenever the anniversary of a birthday came round it was commemorated by a tree. Of course, some of the birthdays were in winter, and we had to wait until spring came to plant the tree, but it was always selected on the day itself.

"As soon as the children grew old enough they did their own planting. Little Tom was only three years old when he toddled home from the woods with a pine sapling and put it in the corner there. It was a few inches high. Look at it now.

"Twice death came to our home and took one of our babies away. But we always remembered their birthdays just the same.

"When the children, one by one, grew up and went away to school, we marked their vacation home-comings by some addition to our garden. When they married we did the same thing. And to this day, whenever they come back to visit the old home, they bring something for the garden in memory of their visit. Charles is a missionary in Japan, you know; he brought and set out those Japanese maples the last time he was home.

"Many of them bring rare trees and shrubs now, and they are very beautiful; but I think I love best the old-fashioned things which my boys and girls planted and tended here long ago, when they were little lads and lasses in blouses and pinafores.

"Nowadays the grandchildren have a share in it, too, and every vacation visit leaves its souvenir here. We have never tried to keep up any formal arrangement. It was an unwritten law that anyone who planted anything here should just stick it in where he pleased.

"We fell into the habit of commemorating our children's successes in this way: For instance, when ten-year-old Teddy carried off the prize for general proficiency in his class he planted one of those clumps of tiger lilies at the gate, and, twelve years later, when he graduated from college, leader of his class, he came home and planted the other clump.

"So you see, my dear, this old garden is just our family history, written out in a script of leaf and blossom. Everything in it has some treasured memory attached to it – sweet or sad or merry.

"Edith planted these lilies of the valley here on the very first day she was able to come to the garden after a long and dangerous illness. Millicent planted the honeysuckle by the trellis on her graduation day, and that big white rose bush came from a little slip in Sara's wedding bouquet of bride roses.

"Do you see that big circle of snowball trees over in the centre of the garden, with the two tall silver poplars behind them? My husband and I planted the poplars on our silver wedding day, and the children planted a snowball each.

"Next year we hope to have our golden wedding, and something more will be added to our garden.

"Last year, when our eldest grandson came home with the soldier boys from South Africa he planted the 'Paardeberg tree'[7] – you see it – that little maple sapling behind the poplars. The boys ran mostly to trees, you know, and the girls to flowers. When I come here all the past seems to live again for me. I wouldn't exchange this rambling old garden for the most beautiful lawn in the world, my dear."

"I shouldn't think you would," I said. "Why, it's sacred! And the whole idea embodied in it is one of the most beautiful I've ever heard of."

WHAT TO TEACH YOUR SON

Teach him to be true to his word and his work.

To respect religion for its own sake.

To face all difficulties with courage and cheerfulness.

To form no friendship that can bring him into degrading associations.

To respect other people's convictions.

To reverence womanhood.

To live a clean life in thought and word, as well as in deed.

Teach him that true manliness always commands success.

That the best things in life are not those which can be bought with money.

That to command he must first learn to obey.

That there can be no compromise between honesty and dishonesty.

That the virtues of punctuality and politeness are excellent things to cultivate.

That a gentleman is just what the word implies – a man who is gentle in all his dealings with the opinions, feelings and weaknesses of other people.

WHAT TO TEACH YOUR DAUGHTER

Teach her to be true and honorable in all her relationships.

To have a solid base for her life, to cultivate fixed habits and the strength of repose.

To have high ideals and live up to them.

To mean what she says and say only what it is right to mean.

To think clearly and judge wisely.

Teach her that the best part of all pleasures is sharing the enjoyment with somebody else.

That work is always worthy when it is well done.

That happiness is living in harmony with God and His laws.

That the more she gives to her friends of her love, her confidence and her loyalty, the more she will receive from them in return.

That everyone's life is a part of God's plan.

That the finest manners are born of unselfishness and loving kindness.

That nobility of character and womanliness are not dependent on education, appearance or social station.

That a woman should be proud of her womanhood and never desecrate it by aping mannishness.

ONE MOTHER'S OPINIONS

The "Little Mother," who was sewing,[8] and the Schoolma'am, who was curled up in an armchair, were talking. The Schoolma'am always said she got many a hint from the "Little Mother" which helped her wonderfully in ruling her motley little subjects in the brown schoolhouse.

Presently five-year-old Winnie ran in, bubbling over with excitement about an accident that had befallen her doll. The "Little Mother's" sewing had to be laid aside while she listened to Winnie's story, sympathized and comforted the little maid, and finally saw her run happily off to her play again.

"How could you stop your work and listen to it all so interestedly, when you were in a hurry to finish your sewing?" asked the Schoolma'am. "I'm sure I wouldn't have had the patience."

The "Little Mother" smiled.

"I'm afraid I wouldn't have, either, always. But last summer I learned a lesson one day, when I was calling on Mrs. Clifford. You know her daughter, Edith Clifford, that bright, handsome girl, who is so clever and ambitious. Mrs. Clifford was talking to me about Edith. She said that Edith never confided in her – never talked to her of her plans and hopes, her failures and successes, as she did to her own girl friends, or as other girls did to their mothers. She said she felt completely shut out of her daughter's inner life. The tears were in her eyes as she spoke. I felt so sorry for her, and yet I couldn't help thinking she was greatly to blame herself for it, although I am sure she would have been much surprised had anyone told her so, for she has always been a most affectionate and self-sacrificing mother. But often when I was there, when Edith was a tiny girl, I have seen her come to her mother, just as Winnie came to me now, eager to tell some little incident or plan which seemed very trifling to a busy woman, but of great importance in the eyes of a child. Mrs. Clifford would push her away, sometimes impatiently, saying: 'Edith, dear, mother is too busy,' or 'There, there, I haven't time to bother now.' Edith's face would cloud over and she would go away with quivering lips. What wonder if, after repeated repulses, the child came to think that none of her little interests mattered to her mother? She has grown up with that impression, and it can never be effaced.[9] I thought of all this while Mrs. Clifford was speaking, and I made a compact with myself never to risk the loss of my child's confidence in like manner. I believe that if Winnie, when she comes to me in her small trials and triumphs now, always finds me ready to listen and sympathize or suggest, she will continue to do so when she grows into young girlhood."

"You are right, 'Little Mother,'" said the Schoolma'am. "I haven't forgotten how grieved and hurt I used to be when I was a wee mite, and found that grown people took no interest in what seemed so wonderful to me, or, what was even worse, laughed at or ridiculed some of my childish thoughts when I tried to express them. Oh, it cut right to the bone and marrow! It is a pity that most folks never seem to realize how sensitive the blossom of a child's confidence is![10] At the first rude touch it shrinks and closes, never to re-open. By the way, 'Little Mother,' what are you doing?"

"Little Mother" laughed.

"Something foolish, I dare say you'll think. You know I made these two print aprons for Lilian to wear to school. They were long, full, high-necked and long-sleeved – very neat and nice, I thought, besides being very serviceable. Well, when Lilian came home from school yesterday there were tears on her face. When I asked her what the trouble was, she said that the girls in her class had laughed at her aprons and called them 'baby dresses.'[11]

"So I am taking out the sleeves and cutting down the necks. I suppose many people would think me very foolish, indeed, but I don't think I am. Of course, I think a mother should stand firm if a real principle were involved, and I don't believe in humoring mere whims, or vanity either. But neither do I think that a mother ought to inflict unnecessary discomfort on a child. Lilian is very sensitive, and would really suffer if she had to go on wearing those aprons, at which her little world laughed. This seems very trifling to me, of course. But suppose I myself were compelled to wear abroad some garment, no matter how serviceable it might be, which my acquaintances ridiculed. I know how I would feel. So I didn't try to scold or ridicule Lilian – and I'm fixing over the aprons."

"I know," nodded the Schoolma'am, "when I was a little tot, an uncle brought me home a pair of embroidered deerskin moccasins from the west. My parents made me wear them to school, and I'll never forget how I suffered. Looking back now, I know that the moccasins were really very sweet and pretty, and I wish somebody would give me a pair like them nowadays. But nothing like them had ever been seen in my small world before, and they seemed to me very odd and bizarre. Nobody else wore such things, and I felt as if everybody were looking at my feet. How I loathed and detested those poor little, gay little moccasins!"

They both laughed. Then the "Little Mother" said:–

"I'm going to 'fess to something else, so that you'll not get too much of a shock when you see him. I had Teddy's curls cut off to-day."

"Oh, 'Little Mother!'" protested the Schoolma'am. "Why did you do it? I've approved of you right along, but I can't – no, I can't – approve of this. His lovely, long, golden curls!"

"Well, I discovered that his lovely, long, golden curls were so many thorns in my little son's soul. Oh, I hated to let them go. They did look so sweet and picturey when I combed them out over his velvet suit and lace collar. But poor Ted's heart was broken. He said the other boys laughed at him and called him 'girl-baby,' and offered him curl-papers; and he just couldn't stand it. I had a bit of a struggle with myself. Then I thought I had no right to make Ted's life a wilderness of woe,[12] just to gratify my maternal vanity. So I took Ted to the barber's, and he is a shorn lamb now, bless his dear little round, close-clipped pate! He isn't half so pretty, but he's a great deal happier."

"What a wise Teddy to choose you for his 'Little Mother,'" said the Schoolma'am, with a resigned sigh.

BRIGHT SAYINGS

Once upon a time there were mothers together, and they were telling the bright things their children had said. There was also a listener, who listened with interest because these were real speeches of real children, and not simply funny column emanations of grown-up brains.

"Yesterday," said Mrs. Wise, "I was giving my little boy a lesson in arithmetic. He is rather dull at figures and addition seems to be a sad stumbling block to him. 'Now, Harry,' I said, 'if you had four candies in one hand and five in the other, how many would you have altogether?' 'A mouthful,' promptly answered Harry."[13]

"That reminds me," said Mrs. Milner, who had once been a

schoolteacher, "of some answers that my pupils used to give me. One little chap, on being asked what a glacier was, said it was 'a man who put in window frames.'"[14]

"Gladys wanted to know the other day," said Mrs. Campbell, "if her kitty had a soul, and if so, would he have a little heaven all to himself when he died."

"Last summer," said Mrs. Price, "my sister's little Mary, a small mite who had never been in the country before, spent a month with us on our farm. One day she said to me, 'Oh, Aunt Lina, I feel so much gooder here than in town. Why, I feel so good that I say my prayers two or three times through the day.'"

"The real humor of children's sayings consists in their earnestness," said Mrs. Haye, laughing. "They are always so very solemn. Last summer we spent a fortnight at a farmhouse, where they had several of those monstrosities known as 'curly' hens. Just as soon as four-year-old Henrietta caught sight of one of them, she exclaimed: 'Oh, mamma, that hen has put on its feathers wrong side out.'"

"There was another small boy in the second primer class who could not learn to spell. All his grey matter went into the theory and practice of mischief apparently. One day I was trying to get him to spell 'speckled,' but he could not get it right at all. At last, after trying every combination of letters you could imagine, besides several you couldn't, he said, 'Well, teacher, I can't spell it but I know what it means.' His impish grin might have warned me, but I was inexperienced, and said, rashly, 'Well, Arthur, what does it mean?' 'George Howatt's face, ma'am.' George was celebrated in the school for his freckles. I had to laugh myself, and so did all the scholars. But I think George paid Arthur up for his joke at recess."[15]

"Since we are on this subject," said Mrs. Sutherland, "I must tell you our latest family joke. The other day a gentleman, who gave his name as Mr. Lord, called to see Robert. I showed him the parlor and went out to find Robert. As I crossed the hall my little three-year-old Jack said, 'Mamma, who is in there?'

'Mr. Lord,' I responded, as I hurried out. Mr. Lord himself told me what happened after that. Jack pattered away to the parlor, pushed open the door softly, and tiptoed in, looking at the caller with an expression of mingled awe and curiosity. Mr. Lord held out his hand and said: 'Well, little chap, come here.' So Jack sidled up, put one grimy little hand on Mr. Lord's knee, and said, very reverently, 'Are you God?'

"It took Mr. Lord some seconds to grasp the situation. Then he couldn't help laughing so heartily that I fear poor Jacky's ideas of Divinity got a rude shock. The tears welled up in his eyes and he ran indignantly away. When I heard the story I had to laugh, too. But it took me a good hour to comfort Jacky and straighten out his theology a bit."[16]

After the laugh which greeted Mrs. Sutherland's story had subsided, Mrs. Norton said:

"That makes me think of what Dottie said the other night. She is just three years old, too. That seems to be the worst age for visitations of acuteness. I had put her to bed at dusk and said to her, 'Now, Dottie, you won't be frightened to go to sleep here alone, will you? Just remember that God is right here with you all the time.' 'All right,' responded Dot, cheerfully. I went down, but in a few minutes heard her calling me. Going to the foot of the stairs, I asked her what she wanted. 'Oh, mamma,' said a tearful voice, 'won't you come up here and stay wif God, and let me go down and stay wif papa?'"

"Now," said the minister's wife, "I'm going to tell you what one of my Sunday School class said last Sunday. The lesson was on the translation of Elijah, and the falling of the mantle on Elisha. 'Now,' I said, at the end, 'what was it Elijah left to Elisha when he went to heaven?' At once a tiny maiden of five lisped out, gravely and reverently, 'His old clo'es.'"[17]

The mothers' meeting broke up at this point, and the listener laughed and scribbled in her notebook.

(1901)

Christmas Shopping in Halifax Stores

In addition to her "Around the Table" column, Montgomery was given by her *Daily Echo* editors a variety of occasional writing assignments, most of which cannot be identified because they are unsigned and omitted from her scrapbooks. One such task, which she mentioned both in her journals and in "The Alpine Path," involved visiting all Halifax stores that advertised in the paper and writing up their holiday specials.[1] Montgomery stated in both accounts that she had hated this work but neglected to mention the sheer volume of it. In nine unsigned instalments published between 9 and 19 December in the *Halifax Daily Echo*, Montgomery wrote up advertising copy for ninety stores, the pieces ranging from fifty to four hundred words; of these, twenty-four were reprinted in the *Morning Chronicle*. These ads amount to nearly thirteen thousand words, which is more than half the length of "The Alpine Path." They cover a wide range of goods, including furniture, meat and groceries, musical instruments, cloth and clothing, kitchen appliances and labour-saving devices, shoes, suitcases, stoves and coal, games and toys, books and stationery, cigars and alcohol, jewellery and silverware, wallpaper, watches, lamps, and hats. Perhaps because Montgomery found this assignment onerous and perhaps due to the sheer volume of write-ups, several key phrases and terms recur throughout, including the qualifiers "splendid," "first-class," and "up-to-date." What follows are some highlights from this assignment.

AGAIN CHRISTMAS TIDE APPROACHES AND THE WIDE-awake shopkeepers have made preparations for a good season's trade. All branches of trade feel the effect of Christmas buying, and the consumer feels it perhaps most than all, but he grows reckless with his money in preparing for the season of peace and goodwill. At times he is bothered in the selection of goods and articles which he may deem suitable and worthy of the occasion, and in order to assist readers who might possibly find themselves in such a dilemma the *Echo* will take the liberty of calling attention to stores and shops where Christmas purchases may be made to advantage.

N.S. FURNISHING CO.

The large building of this well known firm on Barrington street now contains a stock that cannot be eclipsed in the Provinces.[2] The variety is immense and the prices surprisingly low. None need want for the selection of Xmas gifts here. In parlor, chamber and dining-room suites there are hundreds to select from, and chairs of all styles and shapes are to be seen. A branch of this line that is taking well this season is the Morris chair for gentlemen, ladies and children.[3] There are dainty pieces of furniture for the boudoir, cozy corner pieces, wardrobes and bookcases, and everything in the furniture line, including carpets, window curtains, blinds, and a splendid assortment of art furnishing wares. The firm have just fitted up two new art rooms, which are being largely visited. A very fine line of desks and ladies secretaries are shown, and also a complete stock of children's furnishings.

SCOVIL & PAGE

Clothes may not make the man or boy, but they can make him warm and comfortable, and just now Scovil & Page, corner of George and Barrington streets, are showing a stock calculated to make many men and boys happy, and the goods are offered at prices that cannot be beaten. They are showing men's overcoats at from $5 to $18, boys' from $2.75 to $8.50, and boys' reefers[4] at from $1.50 to $5. Suits, coats, vests and pants are offered at equally reasonable prices, and all the goods are well made. The cloths include all the latest shades and patterns. Scovil & Page are agents for the famous Oxford tweeds and homespuns. In gentlemen's furnishings they show a very complete stock. Ties and scarfs in all the newest shades and styles are offered, and the line of silk handkerchiefs is very extensive. Gentlemen's jewelry is shown in profusion, and umbrellas and walking sticks are offered in great variety. They also carry a splendid line of underclothing. The window dressing at Scovil & Page's is in itself a feature that attracts the public to the store.

CRUMP & PERRIOR

The firm at 25, 27 and 29 Barrington street are showing a large stock of kitchen and household requisites, and are receiving a generous patronage. The stock includes all the paraphernalia and hardware necessary to complete equipment of a first-class kitchen, and all the labor-saving novelties designed to lessen labor therein. Cooking utensils of all kinds are offered at the lowest cash prices, and if there is anything needed for the equipment of the kitchen that cannot be found in stock the firm can very quickly make it. They also show a fine line of cooking ranges and stoves, and here again low prices rule, though the goods are of first-class manufacture. Crump & Perrior are noted for first-class sanitary plumbing, and any work in that line can safely be entrusted to them.

WOOD BROS.

At Wood Bros., 107 and 109 Granville Street, you have a very wide range of choice in the selection of your holiday purchases. One window displays warm and handsome dressing jackets and dress goods, while the other is draped with bright figured cretonnes and art muslins, suggestive of cosy corners and comfortable, serviceable cushions. The display of laces is a feature of this store and there are several tables and show cases laden with novelties for the Christmas trade – pin cushions, candle sticks, vases, boxes, pomade jars, plates, inkstands and many more, at prices that are within reach of all. On all cash purchases of $1.00 and upwards a discount of ten per cent. will be given during December. They show some very handsome silk drapes and waists, aprons, umbrellas, woollen and kid gloves, handkerchiefs and silk neckwear, as well as damask tablecloths and napkins. They have a splendid assortment of ladies wrappers and under skirts, the latter coming in silk, flannel, felt, moire and sateen.

They also carry a full stock of ready made capes and jackets in all prices and are prepared to suit every customer who is looking for bargains.

E. & A. THOMPSON

This well known meat and grocery firm at 217 and 214 Barrington street, have arranged for an especially selected stock of meats, poultry, etc., for the holidays and will make a display in this line calculated to make the mouth water. Turkeys, geese, fowls, chickens and ducks are now being fed especially for Thompson's Christmas trade and all will be offered at the lowest possible prices. Meat is likewise being fattened for the trade, the cattle having been selected a short time ago. Besides these lines the firm offer everything in the grocery line, and so extensively are their goods used that three or four delivery teams are kept continuously going. They have a very complete line of canned and preserved goods and are noted for their butter and cheese. "The lowest market prices," is Thompsons' motto.

MCMANUS' SHOE STORE

Everybody must have footwear, particularly this time of year, and many are being supplied at P.J. McManus' store, in the Aberdeen Building, at the corner of Barrington and Duke streets, because he keeps a good stock of boots and shoes and sells them at reasonable prices. Mr. McManus handles the celebrated King Quality shoes,[5] of which it is claimed there are none better on the market. He offers gentlemen's at $4.50 and ladies' at $3. But this is only one line of the many shown. All styles and sizes are to be had and every buyer's pocket can be suited. McManus shows a fine line of patent leather shoes and slippers for both ladies and gentlemen. Of slippers there is a great variety and rubber goods are to be had there in plenty, including low rubbers and high boots. There is a fine stock of overshoes and snowshoes, and hockey boots in different grades may be seen at McManus'.

W. & C. SILVER'S

Nobody is to be cold in Halifax this winter. That is what the display in one of the windows at W. & C. Silver's store at the corner of George and Hollis means. Blankets, cushions and eider-down coverlets marked at holiday prices – the nicest of Christmas gifts to the home. In the other window the display is calculated to gladden the good housewife's heart. It consists of household linen, towelling, tablecloths, napkins, bureau and sideboard scarfs, etc., to suit all tastes and purses.

Inside the store the holiday exhibit of ladies' shirt-waists is one of the most noticeable features. These useful and attractive garments range from 45¢ to $3.60 and higher, prices being marked wonderfully low in honor of the season.

They are made up in sateen, alpaca, peau de soie, taffeta, flannel and flannelette in very dainty shades, such as old rose, pink, cream and blue, besides the darker and more serviceable colors for every day wear. All are made in the latest fashion and are natty and tastefully finished.

This firm also has a fine stock of dress goods, especially in the newest designs of plaids and it has a good assortment of all the little knick-knacks that delight the eyes of Christmas shoppers – handkerchiefs, fans, gloves, purses, chatelaines, hand-bags, the popular lace goods, ties, collars and neckwear.

Ladies' wrappers, underskirts and dressing jackets are also kept in stock and special inducements are offered for the holiday season. Everybody intent on securing bargains in Christmas presents should pay a visit to this firm.

G.M. SMITH & CO.

"We bank on furs," say the well-known firm of G.M. Smith & Co., 119 to 123 Barrington street, and a glance at one of their show windows proves that they do. It contains a magnificent display of furs – fur capes, collars, ruffs, muffs, gloves and coats, in all kinds of furs from the more inexpensive oppossum and coney up to the finest of electric seal and Persian lamb.[6]

Besides furs, this firm make a specialty of kid gloves and have a very attractive display along this line, in dressed and undressed kid and in fur-lined and topped kid gloves. To any person buying two or three pairs of gloves G.M. Smith & Co. give a present of a very handsome box.

Another of their specialties is their silks, made especially for them, elegant in design and moderate in price. They have some very lovely French tea-gowns, bath robes and dressing sacques,[7] and also one thousand dress lengths which are to be sold during the Christmas holidays at only a slight advance in cost in order to clear them completely out.

They have a beautiful assortment of presentation umbrellas with tops in sterling silver, Scotch agate and pearl, and the usual display of the thousand and one dainty holiday belongings that lend a festive air to the show cases and counters, as well as eiderdown quilts and cushions, covered with silk and satin. They have also an excellent variety of underwear and shirt-waists. A special effort will be made to sell these and extra inducements will be given, as long as the holiday season lasts, to persons wishing to purchase.

S. CUNARD & CO.

Stoves are little use without fuel, so when one orders a stove coal is brought to mind. S. Cunard & Co.'s is one of the oldest coal dealing firms in Halifax, and their reputation is built on a solid foundation. They deal in all kinds of coals, hard and soft, and having North and South end depots are in a position to supply all parts of the city at short notice. Much coal is given at Christmas to the poor, and it is a thoughtful and in most cases exceedingly welcome gift.[8] With such arrangements as S. Cunard & Co. are equipped with there is little trouble occasioned by one who wishes coal sent to a poor acquaintance. He simply rings up one of the firm's telephones and gives his order, and the firm does the rest, even to putting the coal in the cellar, if he desires it. Cunard & Co. say that the hard coal with which they supplied their customers the past season turned out to be the best they ever handled. The firm has still a lot of this coal on hand now, and can supply it promptly.

LE BON MARCHE

Knowing fathers, husbands and brothers will go to the Bon Marche, at the corner of Sackville and Barrington streets, to select Christmas gifts this season for daughters, wives and sisters. Why? Because to any rightly constituted woman no gift is more acceptable than a pretty new hat. And at this establishment all tastes and purses may be suited, for the selections displayed range from the plain walking hats up to the most elaborate of imported confections for smart functions. This year a special effort has been made to prepare a large and varied assortment of trimmed hats, because the large sales of former Christmas seasons has led the proprietor to believe that hats make most useful and desirable Christmas presents. They show two windows filled with charming hats, both home-trimmed and imported. After night, especially, these windows are very attractive, owing to the electric illuminations which show up the millinery to the best advantage. A fine assortment of serviceable and natty "ready-to-wear" hats is a feature of the holiday stock. Neither are the small folks forgotten, for there are some exceedingly dainty bonnets for them, which need only a chubby face beneath them to set them off to the best advantage. One of these should be mother's present for the baby. A large assortment of ribbons and silks for fancy work is also shown, and all the latest novelties in veilings may be found at this enterprising and up-to-date millinery establishment.

DeNIGRIS

DeNigris, Ladies' Tailor, at 87½ Barrington street, is prepared to meet the demands of the Christmas trade in fine style. A natty tailor-made suit is what every woman longs for, and this or a stylish coat makes the very nicest of Christmas presents. A fine line of cloths, suitable for making dresses, coats or riding habits, is shown in all the newest materials and designs. The workmanship is up-to-date in every respect, and Christmas purchasers have an exceptional opportunity to get a really good thing.

B.A. BOOK AND TRACT SOCIETY

At the British American Book and Tract Society's Store, at 115 Granville street, there is now shown a magnificent line of the International Art Co.'s calendars. These articles are taking the place of Christmas cards to a great extent and are certainly very much more useful. There is a large line of these goods to select from. All the annuals, *Our Boys*, *Our Girls*, *Young England*,

Leisure Hours, *Chums*, *Sunday at Home*, etc., are to be had at the store, and there is a large stock of gift books for boys as well as all the standard works, presentation volumes, in handsome bindings, religious works of all kinds, and a full line of stationery.

T.C. JOHNSON & SONS

This well known gold and silverware dealing firm, at 187 Barrington street, are showing beside their complete stock of jewelery and silverware several lines particularly adapted to the Christmas trade. They have everything in watches from the tiny toy watch to the elegant gold repeater worth hundreds of dollars.[9] They have a fine line of ladies' watches in gold and silver, and two specials offered for the holiday season are gentlemen's chronograph gold watches at $15 and ladies' in 14 karat gold-filled cases at $13. In rings and ladies' and gentlemen's jewelery there is a fine display, including a very select line of gold brooches, pendants, earrings, etc., set with pearls and diamonds. Rings are shown in all patterns and settings, and there is a splendid line of mantel and other clocks. They show handsome hairdressing sets of ebony backed with silver and a large quantity of button hooks, shoe horns, bracelets, and novelties of all kinds in sterling silver, bracelets of this material being offered as low as $1 per pair.

CLAYTON & SONS

What would Halifax do without Clayton & Sons' establishment for bargains as well as employment? Clayton's is one of the largest clothing firms in Canada, and their immense purchases place them in a position to offer cloth at figures that other clothiers could not think of. The firm does no shoddy work, and any garment bearing their trademark carries with it a guarantee that it is well made. In their retail department Clayton & Sons are offering a splendid value. They have in stock an immense variety of cloths, from which one may make his choice for overcoat, suit, pants, vest or coat, and the goods are made up in the latest styles at prices that cannot be beat. In ready-made clothing the firm deal largely, and all their work is done right here in the city. Ready-made goods receive the attention as regards strength as custom-made goods. Samples may be seen in the large show windows on Jacob street, and the low prices cause amazement. They are showing now a very handsome ready-made overcoat at $8.75, made of goods of the fashionable grey shade and nicely finished. Blue black nap skating reefers are made to order at $13.50, and are a splendid bargain. Beside clothing Clayton & Sons show a complete line of gentlemen's hats and caps, also trunks, valises, satchels, dressing suit cases, and a full line of leather goods. They have added a skate department to their bicycle store, and have laid in a full line of skates for the holidays.

HOLLAND & KUHN

121 Granville street, are now showing a fine collection of pictures intended especially for the Christmas trade. The pictures treat of all subjects, sublime and ridiculous, and are finished in beautiful shades artistically blended. A line that attracts a great deal of attention is the photo work covered in thick glass, bound at the corners and standing in easel style instead of hung on the wall. The firm are also just now showing a very complete line of photo frames. These goods are in brass, silver, leather, wood, enamelled ware, etc., and are of varied sizes and shapes, some being intended for hanging on the wall and others with easel backs for standing on the table.

C.R. HOBEN & CO.

Hoben & Co., at 152 and 154 Granville street, are showing a splendid stock of stoves, kitchen furnishings and household labor-saving novelties. In stoves and ranges they handle the best makes, and their stock of enamelled goods and tinware is so constantly replenished as to be always complete. They offer a very fine line of cutlery of the best known makes, including carving sets in cases that are just the thing for Christmas gifts. Woodenware used about the kitchen and household is to be seen in plenty at Hoben's, and there is a very complete line of coal vases and fire sets in brass and iron, and all the requisites of the stove and fireplace are to be had at the store. Raisin seeders and such like apparatus of use in the kitchen are shown in great variety, and a choice line of bird cages in brass has just been received.

Hockey sticks are kept in stock, and there is a line of toy goods for the children, such as carpenter sets for the boys, tiny clothes wringers and carpet sweepers for the girls, etc.

G.B. MALING

The well known victualler on Jacob street, opposite Trinity Church, is going to treat his patrons this season as he has in the past, to the best. He has closed arrangements with breeders with whom he is personally acquainted for a fine supply of poultry during the holidays. The birds will be killed as needed and the stock will be replenished every day. The line will include some of the finest turkeys and geese to be had in Nova Scotia, and a complete line of game will be provided for customers.

H.L. HART

"Oh, look at these cunning little baby shoes, mamma; they would be just lovely for our baby," exclaimed a little tot outside of H.L. Hart's establishment, 71 Gottingen street, yesterday afternoon, when the *Echo* reporter was passing. The baby shoes were there all right enough, and were pretty and dainty enough to tempt any fond mother or aunty into buying. There were plenty of things for grown-up babies, too. Mr. Hart has an unusually large stock of footwear in, and every corner of his store is filled. He has a splendid assortment of velvet and kid slippers for both men and women, ranging from 75c. up; overshoes, rubbers and rubber boots, gaiters, felt shoes and a novelty in scarlet German slippers for children and misses at 35c. and 45c. Hart's is the place to get Christmas footwear for yourself and other people. Prices are marked as low as possible.

L. HIGGINS & CO.

Higgins & Co., at their Palace Store, 79 Barrington street, have begun their annual holiday souvenir sale and as usual crowds are bustling for the bargains and souvenirs offered. The souvenirs include a fine display of china, pin trays, jars, fern dishes, jewel cases, manicure trays, opal decanters, etc., all splendidly decorated, and wicker basket-ware, etc. Each purchaser receives a souvenir. The firm are showing a splendid stock of footwear, complete in all departments, and including a fine assortment of wool and leather slippers, cloth house shoes, ladies' kid slippers and dancing shoes, etc. There is also a splendid stock of gaiters, etc. With $5 sales an opal fern dish, manicure tray or decanter is given, and with $4 sales a fancy wicker basket, or an opal vase, tobacco jar, collar box or trinket tray is given. The purchaser of $3 worth has his choice of an opal salt and pepper set, soap box, rose tray, powder jar, tooth brush tray, a placque, or a piece of majolica ware, a hand mirror or a necktie box. There are souvenirs for $1 and $2 purchases and even below $1 a present is given with every purchase.

BIGELOW & HOOD

The well known firm, with offices on Upper Water street, at the head of Commercial wharf, report a great business in aerated waters, and their factories here and at Truro are kept working full time, and frequently overtime, in order to supply the demand for B. & H. aerated beverages.[10] The firm is agents for the celebrated Labatt ale and Vale o' Moray whiskey,[11] and they carry a full stock of the various liquors. They are offering a splendid line of claret, sherry and port for the Christmas holidays, and are giving especial value in these Christmas wines.

(1901)

Many Admiring Glances Bestowed upon Graduates

CYNTHIA

This piece, the only known article attributed to Cynthia outside her "Around the Table" column, appeared in the *Halifax Daily Echo* in late April 1902. Far more serious in tone than the discussion about male and female graduates that would appear in her column the following week, this piece highlights the dignity of the graduation ceremony as well as the idea that graduating from university was cause for celebration not only for the graduates but also for their families and the larger community. Writing this piece must have been bittersweet for Montgomery, who continued to regret that she had been able to complete only one year of university-level study.

Stage of the Academy Filled Yesterday with Grave and Reverend Seigniors – A Delightful Ceremony

UPON THE OCCASION OF THE DALHOUSIE CONVOCATION yesterday afternoon the Academy of Music was crowded to the doors with the friends of the students, and the stage, upon which chorus girls and prima donnas are wont to disport themselves was filled with a body of "most potent grave and reverend seigniors,"[1] all looking as serious and learned as the occasion demanded.

The "gods" gallery was filled with undergraduates who were there to assist their fellow students through the ordeal of graduation and the body of the building held the sisters, cousins and aunts, all in various degrees of pride and expectancy. For instance there was Tom's mother, who had come up to see him take his degree. How her heart swelled with pride as Tom bent his head to be capped by the President.[2] Was there ever such a smart boy before? It did not matter whether Tom's name appeared in the roll of honor or not; if not, then that was merely an oversight on the part of the Faculty and Senate. One heart in the auditorium at least believed that her boy was the central figure of the exercises.

Then there were Dick's sisters, in a chattering, keen-eyed group, who might poke fun at Dick for his nervousness or his awkwardness and make sarcastic comments on his manner of wearing his gown, but who were immensely proud of him all the same, and rather inclined to pity other girls who hadn't so clever a brother as Dick.

And, last but not least, there was Harry's sweetheart, who gazed at him with all her soul in her eyes and her girlish face aglow with a pride that announced to all and sundry that she was convinced so noble and handsome and clever a student never graduated from Dalhousie before and she didn't care who knew she thought so. The very way in which he bowed when he received his honor diploma was a revelation of grace.

At the appointed hour the graduates, very imposing in their severe black and white, filed upon the stage, greeted by college yells and encouraging comments by their friends in the upper gallery. The co-eds were given the place of honor in the front row and looked their part of "sweet girl graduates" to the life.[3]

The members of the various faculties were cheered and sung to their seats as they came in and the stage presented an interesting phase of humanity when all were in their places – on the one side those who are now in the thick of the battle of life or have already won their laurels, on the other those who, young, untried and eager, are about to begin the struggle.

After the brief opening prayer came the President's address, which was punctuated by the irrepressibles in the upper gallery, with cheers, coughs, questions and comments, which were doubtless very witty to the initiated. These interruptions did not disconcert the speaker in the least. Probably he is too well used to them to mind them.

Announcements of prizes and scholarships followed and the candidates for the degree of Bachelor of Arts were then presented to Dr. Forrest, twenty-six in number, of whom nine were ladies.

One by one they paused before him and were capped and invested with all the rights and privileges of their degree. This was a moment of exquisite enjoyment to the upper gallery people. Each name was cheered and commented upon with the cheerful frankness peculiar to undergraduates. The graduates bore the ordeal well. Not one was observed to flinch, no matter what caustic remark was hurled at him by his aerial friends and foes.

Two of the ladies, Miss Bentley and Miss Thomas, were presented with bouquets. None of the gentlemen were thus honored, although an attempt was made in one instance, but the intended recipient did not appear to appreciate it.

One degree of Bachelor of Letters was conferred, the graduate being Miss Jeanette Cann, who later on was also presented with the university medal for high honors in philosophy and was cheered to the echo.[4]

Four degrees of Bachelor of Science were then conferred – all on gentlemen. Apparently Science does not appeal to the mind of the co-ed. The hood worn by a B.S., like that of a Doctor of Medicine, is of red silk and looks very nice.

After the presentation for the honor and distinction diplomas and the prizes, medals and scholarships, twelve degrees of Bachelor of Law were conferred on twelve budding barristers, most of whom were not present to receive it in person.

A very large class graduated in medicine. Miss Philip was the only lady in it and she was presented with two charming bouquets tied with the Dalhousie black and yellow. It may be added that one of the gentlemen in this class was also fortunate enough to get a bouquet.

Judge Wallace[5] then addressed the graduates, giving much good advice and encouragement to the members of each class, who all looked as if they meant to take it.

Six degrees of Master of Arts were conferred, two of the recipients being ladies. Miss Forrest came in for a bouquet.

In closing Bishop Courtney[6] and Professor Falconer[7] addressed the graduates. The Bishop's address was delivered with all his own peculiar grace and charm, illumined by flashes of genial humor. In opening he had two or three tilts with the upper gallery people and got decidedly the best of it, whereupon they paid him the high compliment of listening in almost unbroken silence. He spoke seriously and wisely to the graduates on the importance of living earnest and uplifting lives.

Professor Falconer's address was also much appreciated. He urged upon the citizens of Halifax the importance of appreciating a college like Dalhousie in their midst, and made some very practical remarks concerning the work done by the college and the future of the graduates, especially that of the "average" man and woman. He urged them to aim at efficiency – to know and do something well – and above all to be sincere – to do their best and be content to stand or fall by it. University men and women, said the speaker, should set a standard along these lines.

God Save the King was sung, the audience passed out and another class of Dalhousie's sons and daughters was added to those who are winning honor and repute for their alma mater in the busy field of the world's work.

(1902)

Netted Doily

In a journal entry dated January 1902, while working in Halifax, Montgomery mentioned plans to design "a doily pattern for a fancy work journal for which I expect to get a dollar where with I mean to buy myself a new watch chain."[1] Appearing more than a year later in the Boston magazine *The Modern Priscilla*, this is Montgomery's only known publication on women's traditional crafts, which she enjoyed for most of her life. Twenty examples of her needlework are part of the L.M. Montgomery Collection at the University of Guelph archives.

SET THIRTY STITCHES ON A CORD OVER A BONE MESH one-quarter inch wide. Tie ends together and work around.

Net seven rows plain over a coarse knitting-needle.

Net one row of loop-stitch.

Net a row over mesh, putting two stitches in each loop.

Net four rows plain over needle.

Net one row, putting three into one over the mesh.

Net seven rows plain over the needle.

Net one row of loop-stitch.

Net four rows plain over needle.

Net one row plain over mesh.

Net a row over mesh, putting one stitch into four loops at a time.

Net a row over mesh, putting six stitches into every loop.

Net three rows plain over needle.

Net a row plain over mesh.

Net over mesh, putting one stitch into every four loops at once.

FIGURE 6 L.M. Montgomery's netted doily, in *The Modern Priscilla* (Boston, MA), April 1903. (Courtesy of the Christy Woster Collection.)

Net over mesh, putting four stitches into every loop.

Net one row of loop-stitch.

Net two rows plain over needle.

Net five stitches over needle, turn, net four, turn, net three, turn, net two, turn, net one. Break off thread and fasten in at base of point. Net five more and proceed as before.

The whole doily must be worked off in small points in this way. It is then darned with linen floss as shown in illustration.

(1903)

Innocent Irreverence

Like "Netted Doily" above, this next contribution – a short joke about a child's misunderstanding, appearing in *Lippincott's Monthly Magazine* of Philadelphia in July 1905 – is unique for Montgomery. But it does evoke a similar joke made in "Half an Hour with Canadian Mothers," earlier in this volume, so there is little doubt that it came from her pen.

OLIVER WAS IN THE FRONT YARD ONE DAY WHEN A GENtleman passed by on the street. Oliver asked his nurse who it was.

"That was Mr. Lord," she responded.

Oliver flew in to his mother in great excitement.

"Muvver, oh muvver, God has just gone past – and he had a hard hat on!"

(1905)

PART 3

The Upward Climb to Heights Sublime

FIGURE 7 *L.M. Montgomery*. Undated photograph, ca. 1916. (Courtesy of the L.M. Montgomery Collection, Archival and Special Collections, University of Guelph Library.

Two Sides of a Life Story

J.C. NEVILLE

This short story, signed "J.C. Neville" and appearing in one of Montgomery's scrapbooks housed at the University of Guelph Library, uses non-fiction forms – the diary of Mrs. Fitzelroy, a letter written by William Cavendish – to tell a story of miscommunication and regret. As I discuss in more detail in the afterword to this volume, although Montgomery did not leave any evidence that she claimed authorship of this story – it appears in a scrapbook not otherwise concerned with her career – its style and motifs are unmistakably hers, and, furthermore, I have found evidence that she had republished one of her poems as "J.C. Neville" in 1908. But while the story cannot be dated until the original clipping is identified, it is worth noting that Montgomery placed it in a scrapbook following several pages of postcards and photographs pertaining to her honeymoon in England and Scotland – meaning that, regardless of when it was written, she wanted it to be perceived as a story that followed the start of her own marriage.

(EXTRACT FROM THE JOURNAL OF MRS. FITZELROY)

Tuesday, April Ninth

I SAW A GHOST TODAY, HENCE I AM WRITING IN THIS JOURNAL tonight. There is no human being with whom I can discuss the matter, not even my husband – nay, my husband least of all.

When a woman writes such a sentence as the above it is a sign that all is not as it should be in her heart and life. A woman should see no ghosts she must conceal from her husband. For that matter, a woman who is married should have no need of a

TWO SIDES OF A LIFE STORY

By J. C. Neville.

(Extract from the Journal of Mrs. Fitzelroy.)

Tuesday, April Ninth

I SAW a ghost today, hence I am writing in this journal tonight. There is no human being with whom I can discuss the matter, not even my husband—nay, my husband least of all.

When a woman writes such a sentence as the above it is a sign that all is not as it should be in her heart and life. A woman should see no ghosts she must conceal from her husband. For that matter, a woman who is married should have no need of a journal in which to find a vent for her subtle inner moods. Such should flow naturally to her husband in that sweet interchange of mutually sympathetic souls that needs no other outlet. It is a confession of a serious and vital lack when she must resort to an inanimate journal in her crises of feeling.

I never kept a journal before my marriage, nor for some years after. I have never, indeed, kept a journal in any strict sense of the word. But as the years passed away, each seeming a little emptier than the last, a little more purposeless, a little less worth living, I drifted almost unconsciously into the habit of "writing out" the moods of sorrow and pain, of disquiet and discon-

FIGURE 8 "Two Sides of a Life Story" (detail), by "J.C. Neville." Unidentified and undated clipping in L.M. Montgomery's Red Scrapbook 1, the L.M. Montgomery Collection, Archival and Special Collections, University of Guelph Library. (Photograph by Benjamin Lefebvre.)

journal in which to find a vent for her subtle inner moods. Such should flow naturally to her husband in that sweet interchange of mutually sympathetic souls that needs no other outlet. It is a confession of a serious and vital lack when she must resort to an inanimate journal in her crises of feeling.

I never kept a journal before my marriage, nor for some years after. I have never, indeed, kept a journal in any strict sense of the word. But as the years passed away, each seeming a little emptier than the last, a little more purposeless, a little less worth living, I drifted almost unconsciously into the habit of "writing out" the moods of sorrow and pain, of disquiet and discontent that came to me. Somehow, I could not go to my husband with them; he would not have understood my vague dissatisfactions for which I could certainly urge no material or definite cause; at the best, he would have laughed kindly at me. That I could not have borne; so I have made a confidant only of my pen and a blank page.

Yet there is something I have never written of even in this journal. I have striven to forget it. At times – but at times only – I have cheated my heart into believing that I had forgotten. At other times, when I looked the issues of life squarely in the face, I knew I could never forget – never – never – never – not even in the ages of eternity. One cannot forget one's own soul and the emotions that have branded themselves deeply into that soul. There are some things no woman can ever forget. And if she wilfully puts them aside and disregards them she sins against the very laws of her being, and sure and bitter will be her punishment. This I, Ethel Fitzelroy, have found to my cost. But only I and this inanimate confidant of a journal know it.

Well, to my ghost! I met it on the street today, in the person of William Cavendish. I have never seen him since my marriage. I did not expect to see him today, for I had not known he was in St. Martin's. I knew him at once, although he was terribly changed. He looked far older than his years; his hair was gray and his face – the frank, boyish face I remembered so well – was indescribably hard and bitter – cynical, I should say – the face of a man who has very little faith left in man or woman.

After the first shock of mutual recognition flashing from eye to eye I would have stopped and spoken to him. But he raised his hat unsmilingly and passed on. I felt unutterably hurt and chilled. Yet I could not blame him. He is right in scorning me – did I not give him the right? And he is the only man in the world whose contempt has the power to hurt me.

This evening I met Phil Larkins, who said that Will Cavendish had been in town, but had left on the evening train for the West. So I shall not meet him again. I am glad – glad – glad – for to meet him would only be to renew the old agony which the years have softened into a dull but constant aching sense of loss.

Fourteen years ago, when I was a girl of eighteen, as happy and light-hearted as a girl of that age should be, I first met William Cavendish. We were drawn to each other from the beginning. He was a young bank clerk in my native town, and our social set was the same. We continued to meet frequently and ere long we learned to love each other deeply, with all the passionate tenderness of youth. Finally he told me his love and an understanding existed between us – an understanding only, for my parents would not permit a definite engagement. Not that they objected to Will, but they alleged my youth and his somewhat uncertain prospects as excellent reasons why our engagement should not be considered binding on either of us for at least two years more.

Will was ambitious. He became discontented with his narrow and circumscribed round of duties; finally he listened to the lure of the golden West. We parted with fond assurances of mutual love and confidence. Heaven knows I meant to be true to him. During the first weeks of his absence I missed him bitterly and his fond and frequent letters were all that made my life worth while for me.

I had at that time an intimate friend named Emma Ranford. At least, I considered her my friend. I had sometimes thought that she cherished a secret fondness for Will herself. But if so she concealed it well and affected to dislike him. I knew by her contemptuous silence that she affected to disapprove of my relations with him. Not long after his departure she began coming to me with various tales to his discredit. She had a correspondent in the western city where Will was living. This friend wrote to her of the wild life which Will was beginning to lead. He had fallen in with a fast set and was rapidly becoming, so she asserted, as dissipated as they. This and many other rumors were faithfully recounted to me. At first I refused to listen to or credit them. But Emma came to me oftener and oftener with them; constant dropping will wear away the hardest stone – constant insinuations will undermine the strongest faith. Finally I began to listen – and to believe. But in the final event it was Will himself who really gave the death-blow to my faith. His letters began to grow cold and infrequent; the intervals between them longer and longer. I believed, as Emma asserted, that he was ceasing to love me and my pride was bitterly hurt.

Meanwhile, Dr. Fitzelroy, a handsome young surgeon attached to a certain steamer, had declared himself my lover. He was a fine, manly fellow and my parents, who had likewise heard the rumors about Will, favored his suit. I was urged and entreated to accept him. I liked him – respected him. I believed Will false to me, and my own angry pride was so intense that I believed also that I had ceased to love him. In an evil hour – yes, it was in an evil hour – I listened to the dictates of that pride, to Emma Ranford's subtly worded insinuations and to Jack Fitzelroy's pleadings. I became Jack's promised wife, and I announced the fact in one brief, bitter letter to Will.

What effect the letter had upon him I was left to conjecture, for I received no answer. But in the two years that followed I heard through Emma that he was becoming more and more dissipated and reckless. I endeavored to root out his memory from my heart as one utterly unworthy; I fancied that I had succeeded; but suddenly this delusion was rent from my eyes by Will's return home.

He had been unsuccessful in his pursuit of fortune in the West. But upon his return he secured an excellent position in a brokerage house in St. Martin's. We met again; Jack Fitzelroy was away on an indefinite voyage in the steamer to which he was attached, and the old love between myself and Will, which I had thought dead, was renewed with redoubled intensity. But alas, it was not on my part accompanied by a renewal of the old fond faith and confidence. Will avowed repentance for the past three years, which he admitted had been somewhat careless and dissipated, but he averred that the reports which had reached my ears had been exaggerated by malice and jealousy, he vowed that the future should redeem the past,[1] and he implored me to trust in my own love and his.

For a time I wavered. My heart seconded Will's appeal. But my broken trust was not so easily restored. The poison of malicious insinuation had done its work well; my family were now bitterly opposed to Will's suit, and I persuaded myself that it was my duty to fulfill the promise I had made to Dr. Fitzelroy. This was my final decision. I shall never forget Will's face when I told him! He went from me as one stricken with a mortal blow and from that moment until today I have never seen him. He went West again shortly afterwards, and I married Jack Fitzelroy.

I have been his wife for eleven years, and I have realized every day of those years what a fatal mistake the woman makes who marries one man when her heart belongs to another. The world believes that I am a happy woman; I have everything to make me so – an indulgent husband, wealth, social position, charming friends. But I have never been able to delude myself into such a belief. I have learned too well that I bade adieu to my happiness when I sent from me the man I loved. Today, when I read the scorn in Will's eyes, I realized as never before what a failure my life is – my life that might have been such a happy one had I trusted to my own heart.

Oh, life is so empty! I am so tired! And that look on Will's face! How he must hate me! That thought is the hardest of all to bear.

(EXTRACT FROM LETTER WRITTEN BY WILLIAM CAVENDISH TO OLD FRIEND IN ST. MARTIN'S)

Dear Morris:–

What a letter of fatherly good advice you sent me, to be sure. The gist of it seems to be "marry and settle down." Marriage in your eyes seems to be a sort of universal panacea for all the ills of life. It might be so with some. With me I fear it would prove quite otherwise.

You wonder that I have never married. Well, I will tell you why on condition that you forevermore stop preaching marriage to me. When you have heard my brief story you will realize that you are wasting time and breath in doing so.

Years ago, when I was a mere boy, I met and loved Ethel Leah. She was then in all the bloom of her beauty – a tall, slender girl with glorious brown eyes and the sweetest mouth a man could picture in his fairest dreams. She returned, or professed to return, my love, and when I went West to better my fortunes an understanding that amounted to an engagement existed between us.

You know that my first western experiment did not turn out well. Moreover, I got into a fast set and lived a rather wild life. I supposed that rumors of this soon reached Ethel for I soon noticed a subtle difference in the tone of her letters. For my own part, I began to grow discouraged and reckless, owing to my lack of success. My own letters grew colder and fewer. I loved Ethel as fondly as ever but I felt an increasing chasm forming between us. I knew her parents would never consent to her marriage with a man who had failed. At this period I received a brief letter from her announcing her engagement to Dr. Fitzelroy. It came as a fearful blow. I never answered the letter. I said savagely that since she had chosen to discard me I would accept my dismissal with a pride equal to her own. But some motive power seemed gone from my life and during the next two years I went down hill rapidly, becoming more dissipated every day.

In this fatal course I was at last arrested by what seemed at the time to be a dire calamity. The firm with whom I was employed failed, and I found myself face to face with ruin. I returned home. For a time I felt utterly discouraged. Then I obtained a good position in my native city, and my prospects began to look bright again, for I had firmly resolved to live an entirely different life and repair my past mistakes.

At this juncture I again met Ethel Leah, more beautiful than ever. Dr. Fitzelroy was away; we met frequently, and on my part the old love returned with trebled intensity. Before it had been but the love of a boy; now it was the love of a man. She, on her side, professed a similar reawakening of the old affection. But when I urged her to follow the dictates of this affection she failed in the test. Why should I write more of this! It is too painful! In the end she married Fitzelroy and I was left to believe that I had merely been the victim of a coquette, who had never at any time felt any real love for me.

As you know, I again went West. This time fortune was kinder. Today I am a rich man. But life holds nothing for me. No other woman has ever filled Ethel's place. I love her today as I have always loved her, in spite of her treatment of me.

A few weeks ago during a flying trip east I met her on the

street. My heart bounded as our eyes met. She half paused as if she would have spoken, but I passed on – I did not dare to linger. She looked well and happy; life has evidently treated her kindly and no doubt she is perfectly satisfied with it. I would not have it otherwise. I would not have her feel as I do, that all that was vital went out of life when love failed me.

Well, that's all. Don't bore me with any get-married-and-be-happy-ever-after advice again.

Will write you next week about those Montana shares. We ought to be able to make a good thing out of them.

Yours,

Cavendish.

The Alpine Path

The Story of My Career

In 1916, at the height of her career as a novelist, L.M. Montgomery penned a 25,000-word memoir in which she narrated a version of her childhood, her evolution and ultimate success as a writer, and her honeymoon. The invitation to do so came from the Toronto magazine *Everywoman's World* (1914–1923), which had a monthly circulation of over 130,000 copies, according to the front cover of its May 1917 issue. Published in six instalments starting in June and ending in November 1917, "The Alpine Path: The Story of My Career" is the most detailed autobiographical account that Montgomery published during her lifetime. It was remarkably frank compared with earlier essays and interviews, in which she had appeared highly reluctant to reveal even basic biographical details; yet it was also tactful and calculated compared with versions of her childhood and career that she constructed in her journals, which she eventually intended for posthumous publication.

Everywoman's World, which declared itself "Canada's Great Home Magazine," had already run a profile of Montgomery entitled "The Novelist of the Isle" in Mary Josephine Trotter's "Prominent Women" column in 1914. It had also published several of her stories and poems[1] and had included, in its April 1915 issue, both a contribution by Montgomery to a round table entitled "What Twelve Canadian Women Hope to See as the Outcome of the War" and her essay "The Way to Make a Book."[2] The magazine featured first-person and third-person accounts of prominent Canadian women on a regular basis, including five-chapter celebrity memoirs by film actors Margaret Anglin (1876–1958) and Julia Arthur (1869–1950) that appeared throughout mid-1916 and into 1917.[3] Appearing alongside the

August 1917 instalment was an article by Arthur B. Farmer entitled "Will My Daughter Be an Author?," which featured a photograph of Montgomery under the headline "Fiction," along with commentary on her appearance (see figure 1).[4] According to an unsigned editorial appearing alongside the September 1917 instalment, the editors had obtained Montgomery's "intensely human and yet restrained" memoir "only after much persuasion on our part," adding that her title "suggests the hard, upward climb which almost everyone must come through life, and especially in journalistic life, before they arrive anywhere."[5]

When Montgomery wrote in her journal that she had consented to write the piece, she noted that she had chosen the title from "a bit of fugitive verse entitled 'Lines to the Fringed Gentian' by some forgotten author." Carol Gaboury identified the source of this poem in the late 1980s: "The Fringed Gentian" appeared in a sixteen-chapter serial, "Tam: The Story of a Woman," by Ella Rodman Church and Augusta de Bubna, in *Godey's Lady's Book* (Philadelphia) in six instalments published in the first half of 1884, when Montgomery was nine years old. What does not seem to have been discussed before is that Montgomery consistently misquoted part of this poem in her journals and in "The Alpine Path," even though the *Godey's* clipping is in one of her scrapbooks. The poem in its entirety appears as follows:

Lift up thy dewy, fringed eyes,
  O little Alpine flower!
The tear that trembling on them lies
  Has sympathetic power
To move my own; for I, too, dream
  With thee of distant heights,
Whose lofty peaks are all agleam
  With rosy, dazzling lights.

Where aspirations, hopes, desires,
  Combining, fondly dwell –
Where burn the never-dying fires
  Of genius' wondrous spell.
Such towering summits would I reach,
  Who climb and grope in vain:
O little flower! the secret teach –
  The weary way make plain.

Who dreams of wider spheres revealed
Up higher, near the sky,
Within the valley's narrow field
Cannot contented lie;
Who longs for mountain breezes rare,
Is restless down below –
Like me, for stronger, purer air
Thou pinest, too, I know.

Then whisper, blossom, in thy sleep,
How may I upward climb
The Alpine path so hard, so steep,
That leads to heights sublime?
How may I reach the far-off goal
Of true and honored fame,
To write upon its shining scroll
A woman's humble name?[6]

What Church and de Bubna's poem frames as two questions – "How may I upward climb ... ?" and "How may I reach the far-off goal ... ?" – Montgomery reframes as a demand: "Whisper ... how I may upward climb ... how I may reach that far-off goal."[7] Whether the misquotation was deliberate or inadvertent, it shows the degree of her determination to succeed.

The publication of "The Alpine Path" in 1917 coincided with a year of major changes in Montgomery's professional life. After publishing seven books with L.C. Page and Company, she had decided to part ways with her first publisher, partly because of his increasingly unethical business tactics, and partly because of his refusal to publish a book of her poems, which she thought he might agree to as a personal favour given the continually outstanding sales of her novels. *The Watchman and Other Poems* would be published by McClelland, Goodchild, and Stewart in November 1916; the following year, *Anne's House of Dreams* would be published by the same firm in Canada and by the Frederick A. Stokes Company in the United States. This publishing arrangement would continue for the rest of her career. The July 1917 issue of *Everywoman's World* also contained Montgomery's short story "The Schoolmaster's Bride," which would be reworked for *Anne's House of Dreams*.

When Fitzhenry and Whiteside republished "The Alpine Path" in

1974, an unsigned preface called this memoir "the most complete source of information about the childhood and early struggles of this accomplished and well-loved Canadian writer."[8] Indeed, the fact that little was widely known about Montgomery in 1974, the year of the centenary of her birth, made this volume a welcome addition to the conversation, even though it was poorly received.[9] Yet its effects on the beginnings of Montgomery scholarship were immediate: half of the new articles appearing in the "L.M. Montgomery Issue" of *Canadian Children's Literature* in autumn 1975 drew on "The Alpine Path" to provide biographical and cultural context.[10] But as I discuss in the afterword to this book, it was only after several volumes of Montgomery's private journals were published that scholars began to look at "The Alpine Path" as evidence of her creation of a public persona that stood in marked contrast from the supposedly "real" Montgomery of the journals. The book version also omitted twenty photographs and first-person captions that Montgomery had included in the *Everywoman's World* version, many of which were organized in framed clusters that ignored chronology. In this volume, for ease of reference, photographs appear alongside first references to their subject matter in the text.

Revisiting "The Alpine Path" a century after its appearance in *Everywoman's World* and more than forty years after its first book publication by Fitzhenry and Whiteside is important because of how much more we know now about Montgomery's life and about her strategies for self-representation than readers did in either 1917 or 1974. While she noted in her journal that she had snubbed her editor's request for an additional thousand words about her "love affairs,"[11] she remained silent about her decisions concerning what to include and what to exclude in this public account of her life. She did not explain, for instance, why she provided two snapshots captioned "Stuart" and "Chester" as part of a work that does not identify these children as hers or even declare that she had children at all, or why she decided not to name either her husband or the Ontario community to which she had moved after her marriage. Only in a brief note accompanying the penultimate instalment do the magazine editors attempt to correct this absence, referring to Montgomery first as "Lucy Maude [*sic*] Montgomery" and then as "Mrs. Ewan Macdonald, as she is now."[12] She likewise did not reveal what would be difficult to detect prior to the search capabilities of the digital age: she included in her memoir lengthy extracts from her journals, complete with date, but a closer comparison of this text and her private life writing reveals that she mined her journal for far more material than she let on, changing only details that would contradict the story of her life that she aimed to construct for public consumption.

WHEN THE EDITOR OF *EVERYWOMAN'S WORLD* ASKED me to write "The Story of My Career,"[13] I smiled with a little touch of incredulous amusement. My career? *Had* I a career? Was not – should not – a "career" be something splendid, wonderful, spectacular at the very least, something varied and exciting? Could my long, uphill struggle, through many quiet, uneventful years, be termed a "career"? It had never occurred to me to call it so;[14] and, on first thought, it did not seem to me that there was much to be said about that same long, monotonous struggle. But it appeared to be a whim of the aforesaid editor that I should say what little there was to be said; and in those same long years I acquired the habit of accommodating myself to the whims of editors to such an inveterate degree that I have not yet been able to shake it off.[15] So I shall cheerfully tell my tame story. If it does nothing else, it may serve to encourage some other toiler who is struggling along in the weary pathway I once followed to success.

Many years ago, when I was still a child, I clipped from a current magazine a bit of verse, entitled "To the Fringed Gentian,"[16] and pasted it on the corner of the little portfolio on which I wrote my letters and school essays. Every time I opened the portfolio I read one of those verses over; it was the key-note of my every aim and ambition:

"Then whisper, blossom, in thy sleep
How I may upward climb
The Alpine path, so hard, so steep,
That leads to heights sublime;
How I may reach that far-off goal
Of true and honoured fame,
And write upon its shining scroll
A woman's humble name."

It is indeed a "hard and steep" path; and if any word I can

FIGURE 9 *The house at Clifton where I was born. I think that Prince Edward Island is a good place in which to be born, and a good place in which to spend one's childhood.* Undated photograph. (Courtesy of the L.M. Montgomery Collection, Archival and Special Collections, University of Guelph Library.)

write will assist or encourage another pilgrim along that path, that word I gladly and willingly write.

I was born in the little village of Clifton, Prince Edward Island.[17] "Old Prince Edward Island" is a good place in which to be born – a good place in which to spend a childhood. I can think of none better. We Prince Edward Islanders are a loyal race. In our secret soul we believe that there is no place like the little Province that gave us birth. We may suspect that it isn't *quite* perfect, any more than any other spot on this planet, but you will not catch us admitting it. And how furiously we hate any one who does say it! The only way to inveigle a Prince Edward Islander into saying anything in dispraise of his beloved Province is to praise it extravagantly to him. Then, in order to deprecate the wrath of the gods and veil decently his own bursting pride, he will, perhaps, be induced to state that it has one or two drawbacks – mere spots on the sun. But his hearer must not commit the unpardonable sin of agreeing with him!

Prince Edward Island, however, is really a beautiful Province – the most beautiful place in America, I believe. Elsewhere are more lavish landscapes and grander scenery; but for chaste, restful loveliness it is unsurpassed. "Compassed by the inviolate sea,"[18] it floats on the waves of the blue gulf, a green seclusion and "haunt of ancient peace."[19]

Much of the beauty of the Island is due to the vivid colour contrasts – the rich red of the winding roads, the brilliant emerald of the uplands and meadows, the glowing sapphire of the encircling sea. It is the sea which makes Prince Edward Island in more senses than the geographical. You cannot get away from the sea down there. Save for a few places in the interior, it is ever visible somewhere, if only in a tiny blue gap between distant hills, or a turquoise gleam through the dark boughs of spruce fringing an estuary. Great is our love for it; its tang gets into our blood; its siren call rings ever in our ears; and no matter where we wander in lands afar, the murmur of its waves ever summons us back in our dreams to the homeland. For few things am I more thankful than for the fact that I was born and bred beside that blue St. Lawrence Gulf.

And yet we cannot define the charm of Prince Edward Island in terms of land or sea. It is too elusive – too subtle. Sometimes I have thought it was the touch of austerity in an Island landscape that gives it its peculiar charm. And whence comes that austerity? Is it in the dark dappling of spruce and fir? Is it in the glimpses of sea and river? Is it in the bracing tang of the salt air? Or does it go deeper still, down to the very soul of the land? For lands have personalities just as well as human beings; and to know that personality you must live in the land and companion it, and draw sustenance of body and spirit from it; so only can you really know a land and be known of it.[20]

My father was Hugh John Montgomery; my mother was Clara Woolner Macneill.[21] So I come of Scotch ancestry, with a dash of English from several "grands" and "greats."[22] There were many traditions and tales on both sides of the family, to which, as a child, I listened with delight while my elders talked them over around winter firesides. The romance of them was in my blood; I thrilled to the lure of adventure which had led my forefathers westward from the Old Land – a land which I always heard referred to as "Home," by men and women whose parents were Canadian born and bred.

Hugh Montgomery came to Canada from Scotland. He sailed on a vessel bound for Quebec; but the fates and a woman's will took a hand in the thing. His wife was desperately seasick all the way across the Atlantic – and a voyage over the Atlantic was no five days' run then. Off the north shore of Prince Edward Island, then a wild, wooded land, with settlements few and far between, the Captain hove-to in order to replenish his supply of water. He sent a boat ashore, and he told poor Mrs. Montgomery that she might go in it for a little change. Mrs. Montgomery did go in it; and when she felt that blessed dry land under her feet once more, she told her husband that she meant to stay there. Never again would she set foot in any vessel. Expostulation, entreaty, argument, all availed nothing. There the poor lady was resolved to stay, and there, perforce, her husband had to stay with her. So the Montgomerys came to Prince Edward Island.[23]

Their son Donald, my great-grandfather, was the hero of another romance of those early days. I have used this tale in my book, *The Story Girl*. The *Nancy* and *Betty Sherman* of the story told there were Nancy and Betsy Penman, daughters of a United Empire Loyalist who came from the States at the close of the war of Independence.[24] George Penman had been a paymaster in the British Army; having forfeited all his property, he was very poor, but the beauty of the Penman girls, especially Nancy, was so great that they had no lack of suitors from far and near. The *Donald Fraser* of *The Story Girl* was Donald Montgomery, and *Neil Campbell* was David Murray, of Bedeque.[25] The only embroidery I permitted myself in the telling of the tale was to give *Donald* a horse and cutter. In reality, what he had was a half-broken steer, hitched to a rude, old wood-sled, and it was with this romantic equipage that he hied him over to Richmond Bay to propose to *Nancy*![26]

My grandfather, Senator Montgomery, was the son of Donald and Nancy, and inherited his stately presence and handsome face from his mother.[27] He married his first cousin, Annie Murray, of Bedeque, the daughter of David and Betsy. So that Nancy and Betsy were both my great-grandmothers. If Betsy were alive to-day, I have no doubt, she would be an ardent suffragette.[28] The most advanced feminist could hardly spurn old conventions more effectually than she did when she proposed to David. I may add that I was always told that she and David were the happiest couple in the world.

It was from my mother's family – the Macneills – that I inherited my knack of writing and my literary tastes. John Macneill had come to Prince Edward Island in 1775; his family belonged to Argyleshire and had been adherents of the unfortunate Stuarts.[29] Consequently, young Macneill found that a change of climate would probably be beneficial. Hector Macneill, a minor Scottish poet, was a cousin of his. He was the author of several beautiful and well-known lyrics, among them "Saw ye my wee thing, saw ye my ain thing," "I lo'e ne'er a laddie but one," and "Come under my plaidie" – the latter often and erroneously attributed to Burns.[30]

John Macneill settled on a north-shore farm in Cavendish and had a family of twelve children, the oldest being William Macneill, my great-grandfather, commonly known as "Old Speaker Macneill." He was a very clever man, well educated for those times, and exercised a wide influence in provincial politics.[31] He married Eliza Townsend, whose father was Captain John Townsend of the British Navy. His father, James Townsend, had received a grant of Prince Edward Island land from George III.,[32] which he called Park Corner, after the old family estate in England. Thither he came, bringing his wife. Bitterly homesick she was – rebelliously so. For weeks after her arrival she would not take off her bonnet, but walked the floor in it, imperiously demanding to be taken home. We children who heard the tale never wearied of speculating as to whether she took off her bonnet at night and put it on again in the morning, or whether she slept in it. But back home she could not go, so eventually she took off her bonnet and resigned herself to her fate. Very peacefully she sleeps in the little, old, family graveyard on the banks of the *Lake of Shining Waters* – in other words, Campbell's Pond at Park Corner.[33] An old, red sandstone slab marks the spot where she and her husband lie, and on it is carved this moss-grown epitaph – one of the diffuse epitaphs of a generation that had time to carve such epitaphs and time to read them.[34]

"To the memory of James Townsend, of Park Corner, Prince Edward Island. Also of Elizabeth, his wife. They emigrated from England to this Island, A.D. 1775, with two sons and three daughters, viz., John, James, Eliza, Rachel, and Mary. Their son John died in Antigua in the life time of his parents.[35] His afflicted mother followed him into Eternity with patient resignation on the seventeenth day of April, 1795, in the 69th year of her age. And her disconsolate husband departed this life on the 25th day of December, 1806, in the 87th year of his age."[36]

I wonder if any homesick dreams haunt Elizabeth Townsend's slumber of over a hundred years!

William and Eliza Macneill had a large family of which all the members possessed marked intellectual power. Their education consisted only in the scanty, occasional terms of the district school of those rude, early days; but, had circumstances been kinder, some of them would have climbed high. My grandfather, Alexander Macneill, was a man of strong and pure literary tastes, with a considerable knack of prose composition.[37] My great-uncle, William Macneill, could write excellent satirical verse. But his older brother, James Macneill, was a born poet.[38] He composed hundreds of poems, which he would sometimes recite to favoured persons. They were never written down, and not a line of them, so far as I know, is now extant. But I heard my grandfather repeat many of them, and they were real poetry, most of them being satirical or mock-heroic. They were witty, pointed, and dramatic. Uncle James was something of a "mute, inglorious" Burns.[39] Circumstances compelled him to spend his life on a remote Prince Edward Island farm; had he had the advantages of education that are within reach of any schoolboy to-day, I am convinced he would have been neither mute nor inglorious.

The "Aunt Mary Lawson," to whom I dedicated *The Story Girl*, was another daughter of William and Eliza Macneill.[40] No story of my "career" would be complete without a tribute to her, for she was one of the formative influences of my childhood. She was really quite the most wonderful woman in many respects that I have ever known. She had never had any

FIGURE 10 *This is my great aunt, Mrs. Lawson, who told me many of the tales that I subsequently wrote into my stories. I often wished that I had her fund of story material.* Undated photograph. (Courtesy of the L.M. Montgomery Collection, Archival and Special Collections, University of Guelph Library.)

FIGURE 11 *My old home at Cavendish, Prince Edward Island, taken from the front. In the grove to the left was our playhouse with the wonderful door that we made ourselves.* Undated photograph. (Courtesy of the L.M. Montgomery Collection, Archival and Special Collections, University of Guelph Library.)

educational advantages. But she had a naturally powerful mind, a keen intelligence, and a most remarkable memory which retained to the day of her death all that she had ever heard or read or seen. She was a brilliant conversationalist, and it was a treat to get Aunt Mary started on tales and recollections of her youth, and all the vivid doings and sayings of the folk in those young years of the Province.[41] We were "chums," she and I, when she was in the seventies and I was in my teens. I cannot, in any words at my command, pay the debt I owe to Aunt Mary Lawson.

When I was twenty-one months old my mother died, in the old home at Cavendish, after a lingering illness.[42] I distinctly remember seeing her in her coffin – it is my earliest memory. My father was standing by the casket holding me in his arms. I wore a little white dress of embroidered muslin, and Father was crying. Women were seated around the room, and I recall two in front of me on the sofa who were whispering to each other and looking pityingly at Father and me. Behind them the window was open, and green vines were trailing across it, while their shadows danced over the floor in a square of sunshine.

I looked down at Mother's dead face. It was a sweet face, albeit worn and wasted by months of suffering. My mother had been beautiful, and Death, so cruel in all else, had spared the delicate outline of feature, the long silken lashes brushing the hollow cheek, and the smooth masses of golden-brown hair.

I did not feel any sorrow, for I knew nothing of what it all meant. I was only vaguely troubled. Why was Mother so still? And why was Father crying? I reached down and laid my baby hand against Mother's cheek. Even yet I can feel the coldness of that touch. Somebody in the room sobbed and said, "Poor child." The chill of Mother's face had frightened me; I turned and put my arms appealingly about Father's neck and he kissed me. Comforted, I looked down again at the sweet, placid face as he carried me away. That one precious memory is all I have of the girlish mother who sleeps in the old burying-ground of Cavendish, lulled forever by the murmur of the sea.[43]

I was brought up by my grandparents in the old Macneill Homestead in Cavendish. Cavendish is a farming settlement on the north shore of Prince Edward Island. It was eleven miles from a railway and twenty-four miles from the nearest town. It was settled in 1790 by three Scotch families – the Macneills, Simpsons, and Clarks. These families had inter-married to such an extent that it was necessary to be born or bred in Cavendish in order to know whom it was safe to criticize. I heard Aunt Mary Lawson once naively admit that "the Macneills and Simpsons always considered themselves a little better than the common run;"[44] and there was a certain rather ill-natured local saying which was always being cast up to us of the clans by outsiders, "From the conceit of the Simpsons, the pride of the Macneills, and the vain-glory of the Clarks, good Lord deliver us."[45] Whatever were their faults, they were loyal, clannish, upright, God-fearing folk, inheriting traditions of faith and simplicity and aspiration.

I spent my childhood and girlhood in an old-fashioned Cavendish farmhouse, surrounded by apple orchards. The first six years of my life are hazy in recollection. Here and there, a memory picture stands out in vivid colours.[46] One of these was the wonderful moment when, I fondly supposed, I discovered the exact locality of Heaven.

One Sunday, when I could not have been more than four years old, I was in the old Clifton Church with Aunt Emily.[47] I heard the minister say something about Heaven – that strange, mysterious place about which my only definite idea was that it was "where Mother had gone."

"Where is Heaven?" I whispered to Aunt Emily, although I knew well that whispering in church was an unpardonable sin. Aunt Emily did not commit it. Silently, gravely, she pointed upward. With the literal and implicit belief of childhood, I took it for granted that this meant that portion of Clifton Church which was above the ceiling. There was a little square hole in the ceiling. Why could we not go up through it and see Mother? This was a great puzzle to me. I resolved that when I grew bigger I would go to Clifton and find some means of getting up into Heaven and finding Mother. This belief and hope was a great, though secret, comfort to me for several years. Heaven was no remote, unattainable place – "some brilliant but distant shore."[48] No, no! It was only ten miles away, in the attic of Clifton Church! Very, very sadly and slowly I surrendered that belief.[49]

Hood wrote, in his charming *I Remember* that he was farther off from Heaven than when he was a boy.[50] To me, too, the world seemed a colder, lonelier place when age and experience at length forced upon my reluctant seven-year-old consciousness the despairing conviction that Heaven was not so near me as I had dreamed. Mayhap, 'twas even nearer, "nearer than breathing, closer than hands or feet"[51] but the ideas of childhood are, necessarily, very concrete; and when I once accepted the fact that the gates of pearl and streets of gold[52] were not in the attic of Clifton Church, I felt as though they might as well be beyond the farthest star.

Many of those early memories are connected with visits to Grandfather Montgomery's farm at Park Corner.[53] He and his family lived in the "old house" then, a most quaint and delightful old place as I remember it, full of cupboards and nooks, and little, unexpected flights of stairs. It was there, when I was about

FIGURE 12 *The old Presbyterian Church under whose roof I thought Heaven was, and that one could get to it through the little square hole in the ceiling. I planned to go up there some day.* Undated photograph. (Courtesy of the L.M. Montgomery Collection, Archival and Special Collections, University of Guelph Library.)

five years old, that I had the only serious illness of my life – an attack of typhoid fever.[54]

The night before I took ill I was out in the kitchen with the servants, feeling as well as usual, "wide-awake and full of ginger," as the old cook used to declare. I was sitting before the stove, and cook was "riddling" the fire with a long, straight bar of iron used for that purpose. She laid it down on the hearth and I promptly caught it up, intending to do some "riddling" myself, an occupation I much liked, loving to see the glowing red embers fall down on the black ashes.

Alas, I picked the poker up by the wrong end! As a result, my hand was terribly burned. It was my first initiation into physical pain, at least, the first one of which I have any recollection.

I suffered horribly and cried bitterly; yet I took considerable satisfaction out of the commotion I had caused. For the time being I was splendidly, satisfyingly important. Grandfather scolded the poor, distracted cook. Father entreated that something be done for me, frenzied folk ran about suggesting and applying a score of different remedies.[55] Finally I cried myself to sleep, holding my hand and arm to the elbow in a pail of ice-cold water, the only thing that gave me any relief.

I awoke the next morning with a violent headache that grew worse as the day advanced. In a few days the doctor pronounced my illness to be typhoid fever. I do not know how long I was ill, but several times I was very low and nobody thought I could possibly recover.

Grandmother Macneill was sent for at the beginning of my illness. I was so delighted to see her that the excitement increased my fever to an alarming pitch, and after she had gone out, Father, thinking to calm me, told me that she had gone home. He meant well, but it was an unfortunate statement. I believed it implicitly – too implicitly. When Grandmother came in again I could not be convinced that it was she. No! She *had* gone home. Consequently, this woman must be Mrs. Murphy, a woman who worked at Grandfather's frequently, and who was tall and thin, like Grandmother.

I did not like Mrs. Murphy and I flatly refused to have her near me at all. Nothing could convince me that it was Grandmother. This was put down to delirium, but I do not think it was. I was quite conscious at the time. It was rather the fixed impression made on my mind in its weak state by what Father had told me. Grandmother *had* gone home, I reasoned, hence, she could *not* be there. *Therefore*, the woman who looked like her must be some one else.

It was not until I was able to sit up that I got over this delusion. One evening it simply dawned on me that it really was Grandmother. I was so happy, and could not bear to be out of her arms. I kept stroking her face constantly and saying in amazement and delight, "Why, you're *not* Mrs. Murphy, after all; you *are* Grandma."

Typhoid fever patients were not dieted so strictly during convalescence in those days as they are now. I remember one day, long before I was able to sit up, and only a short time after the fever had left me, that my dinner consisted of fried sausages – rich, pungent, savoury, home made sausages, such as are never found in these degenerate days. It was the first day that I had felt hungry, and I ate ravenously. Of course, by all the rules of the game, those sausages should have killed me, and so cut short that "career" of which I am writing. But they did not. These things are fated. I am sure that nothing short of predestination saved me from the consequences of those sausages.

Two incidents of the following summer stand out in my memory, probably because they were so keenly and so understandably bitter. One day I heard Grandmother reading from a newspaper an item to the effect that the end of the world was to come the following Sunday.[56] At that time I had a most absolute and piteous belief in everything that was "printed." Whatever was in a newspaper must be true. I have lost this touching faith, I regret to say, and life is the poorer by the absence of many thrills of delight and horror.

From the time I heard that awesome prediction until Sunday was over I lived in an agony of terror and dread. The grown-up folk laughed at me, and refused to take my questions seriously. Now, I was almost as much afraid of being laughed at as of the Judgment Day. But all through the Saturday before that fateful Sunday I vexed Aunt Emily to distraction by repeatedly asking her if we should go to Sunday-school the next afternoon. Her assurance that of course we should go was a considerable comfort to me. If she really expected that there would be Sunday-school she could not believe that the next day would see the end of the world.

But then – it had been *printed*. That night was a time of intense wretchedness for me. Sleep was entirely out of the question. Might I not hear "the last trump" at any moment?[57] I can laugh at it now – any one would laugh. But it was real torture to a credulous child, just as real as any mental agony in after life.

Sunday was even more interminable than Sundays usually were, then. But it came to an end at last, and, as its "dark, descending sun" dimpled the purple sky-line of the Gulf,[58] I drew a long breath of relief. The beautiful green world of blossom and sunshine had not been burned up; it was going to last for a while longer. But I never forgot the suffering of that Sunday.

Many years later I used the incident as the foundation of the chapter "The Judgment Sunday" in *The Story Girl*. But the children of *King Orchard* had the sustaining companionship of each other. I had trodden the wine-press alone.[59]

The other incident was much more trifling. The *Martin Forbes* of *The Story Girl* had his prototype in an old man who visited at my grandfather's for a week. *Forbes* was not his name, of course.[60] He was, I believe, an amiable, respectable, and respected, old gentleman. But he won my undying hatred by calling me "Johnny" every time he spoke to me.

How I raged at him! It seemed to me a most deadly and unforgivable insult. My anger amused him hugely and incited him to persist in using the objectionable name. I could have torn that man in pieces had I had the power! When he went away I refused to shake hands with him, whereupon he laughed uproariously and said, "Oh, well, I won't call you 'Johnny' any more. After this I'll call you 'Sammy,'" which was, of course, adding fuel to the fire.

For years I couldn't hear that man's name without a sense of hot anger. Fully five years afterward, when I was ten, I remember writing this in my diary: "Mr. James Forbes is dead. He is the brother of a horrid man in Summerside who called me 'Johnny.'"

I never saw poor old Mr. Forbes again, so I never had to endure the indignity of being called "Sammy." He is now dead himself, and I daresay the fact that he called me "Johnny" was not brought up in judgment against him. Yet he may have committed what might be considered far greater sins that yet would not inflict on any one a tithe of the humiliation which his teasing inflicted on a child's sensitive mind.

That experience taught me one lesson, at least. I never tease a child. If I had any tendency to do so, I should certainly be prevented by the still keen recollection of what I suffered at Mr. Forbes' hands. To him, it was merely the "fun" of teasing a "touchy" child. To me, it was the poison of asps.[61]

The next summer, when I was six, I began to go to school. The Cavendish school-house was a white-washed, low-eaved building on the side of the road just outside our gate. To the west and south was a spruce grove, covering a sloping hill. That old spruce grove, with its sprinkling of maple, was a fairy realm of beauty and romance to my childish imagination. I shall always be thankful that my school was near a grove – a place with winding paths and treasure-trove of ferns and mosses and wood-flowers. It was a stronger and better educative influence in my life than the lessons learned at the desk in the school-house.[62]

And there was a brook in it, too – a delightful brook, with a big, deep, clear spring – where we went for buckets of water, and no end of pools and nooks where the pupils put their bottles of milk to keep sweet and cold until dinner hour. Each pupil had his or her own particular place, and woe betide a lad or lass who usurped another's prescriptive spot. I, alas, had no rights in the brook. Not for me was the pleasure of "scooting" down the winding path before school-time to put my bottle against a mossy log, where the sunlit water might dance and ripple against its creamy whiteness.

I had to go home to my dinner every day, and I was scandalously ungrateful for the privilege. Of course, I realize now that I was very fortunate in being able to go home every day for a good, warm dinner. But I could not see it in that light then. It was not half so interesting as taking lunch to school and eating it in sociable rings on the playground, or in groups under the trees. Great was my delight on those few stormy winter days when I had to take my dinner, too. I was "one of the crowd" then, not set apart in any lonely distinction of superior advantages.

Another thing that worried me with a sense of unlikeness was the fact that I was never allowed to go to school barefooted. All the other children went so, and I felt that this was a humiliating difference. At home I could run barefoot, but in school I must wear "buttoned boots." Not long ago, a girl who went to school with me confessed that she had always envied me those "lovely buttoned boots." Human nature always desirous of what it has not got! There was I, aching to go barefoot like my mates; there were they, resentfully thinking that it was bliss to wear buttoned boots!

I do not think that the majority of grown-ups have any real conception of the tortures sensitive children suffer over any marked difference between themselves and the other denizens of their small world. I remember one winter I was sent to school wearing a new style of apron. I think still that it was rather ugly. *Then* I thought it was hideous. It was a long, sack-like garment,

FIGURE 13 *As I looked at six years of age, when I started to go to school. We lived so near that I could not take my dinner as the others did. They put their milk bottles in the pools and nooks of the brook to keep cool – I had to go home for mine.* Undated photograph, ca. 1881. (Courtesy of the L.M. Montgomery Collection, Archival and Special Collections, University of Guelph Library.)

FIGURE 14 *The school at Cavendish. I envied the other children who were allowed to go barefoot, while I had to wear "buttoned boots."* Undated photograph. (Courtesy of the L.M. Montgomery Collection, Archival and Special Collections, University of Guelph Library.)

with *sleeves*. Those sleeves were the crowning indignity. Nobody in school had ever worn aprons with sleeves before. When I went to school one of the girls sneeringly remarked that they were *baby aprons*. This capped all! I could not bear to wear them, but wear them I had to. The humiliation never grew less. To the end of their existence, and they *did* wear horribly well, those "baby" aprons marked for me the extreme limit of human endurance.[63]

I have no especial remembrance of my first day in school. Aunt Emily took me down to the school-house and gave me into the charge of some of the "big girls," with whom I sat that day. But my second day – ah! I shall not forget it while life lasts. I was late and had to go in alone. Very shyly I slipped in and sat down beside a "big girl."[64] At once a wave of laughter rippled over the room. *I had come in with my hat on.*

As I write, the fearful shame and humiliation I endured at that moment rushes over me again. I felt that I was a target for the ridicule of the universe. Never, I felt certain, could I live down such a dreadful mistake. I crept out to take off my hat, a crushed morsel of humanity.

My novelty with the "big girls" – they were ten years old and seemed all but grown-up to me – soon grew stale, and I gravitated down to the girls of my own age.[65] We "did" sums, and learned the multiplication table, and wrote "copies," and read lessons, and repeated spellings. I could read and write when I went to school. There must have been a time when I learned, as a first step into an enchanted world, that *A* was *A*; but for all the recollection I have of the process I might as well have been born with a capacity for reading, as we are for breathing and eating.

I was in the second book of the old Royal Reader series.[66] I had gone through the primer at home with all its cat and rat formulæ, and then had gone into the Second Reader, thus skipping the First Reader. When I went to school and found that there was a First Reader I felt greatly aggrieved to think that I had never gone through it. I seemed to have missed something, to suffer, in my own estimation, at least, a certain loss of standing because I had never had it. To this day there is a queer, absurd regret in my soul over missing that First Reader.[67]

Life, from my seventh year, becomes more distinct in remembrance. In the winter following my seventh birthday, Aunt Emily married and went away. I remember her wedding as a most exciting event, as well as the weeks of mysterious preparation before; all the baking and frosting and decorating of cakes which went on! Aunt Emily was only a young girl then, but in my eyes she was as ancient as all the other grown-ups. I had no conception of age at that time. Either you were grown-up or you were not, that was all there was about it.

The wedding was one of the good, old-fashioned kind that is not known nowadays. All the big "connection" on both sides were present, the ceremony at seven o'clock, supper immediately afterward, then dancing and games, with another big supper at one o'clock.

For once I was permitted to stay up, probably because there was no place where I could be put to bed, every room being used for some gala purpose, and between excitement and unwatched indulgence in good things I was done up for a week.

FIGURE 15 *The old orchard at Cavendish. This is one of the two orchards of which the "King Orchard" in* The Story Girl *is a composite. The trees here were beautiful.* Undated photograph. (Courtesy of the L.M. Montgomery Collection, Archival and Special Collections, University of Guelph Library.)

But it was worth it! Also, I regret to say, I pounded my new uncle with my fists and told him I hated him because he was taking Aunt Emily away.[68]

The next summer two little boys came to board at my grandfather's and attend school, Wellington and David Nelson, better known as "Well" and "Dave." Well was just my age. Dave, a year younger. They were my playmates for three happy years; we *did* have fun in abundance, simple, wholesome, delightful fun, with our playhouses and our games in the beautiful summer twilights, when we ranged happily through fields and orchards, or in the long winter evenings by the fire.

The first summer they came we built a playhouse in the spruce grove to the west of our front orchard. It was in a little circle of young spruces. We built our house by driving stakes into the ground between the trees, and lacing fir boughs in and out. I was especially expert at this, and always won the boys' admiration by my knack of filling up obstreperous holes in our verdant castle. We also manufactured a door for it, a very rickety affair, consisting of three rough boards nailed uncertainly across two others, and hung to a long-suffering birch tree by ragged leather hinges cut from old boots. But that door was as beautiful and precious in our eyes as the Gate Beautiful of the Temple was to the Jews of old.[69] You see, we had made it ourselves!

Then we had a little garden, our pride and delight, albeit it rewarded all our labour very meagrely. We planted live-forevers around all our beds, and they grew as only live-forevers *can* grow.[70] They were almost the only things that *did* grow. Our carrots and parsnips, our lettuces and beets, our phlox and sweet-peas – either failed to come up at all, or dragged a pallid, spindling existence to an ignoble end, in spite of all our patient digging, manuring, weeding, and watering, or, perhaps, because of it, for I fear we were more zealous than wise. But we worked persistently, and took our consolation out of a few hardy sunflowers which, sown in an uncared-for spot, throve better than all our petted darlings, and lighted up a corner of the spruce grove with their cheery golden lamps. I remember we were in great tribulation because our beans persisted in coming up with their skins over their heads. We promptly picked them off, generally with disastrous consequences to the beans.[71]

FIGURE 16 *A view of my old home from a distance. The window of the gable was in my room where I sat to write my first four books. The "cross" is just above the spot on the dyke, under the old tamarack tree, where we saw our "ghost."* [In the copy of this photograph appearing in *Everywoman's World*, a handwritten "X" appears in the horizontal centre of the image, above the trees.] Undated photograph. (Courtesy of the L.M. Montgomery Collection, Archival and Special Collections, University of Guelph Library.)

Readers of *Anne of Green Gables* will remember the Haunted Wood.[72] It was a gruesome fact to us three young imps. Well and Dave had a firm and rooted belief in ghosts. I used to argue with them over it with the depressing result that I became infected myself. Not that I really believed in ghosts, pure and simple; but I was inclined to agree with *Hamlet* that there might be more things in heaven and earth than were commonly dreamed of – in the philosophy of Cavendish authorities, anyhow.[73]

The Haunted Wood was a harmless, pretty spruce grove in the field below the orchard. We considered that all our haunts were too commonplace, so we invented this for our own amusement.

None of us really believed at first, that the grove *was* haunted, or that the mysterious "white things" which we pretended to see flitting through it at dismal hours were aught but the creations of our own fancy. But our minds were weak and our imaginations strong; we soon came to believe implicitly in our myths, and not one of us would have gone near that grove after sunset on pain of death. Death! What was death compared to the unearthly possibility of falling into the clutches of a "white thing"?

In the evenings, when, as usual, we were perched on the back porch steps in the mellow summer dusk, Well would tell me blood-curdling tales galore, until my hair fairly stood on end, and I would not have been surprised had a whole army of "white things" swooped suddenly on us from round the corner. One tale was that his grandmother having gone out one evening to milk the cows, saw his grandfather, as she supposed, come out of the house, drive the cows into the yard and then go down the lane.

The "creep" of this story consisted in the fact that she went straightway into the house and found him lying on the sofa where she had left him, he having never been out of the house at all. Next day something happened to the poor old gentleman, I forget what, but doubtless it was some suitable punishment for sending his wraith out to drive cows![74]

Another story was that a certain dissipated youth of the community, going home one Saturday night, or rather Sunday morning, from some unhallowed orgy, was pursued by a lamb of fire, with its head cut off and hanging by a strip of skin or flame. For weeks afterward I could not go anywhere after dark without walking with my head over my shoulder, watching apprehensively for that fiery apparition.

One evening Dave came down to me in the apple orchard at dusk, with his eyes nearly starting out of his head, and whispered that he had heard a bell ringing in the then deserted house. To be sure, the marvellous edge was soon taken off this by the discovery that the noise was simply a newly-cleaned clock striking the hours, which it had never done before. This furnished the foundation of the "Ghostly Bell" chapter in *The Story Girl*.

But, one night we had a real ghost scare – the "real" qualifying "scare," not "ghost." We were playing at twilight in the hayfield south of the house, chasing each other around the fragrant coils of new-cut hay. Suddenly I happened to glance up in the direction of the orchard dyke. A chill began galloping up and down my spine, for there, under the juniper tree, was really a "white thing," shapelessly white in the gathering gloom. We all stopped and stared as though turned to stone.

"It's Mag Laird," whispered Dave in terrified tones.

Mag Laird, I may remark, was a harmless creature who wandered begging over the country side, and was the bugbear of children in general and Dave in particular. As poor Mag's usual apparel was dirty, cast-off clothes of other persons, it did not seem to me likely that this white visitant were she. Well and I would have been glad to think it was, for Mag was at least flesh and blood while this – !

"Nonsense!" I said, trying desperately to be practical. "It must be the white calf."

Well agreed with me with suspicious alacrity, but the shapeless, grovelling thing did not look in the least like a calf.

"It's coming here!" he suddenly exclaimed in terror.

I gave one agonized glance. Yes! It was creeping down over the dyke, as no calf ever did or could creep. With a simultaneous shriek we started for the house, Dave gasping at every step, "It's Mag Laird," while all that Well and I could realize was that it was a "white thing" after us at last!

We reached the house and tore into Grandmother's bedroom, where we had left her sewing. She was not there. We swung round and stampeded for a neighbour's, where we arrived trembling in every limb. We gasped out our awful tale and were laughed at, of course. But no persuasion could induce us to go back, so the French-Canadian servants, Peter and Charlotte, set off to explore, one carrying a pail of oats, the other armed with a pitchfork.

They came back and announced that there was nothing to be seen. This did not surprise us. Of course, a "white thing" would vanish, when it had fulfilled its mission of scaring three wicked children out of their senses. But go home we would not until Grandfather appeared and marched us back in disgrace. For what do you think it was?

A white tablecloth had been bleaching on the grass under the juniper tree, and, just at dusk, Grandmother, knitting in hand, went out to get it. She flung the cloth over her shoulder and then her ball fell and rolled over the dyke. She knelt down and was reaching over to pick it up when she was arrested by our sudden stampede and shrieks of terror. Before she could move or call out we had disappeared.

So collapsed our last "ghost," and spectral terrors languished after that, for we were laughed at for many a long day.

But we played house and gardened and swung and picnicked and climbed trees. How we did love trees! I am grateful that my childhood was spent in a spot where there were many trees, trees of personality, planted and tended by hands long dead, bound up with everything of joy or sorrow that visited our lives. When I have "lived with" a tree for many years it seems to me like a beloved human companion.

Behind the barn grew a pair of trees I always called "The Lovers," a spruce and a maple, and so closely intertwined that the boughs of the spruce were literally woven into the boughs of the maple. I remember that I wrote a poem about them and called it "The Tree Lovers."[75] They lived in happy union for many years. The maple died first; the spruce held her dead form in his green, faithful arms for two more years. But his heart was broken and he died, too. They were beautiful in their lives and in death not long divided;[76] and they nourished a child's heart with a grace-giving fancy.[77]

In a corner of the front orchard grew a beautiful young birch tree. I named it "The White Lady," and had a fancy about it to the effect that it was the beloved of all the dark spruces near, and that they were rivals for her love. It was the whitest straightest thing ever seen, young and fair and maiden-like.

On the southern edge of the Haunted Wood grew a most magnificent old birch. This was the tree of trees to me. I worshipped it, and called it "The Monarch of the Forest." One of my earliest "poems" – the third I wrote – was written on it, when I was nine. Here is all I remember of it:

"Around the poplar and the spruce
The fir and maple stood;
But the old tree that I loved the best
Grew in the Haunted Wood.

FIGURE 17 *"The White Lady." I had a fancy about this beautiful white birch that she was beloved of all the park spruces near, and that they were rivals for her love.* Undated photograph. (Courtesy of the L.M. Montgomery Collection, Archival and Special Collections, University of Guelph Library.)

It was a stately, tall old birch,
With spreading branches green;
It kept off heat and sun and glare –
'Twas a goodly tree, I ween.[78]

'Twas the Monarch of the Forest,
A splendid kingly name,
Oh, it was a beautiful birch tree,
A tree that was known to fame."

The last line was certainly a poetic fiction. Oliver Wendell Holmes says

"There's nothing that keeps its youth,
So far as I know, but a tree and truth."[79]

But even a tree does not live forever. The Haunted Wood was cut down. The big birch was left standing. But, deprived of the shelter of the thick-growing spruces, it gradually died before the bitter northern blasts from the Gulf. Every spring more of its boughs failed to leaf out. The poor tree stood like a discrowned, forsaken king in a ragged cloak. I was not sorry when it was finally cut down. "The land of dreams among,"[80] it resumed its sceptre and reigns in fadeless beauty.

Every apple tree in the two orchards had its own individuality and name – "Aunt Emily's tree," "Uncle Leander's tree," the "Little Syrup tree," the "Spotty tree," the "Spider tree," the "Gavin tree," and many others. The "Gavin" tree bore small, whitish-green apples, and was so called because a certain small boy named Gavin, hired on a neighbouring farm, had once been caught stealing them. Why the said Gavin should have imperiled his soul and lost his reputation by electing to steal apples from that especial tree I could never understand, for they were hard, bitter, flavourless things, good neither for eating or cooking.

Dear old trees! I hope they all had souls and will grow again for me on the hills of Heaven. I want, in some future life, to meet the old "Monarch" and the "White Lady," and even poor, dishonest little "Gavin's tree" again.[81]

When I was eight years old Cavendish had a very exciting

summer, perhaps the most exciting summer it ever had, and of course we children revelled in the excitement. The *Marcopolo* was wrecked on the sandshore.[82]

The *Marcopolo* was a very famous old ship and the fastest sailing vessel of her class ever built. She had a strange, romantic history, and was the nucleus of many traditions and sailors' yarns. She had finally been condemned in England under the Plimsoll Bill.[83] Her owners evaded the Bill by selling her to a Norwegian firm, and then chartering her to bring a cargo of deal plank from Quebec.[84] On her return she was caught in a furious storm out in the Gulf, sprung a leak, and became so waterlogged that the captain determined to run her on shore to save crew and cargo.

That day we had a terrible windstorm in Cavendish. Suddenly the news was spread that a vessel was coming ashore. Every one who could rushed to the sandshore and saw a magnificent sight! – a large vessel coming straight on before the northern gale with every stitch of canvas set. She grounded about three hundred yards from the shore and as she struck the crew cut the rigging, and the huge masts went over with a crash that was heard for a mile, above the roaring of the storm.[85]

The next day the crew of twenty men got ashore and found boarding places about Cavendish. Being typical tars,[86] they painted our quiet settlement a glowing scarlet for the remainder of the summer. It was their especial delight to crowd into a truck-wagon, and go galloping along the roads yelling at the top of their voices. They were of many nationalities, Irishmen, Englishmen, Scotchmen, Spaniards, Norwegians, Swedes, Dutchmen, Germans, and – most curious of all – two Tahitians, whose woolly heads, thick lips, and gold earrings were a never-failing joy to Well and Dave and me.

There was an immense amount of red tape in connection with the affair, and the *Marcopolo* men were in Cavendish for weeks. The captain boarded with us.[87] He was a Norwegian, a delightful, gentlemanly old fellow who was idolized by his crew. He spoke English well, but was apt to get rather mixed up in his prepositions.

"Thank you for your kindness *against* me, little Miss Maud," he would say with a grand bow.

Owing to the presence of the captain, the crew haunted our domain also. I remember the night they were all paid off; they all sat out on the grass under the parlour windows, feeding our old dog Gyp with biscuits. Well and Dave and I saw, with eyes as big as owls', the parlour table literally covered with gold sovereigns, which the captain paid out to the men. Never had we imagined there was so much wealth in the world.

Naturally the shore was a part of my life from my earliest consciousness. I learned to know it and love it in every mood. The Cavendish shore is a very beautiful one; part of it is rock shore, where the rugged red cliffs rise steeply from the boulder-strewn coves. Part is a long, gleaming sandshore, divided from the fields and ponds behind by a row of rounded sand-dunes, covered by coarse sand-hill grass. This sandshore is a peerless spot for bathing.

All through my childhood I spent much of my time on the shore. It was not so quiet and solitary then as it is to-day.[88] Those were the days when the mackerel fishing was good, and the shore was dotted with fishing houses. Many of the farmers had a fishing house on the shore field of their farms, with a boat drawn up on the skids below. Grandfather always fished mackerel in the summer, his boat manned by two or three French Canadians, fishing on the shores. Just where the rocks left off and the sandshore began was quite a little colony of fishing houses. This place was called Cawnpore, owing to the fact that on the day and hour when the last nail was being driven into the last house news arrived of the massacre of Cawnpore in the Indian Mutiny.[89] There is not a house left there now.

The men would get up at three or four in the morning and go out fishing. Then we children had to take their breakfast down at eight, later on their dinner, and, if the fish "schooled" all day, their supper also. In vacations we would spend most of the day there, and I soon came to know every cove, headland, and rock on that shore. We would watch the boats through the sky-glass, paddle in the water, gather shells and pebbles and mussels, and sit on the rocks and eat dulse, literally, by the yard. The rocks at low tide were covered by millions of snails, as we called them. I think the correct name is periwinkle. We often found great, white, empty "snail" shells, as big as our fists, that had been washed ashore from some distant strand or deep sea haunt. I early learned by heart, Holmes' beautiful lines on "The

Chambered Nautilus," and I rather fancied myself sitting dreamily on a big boulder with my bare, wet feet tucked up under my print skirt, holding a huge "snail" shell in my sunburned paw and appealing to my soul to "build thee more stately mansions."

There were many "outgrown shells" by that "unresting sea,"[90] and we carried them home to add to our collection, or to encircle our flower beds. Up by the sea run, where the ponds empty into the Gulf, we always found beautiful, white, quahog-clam shells galore.

The waves constantly dashing against the soft sandstone cliffs wore them away into many beautiful arches and caves. Somewhat to the east of our fishing house was a bold headland against which the water lapped at lowest tide. Through the neck of this headland a hole became worn – a hole so small that we could scarcely thrust a hand through it. Every season it grew a little larger. One summer an adventurous school chum and I crawled through it.[91] It was a tight squeeze, and we used to exult with a fearful joy over having dared it, and speculate as to what would have happened if one of us had got stuck half-way through!

In a few more years we could walk upright through the opening. Then a horse and carriage could have been driven through it. Finally, in about fifteen years from the beginning the thin bridge of rock at the top gave way, and the headland became an island, as though a gateway had been cleft through its wall.[92]

There were many stories and legends connected with the shore, of which I heard older persons talk. Grandfather liked a dramatic story, had a good memory for its fine points, and could tell it well. He had many tales to relate of the terrible American gale – or "Yankee storm," as it was called – when hundreds of American fishing vessels out in the Gulf were wrecked upon the north shore.[93]

The story of the *Franklin Dexter* and the four brothers who sailed in her, which is related in *The Golden Road*, is literally true. Grandfather was among those who found the bodies, helped to bury them in Cavendish churchyard, helped to take them up when the broken-hearted old father came, and helped to put them on the ill-fated *Seth Hall*.[94]

Then there was the story of Cape Leforce, a bit of tragic, unwritten history harking back to the days when the "Island of

FIGURE 18 *Cape Leforce. The hole through which I could just thrust my hand. It widened so that it severed all connection with the mainland.* Undated photograph. (Courtesy of the L.M. Montgomery Collection, Archival and Special Collections, University of Guelph Library.)

St. John" belonged to France.[95] It was some time in the 1760's. I can never remember dates. The only two dates which remain in my memory out of all those so painstakingly learned in schooldays are that Julius Cæsar landed in England 55 B.C. and the Battle of Waterloo was fought in 1815. France and England were at war. French privateers infested the Gulf sallying therefrom to plunder the commerce of the New England Colonies. One of these was commanded by a captain named Leforce.

One night they anchored off the Cavendish shore, at that time an unnamed, wooded solitude. For some reason the crew came ashore and camped for the night on the headland now known as Cape Leforce. The captain and his mate shared a tent, and endeavoured to come to a division of their booty. They quarrelled, and it was arranged that they should fight a duel at sunrise. But in the morning, as the ground was being paced off, the mate suddenly raised his pistol and shot Captain Leforce dead.

I do not know if the mate was ever punished for this deed. Probably not. It was a mere brief sentence in a long page of bloodshed. But the captain was buried by his crew on the spot where he fell, and I have often heard Grandfather say that *his* father had seen the grave in his boyhood. It had long ago crumbled off into the waves, but the name still clings to the red headland.

Away to the westward, six or seven miles the view was bounded by New London Cape, a long, sharp point, running far out to sea. In my childhood I never wearied of speculating what was on the other side of that point, a very realm of enchantment, surely, I thought. Even when I gradually drew into the understanding that beyond it was merely another reach of shore like my own it still held a mystery and a fascination for me. I longed to stand out on that lonely, remote, purple point, beyond which was the land of lost sunsets.[96]

I have seen few more beautiful sights than a sea-sunset off that point. In later years a new charm was added, a revolving light that flashed like a magnificent star through the dusk of summer nights, like a beacon on an out-post of fairyland.[97]

I did not often fare far afield. An occasional trip to town – Charlottetown[98] – and another to Uncle John Campbell's at Park Corner, were my only excursions beyond my horizon line, and both were looked on as great pleasures.[99] A trip to Park Corner was of comparatively frequent occurrence, once a year at least, and perhaps twice. A trip to town was a very rare treat, once in three years, and loomed up in about the same proportions of novelty, excitement, and delight as a trip to Europe would now – or before the war. It meant a brief sojourn in a wonderful and fascinating place, where every one was dressed up and could have all the nuts, candies, and oranges they wanted, to say nothing of the exquisite pleasure of looking at all the beautiful things in the shop windows.

I remember distinctly my first trip to town at the age of five. I had a glorious day, but the most delightful part was a tiny adventure I had just before leaving for home. Grandfather and Grandmother had met some friends at a street corner and stopped to talk. Finding that I wasn't being looked after, I promptly shot down a near-by side street, agog for adventures. It was *so* jolly and independent to be walking down a street all alone. It was a wonderful street, I've never seen it since – not with the same eyes, anyway. No other street has ever had the charm that one had. The most amazing sight I saw was a woman shaking rugs on *the top of a house*. I felt dizzy with astonishment over such a topsy-turvy sight. *We* shook rugs in the yard. Who ever heard of shaking them on the top of a house!

Arriving at the bottom of the street I coolly ran down the steps of an open door I found there, and discovered myself to be in a charming dim spot, full of barrels, with a floor ankle-deep with beautiful curly shavings. But, seeing some one moving in a distant corner I was overcome, not by fear but by shyness, and beat a hasty retreat. On my way back I met a little girl with a pitcher in her hand. We both stopped, and with the instinctive, unconventional *camaraderie* of childhood plunged into an intimate, confidential conversation. She was a jolly little soul, with black eyes and two long braids of black hair. We told each other how old we were, and how many dolls we had, and almost everything else there was to tell except our names which neither of us thought about. When we parted, I felt as though I were leaving a life long friend. We never met again.

When I rejoined my grown-ups they had not missed me at all, and knew nothing of my rapturous voyage into Wonderland.[100]

The Park Corner jaunts were always delightful. To begin with, it was such a pretty drive, those winding thirteen miles through hill and wood, and by river and shore.[101] There were many bridges to cross, two of them, with drawbridges. I was always horribly frightened of drawbridges, and am to this day. Do what I will, I cringe secretly from the time the horse steps on the bridge until I am safely over the draw.[102]

Uncle John Campbell's house was a big white one, smothered in orchards. Here, in other days, there was a trio of merry cousins to rush out and drag me in with greeting and laughter. The very walls of that house must have been permeated by the essence of good times. And there was a famous old pantry, always stored with goodies, into which it was our habit to crowd at bedtime and devour unholy snacks with sounds of riot and mirth.

There is a certain old screw sticking out from the wall on the stair landing which always makes me realize clearly that I am really grown-up. When I used to visit at Park Corner in the dawn of memory that screw was just on a level with my nose! *Now*, it comes to my knees. I used to measure myself by it every time I went over.

I was very fond of trouting and berry picking. We fished the brooks up in the woods, using the immemorial hook and line, with "w'ums" for bait. Generally I managed to put my worm on myself, but I expended a fearful amount of nervous energy in doing it. However, I managed to catch fish. I remember the thrill of pride I felt one day when I caught quite a large trout, as large as some of the grown-ups had caught in the pond. Well and Dave were with me, and I felt that I went up five per cent. in their estimation.[103] A girl who could catch a trout like that was not to be altogether despised.

We picked berries in the wild lands and fields back of the woods, going to them through wooded lanes fragrant with June bells, threaded with sunshine and shadow, carpeted with mosses, where we saw foxes and rabbits in their native haunts. I have never heard anything sweeter than the whistling of the robins at sunset in the maple woods around those fields.[104]

To go through woods with company was very pleasant; to go through them alone was a very different thing. A mile in along the road lived a family who kept a small shop where they sold tea and sugar, etc. I was frequently sent in to buy some household supplies, and I shall never forget the agony of terror I used to endure going through those woods. The distance through the woods was not more than a quarter of a mile, but it seemed endless to me.

I cannot tell just what I was afraid of. I *knew* there was nothing in the wood worse than rabbits or as the all-wise grown-ups told me "worse than yourself." It was just the old, primitive fear handed down to me from ancestors who, in the dawn of time, were afraid of the woods with good reason. With me, it was a blind, unreasoning terror.[105] And this was in daylight; to go through those woods *after dark* was something simply unthinkable. There were persons who did it. A young schoolmaster who boarded with us thought nothing apparently of walking through them at night. In my eyes he was the greatest hero the world had ever seen![106]

I have spoken of the time I realized physical pain. My first realization of the mental pain of sorrow came when I was nine years old.

I had two pet kittens, Catkin and Pussy-willow. Catkin was a little too meek and pink-nosed to suit me, but Pussy-willow was the prettiest, "cutest" little scrap of gray-striped fur ever seen and I loved her passionately.

One morning I found her dying of poison. I shall never forget my agony of grief as I watched my little pet's bright eyes glazing, and her tiny paws growing stiff and cold. And I have never laughed with grown-up wisdom at my passionate sorrow over the little death. It was too real, too symbolical! It was the first time I *realized* death, the first time, since I had become conscious of loving, that anything I loved had left me forever. At that moment the curse of the race came upon me, "death entered into my world"[107] and I turned my back on the Eden of childhood where everything had seemed everlasting. I was barred out of it forevermore by the fiery sword of that keen and unforgettable pain.[108]

We were Presbyterians, and went every Sunday to the old Cavendish Presbyterian Church on the bleak hill.[109] It was never a handsome church, inside or out, but it was beautified in its worshippers' eyes by years of memories and sacred associations. Our pew was by a window and we looked out over the slope of the long western hill and the blue pond down to the curving rim of the sandhills and the fine sweep of the blue Gulf.

There was a big gallery at the back of the church. I always hankered to sit there, principally because I wasn't allowed to, no doubt, another instance of forbidden fruit! Once a year, on Sacrament Sunday,[110] I was permitted to go up there with the other girls, and I considered it a great treat. We could look down over the whole congregation, which always flowered out that day in full bloom of new hats and dresses. Sacrament Sunday, then, was to us what Easter is to the dwellers in cities. We all had new hats or dresses, sometimes, oh, bliss, we had both! And I very much fear that we thought more about them than we did about the service and what it commemorated. It was rather a long service in those days, and we small fry used to get very tired and rather inclined to envy certain irresponsible folk who went out while the congregation sang "'Twas on that night when doomed to know."[111] We liked the Sunday School much better than the church services. Some of my sweetest memories are of the hours spent in that old church with my little mates, with our testaments and lesson sheets held in our cotton-gloved hands. Saturday night we had been made to learn our catechism and our Golden texts and our paraphrases.[112] I always enjoyed reciting those paraphrases, particularly any that had dramatic lines.

The London *Spectator*, in a very kind review of *Anne of Green Gables* said that possibly Anne's precocity was slightly overdrawn in the statement that a child of eleven could appreciate the dramatic effect of the lines,

"Quick as the slaughtered squadrons fell
In Midian's evil day."[113]

But I was only nine when those lines thrilled my very soul as I recited them in Sunday School. All through the sermon following I kept repeating them to myself. To this day they give me a mysterious pleasure and a pleasure quite independent of their meaning.

So ran the current of my life in childhood, very quiet and simple, you perceive. Nothing at all exciting about it, nothing that savours of a "career." Some might think it dull. But life never held for me a dull moment. I had, in my vivid imagination, a passport to the geography of Fairyland. In a twinkling I could – and did – whisk myself into regions of wonderful adventures, unhampered by any restrictions of time or place.

Everything was invested with a kind of fairy grace and charm, emanating from my own fancy, the trees that whispered nightly around the old house where I slept, the woodsy nooks I explored, the homestead fields, each individualized by some oddity of fence or shape, the sea whose murmur was never out of my ears – all were radiant with "the glory and the dream."[114]

I had always a deep love of nature. A little fern growing in the woods, a shallow sheet of June-bells under the firs, moonlight falling on the ivory column of a tall birch, an evening star over the old tamarack on the dyke, shadow-waves rolling over a field of ripe wheat – all gave me "thoughts that lay too deep for tears" and feelings which I had then no vocabulary to express.[115]

It has always seemed to me, ever since early childhood, that, amid all the commonplaces of life, I was very near to a kingdom of ideal beauty. Between it and me hung only a thin veil. I could never draw it quite aside, but sometimes a wind fluttered it and I caught a glimpse of the enchanting realm beyond – only a glimpse – but those glimpses have always made life worth while.[116]

It goes without saying that I was passionately fond of reading.[117] We did not have a great many books in the house, but there were generally plenty of papers and a magazine or two. Grandmother took *Godey's Lady's Book*.[118] I do not know if I would think much of that magazine now, but then I thought it wonderful, and its monthly advents were epochs to me. The opening pages were full of fashion plates and were a perpetual joy; I hung over them with delight, and whiled away many an hour choosing what frocks I would have if I could. Those were the days of bangs, bristles, and high-crowned hats, all of which I considered extremely beautiful and meant to have as soon as I was old enough. Beyond the fashion pages came the literary pabulum, short stories and serials, which I devoured ravenously, crying my eyes out in delicious woe over the agonies of the heroines who were all superlatively beautiful and good. Every one in fiction was either black or white in those days. There were no grays. The villains and villainesses were all neatly labelled and you were sure of your ground. The old method had its merits. Nowadays it is quite hard to tell which is the villain and which the hero. But there was never any doubt in *Godey's Lady's Book*. What books we had were well and often read. I had my especial favourites. There were two red-covered volumes of *A History of the World*,[119] with crudely-coloured pictures, which were a never-failing delight. I fear that, as history, they were rather poor stuff, but as story books they were very interesting. They began with Adam and Eve in Eden, went through "the glory that was Greece and the grandeur that was Rome,"[120] down to Victoria's reign.[121]

Then there was a missionary book dealing with the Pacific Islands, in which I revelled because it was full of pictures of cannibal chiefs with the most extraordinary hair arrangements. Hans Andersen's *Tales* were a perennial joy.[122] I always loved fairy tales and delighted in ghost stories. Indeed, to this day I like nothing better than a well-told ghost story, warranted to send a cold creep down your spine. But it must be a real ghost story, mark you. The spook must not turn out a delusion and a snare.[123]

I did not have access to many novels. Those were the days when novels were frowned on as reading for children. The only novels in the house were *Rob Roy*, *Pickwick Papers*, and Bulwer Lytton's *Zanoni*;[124] and I pored over them until I knew whole chapters by heart.

Fortunately poetry did not share the ban of novels. I could revel at will in Longfellow, Tennyson, Whittier, Scott, Byron, Milton, Burns.[125] Poetry pored over in childhood becomes part of one's nature more thoroughly than that which is first read in mature years can ever do. Its music was woven into my growing soul and has echoed through it, consciously and subconsciously, ever since; "the music of the immortals, of those great, beautiful souls whose passing tread has made of earth holy ground."[126]

But even poetry was barred on Sundays. Then our faithful standbys were *Pilgrims' Progress* and Talmage's *Sermons*.[127] *Pilgrims' Progress* was read and re-read with never-failing delight. I am proud of this; but I am not quite so proud of the fact that I found just as much delight in reading Talmage's *Sermons*. That was Talmage's palmy day. All the travelling colporteurs carried his books, and a new volume of Talmage's meant then to us pretty much what a "best seller" does now. I cannot claim that it was the religion that attracted me, though at that age I liked the Talmage brand much; it was the anecdotes and the vivid, dramatic word-pictures. His sermons were as interesting as fiction. I am sure I couldn't read them with any patience now; but I owe Talmage a very real debt of thanks for pleasure given to a child craving the vividness of life.

My favourite Sunday book, however, was a thin little volume entitled *The Memoir of Anzonetta Peters*.[128] I shall never forget that book. It belonged to a type now vanished from the earth – fortunately – but much in vogue at that time. It was the biography of a child who at five years became converted, grew very ill soon afterward, lived a marvellously patient and saintly life for several years, and died, after great sufferings, at the age of ten.

I must have read that book a hundred times if I did once. I don't think it had a good effect on me. For one thing it discouraged me horribly. Anzonetta was so hopelessly perfect that I felt it was no use to try to imitate her. Yet I did try. She never seemed by any chance to use the ordinary language of childhood at all. She invariably responded to any remark, if it were only "How are you to-day, Anzonetta?" by quoting a verse of scripture or a hymn stanza. Anzonetta was a perfect hymnal. She died to a hymn, her last, faintly-whispered utterance being

"Hark, they whisper, angels say,
Sister spirit, come away."[129]

I dared not attempt to use verses and hymns in current conversation. I had a wholesome conviction that I should be laughed at, and moreover, I doubted being understood. But I did my best; I wrote hymn after hymn in my little diary, and patterned the style of my entries after Anzonetta's remarks. For example, I remember writing gravely "I wish I were in Heaven now, with Mother and George Whitefield and Anzonetta B. Peters."[130]

But I didn't really wish it. I only thought I *ought* to. I was, in reality, very well contented with my own world, and my own little life full of cabbages and kings.[131]

I have written at length about the incidents and environment of my childhood, because they had a marked influence on the development of my literary gift. A different environment would have given it a different bias. Were it not for those Cavendish years, I do not think *Anne of Green Gables* would ever have been written.

When I am asked "When did you begin to write?" I say, "I wish I could remember."[132] I cannot remember the time when I was not writing, or when I did not mean to be an author. To write has always been my central purpose around which every effort and hope and ambition of my life has grouped itself. I was an indefatigable little scribbler, and stacks of manuscripts, long ago reduced to ashes, alas, bore testimony to the same. I wrote about all the little incidents of my existence. I wrote descriptions of

FIGURE 19 *I was in a pensive mood when this was taken, and just ten years old.* Undated photograph, ca. 1885. (Courtesy of the L.M. Montgomery Collection, Archival and Special Collections, University of Guelph Library.)

my favourite haunts, biographies of my many cats, histories of visits, and school affairs, and even critical reviews of the books I had read.

One wonderful day, when I was nine years old, I discovered that I could write poetry. I had been reading Thompson's *Seasons*,[133] of which a little black, curly-covered atrociously printed copy had fallen into my hands. So I composed a "poem" called "Autumn" in blank verse in imitation thereof. I wrote it, I remember, on the back of one of the long red "letter bills" then used in the postal service. It was seldom easy for me to get all the paper I wanted, and those blessed old letter bills were positive boons. Grandfather kept the post office, and three times a week a discarded "letter bill" came my grateful way. The Government was not so economical then as now, at least in the matter of letter bills; they were then half a yard long.[134]

As for "Autumn," I remember only the opening lines:

> "Now autumn comes, laden with peach and pear;
> The sportsman's horn is heard throughout the land,
> And the poor partridge, fluttering, falls dead."

True, peaches and pears were not abundant in Prince Edward Island at any season, and I am sure nobody ever heard a "sportsman's horn" in that Province, though there really was some partridge shooting. But in those glorious days my imagination refused to be hampered by facts. Thompson had sportsman's horns and so forth; therefore I must have them too.

Father came to see me the very day I wrote it, and I proudly read it to him. He remarked unenthusiastically that "it didn't sound much like poetry."[135] This squelched me for a time; but if the love of writing is bred in your bones, you will be practically non-squelchable. Once I had found out that I could write poetry I overflowed into verse over everything. I wrote in rhyme after that, though, having concluded that it was because "Autumn" did not rhyme that Father thought it wasn't poetry. I wrote yards of verses about flowers and months and trees and stars and sunsets. And I addressed "Lines" to my friends.[136]

A school chum of mine, Alma M—,[137] had also a knack of writing rhyme. She and I had a habit, no doubt, a reprehensible one, of getting out together on the old side bench at school, and writing "po'try" on our slates, when the master fondly supposed we were sharpening our intellects on fractions.

We began by first writing acrostics on our names;[138] then we wrote poems addressed to each other in which we praised each other fulsomely; finally, one day, we agreed to write up in stirring rhyme all our teachers, including the master himself. We filled our slates; two verses were devoted to each teacher, and the two concerning the reigning pedagogue were very sarcastic effusions dealing with some of his flirtations with the Cavendish belles. Alma and I were gleefully comparing our productions when the master himself, who had been standing before us but with his back toward us, hearing a class, suddenly wheeled about and took my slate out of my paralyzed hand. Horrors! I stood up, firmly believing that the end of all things was at hand. Why he did not read it I do not know, it may be he had a dim suspicion what it was and wanted to save his dignity. Whatever his reason, he handed the slate back to me in silence, and I sat down with a gasp, sweeping off the accusing words as I did so lest he might change his mind. Alma and I were so badly scared that we gave up at once and forever the stolen delight of writing poetry in company on the side bench!

I remember – who could ever forget it? – the first commendation my writing received. I was about twelve and I had a stack of poems written out and hidden jealously from all eyes, for I was very sensitive in regard to my scribblings and could not bear the thought of having them seen and laughed at. Nevertheless, I wanted to know what others would think of them, not from vanity, but from a strong desire to find out if an impartial judge would see any merit in them. So I employed a little ruse to find out. It all seems very funny to me now, and a little pitiful; but then it seemed to me that I was at the bar of judgment for all time. It would be too much to say that, had the verdict been unfavourable, I would have forever surrendered my dreams, but they would certainly have been frosted for a time.

A lady was visiting us who was something of a singer.[139] One evening I timidly asked her if she had ever heard a song called "Evening Dreams."

She certainly had not, for the said "Evening Dreams" was a poem of my own composition, which I then considered my masterpiece. It is not now extant, and I can remember the first two verses only. I suppose that they were indelibly impressed on my memory by the fact that the visitor asked me if I knew any of the words of the "song." Whereupon I, in a trembling voice, recited the two opening verses:

"When the evening sun is setting
Quietly in the west,
In a halo of rainbow glory,
I sit me down to rest.

I forget the present and future,
I live over the past once more,
As I see before me crowding
The beautiful days of yore."

Strikingly original! Also, a child of twelve would have a long "past" to live over!

I finished up with a positive gasp, but the visitor was busy with her fancy work, and did not notice my pallor and general shakiness. For I *was* pale, it was a moment of awful import to me. She placidly said that she had never heard the song, but "the words were very pretty."

The fact that she was sincere must certainly detract from her reputation for literary discrimination. But to me it was the sweetest morsel of commendation that had ever fallen to my lot, or that ever has fallen since, for that matter. Nothing has ever surpassed that delicious moment. I ran out of the house – it wasn't big enough to contain my joy, I must have all outdoors for that – and danced down the lane under the birches in a frenzy of delight, hugging to my heart the remembrance of those words.

Perhaps it was this that encouraged me sometime during the following winter to write out my "Evening Dreams" very painstakingly – on both sides of the paper, alas! – and to send them to the editor of *The Household*, an American magazine we took.[140] The idea of being paid for them never entered my head. Indeed, I am not at all sure that I knew at that time that people were ever paid for writing. At least, my early dreams of literary fame were untainted by any mercenary speculations.

Alack! the editor of *The Household* was less complimentary

than our visitor. He sent the verses back, although I had *not* "enclosed a stamp" for the purpose, being in blissful ignorance of any such requirement.

My aspirations were nipped in the bud for a time. It was a year before I recovered from the blow. Then I essayed a more modest flight. I copied out my "Evening Dreams" again and sent them to the Charlottetown *Examiner*.[141] I felt quite sure it would print them, for it often printed verses which I thought, and, for that matter, still think, were no better than mine.

For a week I dreamed delicious dreams of seeing my verses in the Poet's Corner, with my name appended thereto. When the *Examiner* came, I opened it with tremulous eagerness. There was not a sign of an evening dream about it!

I drained the cup of failure to the very dregs. It seems very amusing to me now, but it was horribly real and tragic to me then. I was crushed in the very dust of humiliation and I had no hope of rising again. I burned my "Evening Dreams," and, although I continued to write because I couldn't help it, I sent no more poems to the editors.

Poems, however, were not all I wrote. Very soon after I began to write verses I also began to write stories. The "Story Club" in *Anne of Green Gables* was suggested by a little incident of school-days when Janie S—, Amanda M— and I all wrote a story with the same plot.[142] I remember only that it was a very tragic plot, and the heroines were all drowned while bathing on Cavendish sandshore! Oh, it was very sad! It was the first, and probably the last, time that Janie and Amanda attempted fiction, but I had already quite a library of stories in which almost everyone died. A certain lugubrious yarn, "My Graves," was my masterpiece.[143] It was a long tale of the peregrinations of a Methodist minister's wife, who buried a child in every circuit to which she went. The oldest was buried in Newfoundland, the last in Vancouver, and all Canada between was dotted with those graves. I wrote the story in the first person, described the children, pictured out their death beds, and detailed their tombstones and epitaphs.

Then there was "This History of Flossy Brighteyes," the biography of a doll. I couldn't kill a doll, but I dragged her through every other tribulation. However, I allowed her to have a happy old age with a good little girl who loved her for the dangers she had passed and overlooked her consequent lack of beauty.

FIGURE 20 *At fourteen I wrote "The History of Flossy Brighteyes," the biography of a doll. I couldn't kill a doll, but I dragged her through every other tribulation and then allowed her a happy old age with a good little girl who loved her for the dangers she had passed through and overlooked her consequent lack of beauty.* Undated photograph, ca. 1889. (Courtesy of the L.M. Montgomery Collection, Archival and Special Collections, University of Guelph Library.)

FIGURE 21 *This picture was made when I was sixteen and the flame of an ambition to write something big was beginning to sear my soul.* Undated photograph, ca. 1892. (*Everywoman's World*, Toronto.)

Nowadays, my reviewers say that my forte is humour.[144] Well, there was not much humour in those early tales, at least, it was not intended there should be. Perhaps I worked all the tragedy out of my system in them, and left an unimpeded current of humour. I think it was my love of the dramatic that urged me to so much infanticide. In real life I couldn't have hurt a fly, and the thought that superfluous kittens had to be drowned was torture to me. But in my stories battle, murder and sudden death were the order of the day.

When I was fifteen I had my first ride on a railway train, and it was a long one.[145] I went with Grandfather Montgomery to Prince Albert, Saskatchewan, where Father had married again and was then living. I spent a year in Prince Albert and attended the High School there.

It was now three years since I had suffered so much mortification over "Evening Dreams." By this time my long-paralyzed ambition was beginning to recover and lift its head again. I wrote up the old Cape Leforce legend in rhyme and sent it down home to the *Patriot*, no more of the *Examiner* for me![146]

Four weeks passed. One afternoon Father came in with a copy of the *Patriot*. My verses were in it! It was the first sweet bubble on the cup of success and of course it intoxicated me. There were some fearful printers' errors in the poem which fairly made the flesh creep on my bones, but it was my poem, and in a real newspaper! The moment we see our first darling brain-child arrayed in black type is never to be forgotten. It has in it some of the wonderful awe and delight that comes to a mother when she looks for the first time on the face of her first born.[147]

During that winter I had other verses and articles printed. A story I had written in a prize competition was published in the Montreal *Witness*, and a descriptive article on Saskatchewan was printed in the Prince Albert *Times*, and copied and commented on favourably by several Winnipeg papers.[148] After several effusions on "June" and kindred subjects appeared in that long-suffering *Patriot*,[149] I was beginning to plume myself on being quite a literary person.[150]

But the demon of filthy lucre was creeping into my heart.[151] I wrote a story and sent it to the New York *Sun*, because I had been told that it paid for articles; and the New York *Sun* sent it back to me. I flinched, as from a slap in the face, but went on writing. You see, I had learned the first, last, and middle lesson – "Never give up!"

The next summer I returned to Prince Edward Island and spent the following winter in Park Corner, giving music lessons and writing verses for the *Patriot*. Then I attended the Cavendish school for another year, studying for the Entrance Examination into Prince of Wales College. In the fall of 1893 I went to Charlottetown, and attended the Prince of Wales College that winter, studying for a teacher's license.

I was still sending away things and getting them back. But one day I went into the Charlottetown post office and got a thin letter with the address of an American magazine in the corner. In it was a brief note accepting a poem, "Only a Violet." The editor offered me two subscriptions to the magazine in payment. I kept one for myself and gave the other to a friend, and those magazines, with their vapid little stories, were the first tangible recompense my pen brought me.[152]

"It is a start, and I mean to keep on," I find written in my old journal of that year. "Oh, I wonder if I shall ever be able to do anything worth while in the way of writing. It is my dearest ambition."[153]

After leaving Prince of Wales College I taught school for a year in Bideford, Prince Edward Island. I wrote a good deal and learned a good deal, but still my stuff came back, except from two periodicals the editors of which evidently thought that literature was its own reward, and quite independent of monetary considerations. I often wonder that I did not give up in utter discouragement. At first I used to feel dreadfully hurt when a story or poem over which I had laboured and agonized came back, with one of those icy little rejection slips. Tears of disappointment *would* come in spite of myself, as I crept away to hide the poor, crimpled manuscript in the depths of my trunk. But after a while I got hardened to it and did not mind. I only set my teeth and said "I will succeed." I believed in myself and I struggled on alone, in secrecy and silence. I never told my ambitions and efforts and failures to any one. Down, deep down, under all the discouragement and rebuff, I knew I would "arrive" some day.

In the autumn of 1895 I went to Halifax and spent the winter taking a selected course in English literature at Dalhousie College. Through the winter came a "Big Week" for me. On Monday I received a letter from *Golden Days*, a Philadelphia juvenile, accepting a short story I had sent there and enclosing a cheque for five dollars.[154] It was the first money my pen had ever earned; I did not squander it in riotous living,[155] neither did I invest it in necessary boots and gloves. I went up town and bought five volumes of poetry with it – Tennyson, Byron, Milton, Longfellow, Whittier. I wanted something I could keep for ever in memory of having "arrived."[156]

On Wednesday of the same week I won the prize of five dollars

FIGURE 22 *My "red letter day" came when I was nineteen and received my first cheque for a short story. I did not squander that five dollars in riotous living, nor invest it in necessary boots and gloves; no, I bought five volumes of poetry with it. I wanted something I could keep forever in memory of having "arrived."* (Courtesy of the L.M. Montgomery Collection, Archival and Special Collections, University of Guelph Library.)

offered by the Halifax *Evening Mail* for the best letter on the subject, "Which has the greater patience – man or woman?"

My letter was in the form of some verses, which I had composed during a sleepless night and got up at three o'clock in the wee sma' hours to write down.[157] On Saturday the *Youth's Companion* sent me a cheque for twelve dollars for a poem.[158] I really felt quite bloated with so much wealth. Never in my life, before or since have I been so rich!

After my Dalhousie winter I taught school for two more years. In those two years I wrote scores of stories, generally for Sunday School publications and juvenile periodicals. The following entry from my journal refers to this period:

"I have grubbed away industriously all this summer and ground out stories and verses on days so hot that I feared my very marrow would melt and my gray matter be hopelessly sizzled up. But oh, I love my work! I love spinning stories, and I love to sit by the window of my room and shape some 'airy fairy' fancy into verse. I have got on well this summer and added several new journals to my list. They are a varied assortment, and their separate tastes all have to be catered to. I write a great many juvenile stories. I like doing these, but I should like it better if I didn't have to drag a 'moral' into most of them. They won't sell without it, as a rule. So in the moral must go, broad or subtle, as suits the fibre of the particular editor I have in view. The kind of juvenile story I like best to write – and read, too, for the matter of that – is a good, jolly one, 'art for art's sake,' or rather 'fun for fun's sake,' with no insidious moral hidden away in it like a pill in a spoonful of jam!"[159]

It was not always hot weather when I was writing. During one of those winters of school teaching I boarded in a very cold farmhouse. In the evenings, after a day of strenuous school work, I would be too tired to write. So I religiously arose an hour earlier in the mornings for that purpose. For five months I got up at six o'clock and dressed by lamplight. The fires would not yet be on, of course, and the house would be very cold. But I would put on a heavy coat, sit on my feet to keep them from freezing, and with fingers so cramped that I could scarcely hold the pen, I would write my "stint" for the day.[160] Sometimes it would be a poem in which I would carol blithely of blue skies and rippling brooks and flowery meads! Then I would thaw out my hands, eat breakfast and go to school.

When people say to me, as they occasionally do, "Oh, how I envy you your gift, how I wish I could write as you do," I am inclined to wonder, with some inward amusement, how much they would have envied me on those dark, cold, winter mornings of my apprenticeship.[161]

Grandfather died in 1898 and Grandmother was left alone in the old homestead. So I gave up teaching and stayed home with her. By 1901 I was beginning to make a "livable" income for myself by my pen, though that did not mean that everything I wrote was accepted on its first journey. Far from it. Nine out of ten manuscripts came back to me. But I sent them out over and over again, and eventually they found resting places. Another extract from my journal may serve as a sort of milestone to show how far I had travelled.

"March 21, 1901.

"*Munsey's* came to-day with my poem 'Comparisons' in it, illustrated.[162] It really *looked* nice. I've been quite in luck of late, for several new and good magazines have opened their portals to this poor wandering sheepkin of thorny literary ways. I feel that I am improving and developing in regard to my verses. I suppose it would be strange if I did not, considering how hard I study and work. Every now and then I write a poem which serves as a sort of landmark to emphasize my progress. I know, by looking back, that I could not have written it six months, or a year, or four years ago, any more than I could have made a garment the material of which was still unwoven. I wrote two poems this week. A year ago, I could not have written them, but now they come easily and naturally. This encourages me to hope that in the future I may achieve something worth while. I never expect to be famous. I merely want to have a recognized place among good workers in my chosen profession. That, I honestly believe, is happiness, and the harder to win the sweeter and more lasting when won."[163]

In the fall of 1901 I went again to Halifax and worked for the winter on the staff of the *Daily Echo*, the evening edition of the *Chronicle*. A series of extracts from my journal will tell the tale of that experience with sufficient fulness.

"11 November, 1901.

"I am here alone in the office of the *Daily Echo*. The paper is gone to press and the extra proofs have not yet begun to come down. Overhead, in the composing room, they are rolling machines and making a diabolical noise. Outside of the window the engine exhaust is puffing furiously. In the inner office two reporters are having a wrangle. And here sit I – the *Echo* proof-reader and general handy-man. Quite a 'presto change' from last entry![164]

"I'm a newspaper woman!

"Sounds nice? Yes, and the reality is very nice, too. Being of the earth, it is earthy, and has its drawbacks. Life in a newspaper office isn't all 'beer and skittles' any more than anywhere else.[165] But on the whole it is not a bad life at all![166] I rather like proof-reading, although it is tedious. The headlines and editorials are my worst thorns in the flesh.[167] Headlines have a natural tendency to depravity, and the editor-in-chief has a ghastly habit of making puns over which I am apt to come to grief. In spite of all my care 'errors will creep in' and then there is the mischief to pay. When I have nightmares now they are of headlines wildly askew and editorials hopelessly hocussed, which an infuriated chief is flourishing in my face.

"The paper goes to press at 2.30, but I have to stay till six to answer the 'phone, sign for wires, and read extra proofs.

"On Saturdays the *Echo* has a lot of extra stuff, a page of 'society letters' among the rest. It usually falls to my lot to edit these. Can't say I fancy the job much, but the only thing I positively abhor is 'faking' a society letter. This is one of the tricks of newspaperdom. When a society letter fails to turn up from a certain place – say from Windsor – in due time, the news editor slaps a Windsor weekly down before me and says blandly, 'Fake up a society letter from that, Miss Montgomery.'

"So poor Miss Montgomery goes meekly to work, and concocts an introductory paragraph or so about 'autumn leaves' and 'mellow days' and 'October frosts,' or any old stuff like that to suit the season. Then I go carefully over the columns of the weekly, clip out all the available personals and news items, about weddings, and engagements, and teas, etc., hash them up in epistolary style, forge the Windsor correspondent's nom de plume – and there's your society letter![168] I used to include funerals, too, but I found the news editor blue-pencilled them. Evidently funerals have no place in society.

"Then I write a column or so of giddy paragraphs for Monday's *Echo*. I call it 'Around the Tea-Table,' and sign it 'Cynthia.'[169]

"My office is a back room looking out on a back yard in the middle of the block. I don't know that all the Haligonian washerwomen live around it, but certainly a good percentage of them must, for the yard is a network of lines from which sundry and divers garments are always streaming gaily to the breezes. On the ground and over the roof cats are prowling continually, and when they fight, the walls resound with their howls. Most of them are lank, starved-looking beasties enough, but there is one lovely gray fellow who basks on a window sill opposite me and looks so much like 'Dafty' that, when I look at him, I could squeeze out a homesick tear if I were not afraid that it would wash a clean spot on my grimy face.[170] This office is really the worst place for getting dirty I ever was in."

"November 18, 1901.[171]

"Have had a difficult time trying to arrange for enough spare minutes to do some writing. I could not write in the evenings, I was always too tired. Besides, I had to keep my buttons sewed on and my stockings darned. Then I reverted to my old practice, and tried getting up at six in the morning. But it did not work, as of yore. I could never get to bed as early as I could when I was a country 'schoolma'am' and I found it impossible to do without a certain amount of sleep.

"There was only one alternative.

"Hitherto, I had thought that undisturbed solitude was necessary that the fire of genius might burn and even the fire for pot-boiling. I must be alone, and the room must be quiet. I could never have even imagined that I could possibly write anything in a newspaper office, with rolls of proof shooting down every ten minutes, people coming and conversing, telephones ringing, and machines being thumped and dragged overhead. I would have laughed at the idea, yea, I would have laughed it to scorn. But the impossible has happened. I am of one mind with the Irishman who said you could get used to anything, even to being hanged![172]

"All my spare time here I write, and not such bad stuff either, since the *Delineator*, the *Smart Set* and *Ainslies'* have taken some of it.[173] I have grown accustomed to stopping in the middle of a paragraph to interview a prowling caller, and to pausing in full career after an elusive rhyme, to read a lot of proof, and snarled-up copy."

"Saturday, December 8, 1901.[174]

"Of late I've been Busy with a capital B. 'Tending to office work, writing pot-boilers, making Christmas presents, etc., mostly etc.

"One of the 'etcs.' is a job I heartily detest. It makes my soul cringe. It is bad enough to have your flesh cringe, but when it strikes into your soul it gets on your spiritual nerves terribly. We are giving all the firms who advertise with us a free 'write-up' of their holiday goods, and I have to visit all the stores, interview the proprietors, and crystallize my information into two 'sticks' of copy. From three to five every afternoon I potter around the business blocks until my nose is purple with the cold and my fingers numb from much scribbling of notes."[175]

"Wednesday, December 12, 1901.[176]

"It is an ill wind that blows no good and my disagreeable assignment has blown me some. The other evening I went in to write up the *Bon Marche*, which sets up to be the millinery establishment of Halifax, and I found the proprietor very genial.[177] He said he was delighted that the *Echo* had sent a lady, and by way of encouraging it not to weary in well doing[178] he would send me up one of the new walking hats if I gave the *Bon Marche* a good write-up. I rather thought he was only joking, but sure enough, when the write-up came out yesterday, up came the hat, and a very pretty one it is too."

"Thursday, December 20, 1901.[179]

"All the odd jobs that go a-begging in this office are handed over to the present scribe. The very queerest one up to date came yesterday.

"The compositors were setting up, for the weekly edition, a story called 'A Royal Betrothal,' taken from an English paper, and when about half through they lost the copy. Whereupon the news-editor requested me to go to and write an 'end' for the story. At first I did not think I could. What was set up of the story was not enough to give me any insight into the solution of the plot. More over, my knowledge of royal love affairs is limited, and I have not been accustomed to write with flippant levity of kings and queens.

"However, I fell to work and somehow got it done. To-day it came out, and as yet nobody has guessed where the 'seam' comes in. If the original author ever beholds it, I wonder what he will think."[180]

I may remark, in passing, that more than ten years afterward I came across a copy of the original story in an old scrapbook, and was much amused to discover that the author's development of the plot was about as different from mine as anything could possibly be.

"Thursday, December 27th, 1901.

"Christmas is over. I had been rather dreading it, for I had been expecting to feel very much the stranger in a strange land.[181] But, as usual, anticipation was discounted by realization. I had a very pleasant time although not, of course, so wildly exhilarating as to endanger life, limb or nerves, which was, no doubt, just as well.

"I had a holiday, the first since coming here, and so was haunted all day by the impression that it was Sunday. I had dinner at the *Halifax* with B. and spent the afternoon with her. In the evening we went to the opera to see *The Little Minister*. It was good but not nearly so good as the book. I don't care for dramatized novels. They always jar on my preconceptions of the characters. Also, I had to write a criticism of the play and cast for the *Chronicle* and I dislike that very much."[182]

"Saturday, March 29, 1902.[183]

"This week has been a miserable one of rain and fog and neuralgia. But I've lived through it. I've read proofs and dissected headlines and fought with compositors and bandied jokes with the marine editor. I have ground out various blameless rhymes for a consideration of filthy lucre, and I've written one real poem out of my heart.

"I hate my 'pot-boiling' stuff. But it gives me the keenest pleasure to write something that is good, a fit and proper incarnation of the art I worship. The news-editor has just been in to give me an assignment for to-morrow, bad 'cess to him.[184] It is Easter Sunday, and I have to write up the 'parade' down Pleasant Street after church, for Monday's *Echo*."[185]

"Palmday,[186] May 3, 1902.

"I spent the afternoon 'expurgating' a novel for the news-editor's use and behoof. When he was away on his vacation his substitute began to run a serial in the *Echo* called 'Under the Shadow.'[187] Instead of getting some A.P.A.[188] stuff as he should have done, he simply bought a sensational novel and used it. It was very long and was only about half done when the news-editor returned. So, as it would run all summer, in its present form, I was bidden to take it and cut mercilessly out all unnecessary stuff. I have followed instructions, cutting out most of the kisses and embraces, two-thirds of the love-making, and all the descriptions, with the happy result that I have reduced it to about a third of its normal length, and all I can say is 'Lord, have mercy on the soul of the compositor who has to set it up in its present mutilated condition.'"[189]

"Saturday, May 31, 1901.

"I had a good internal laugh to-night. I was in a street car and two ladies beside me were discussing the serial that had just ended in the *Echo*. 'You know,' said one, 'it was the strangest story I ever read. It wandered on, chapter after chapter, for weeks, and never seemed to get anywhere; and then it just finished up in eight chapters, *licketty-split*. I can't understand it!'

"I could have solved the mystery, but I didn't."[190]

I WRITE *ANNE OF GREEN GABLES*

In June, 1902, I returned to Cavendish, where I remained unbrokenly for the next nine years. For the first two years after my return I wrote only short stories and serials as before. But I was beginning to think of writing a book.[191] It had always been my hope and ambition to write one. But I never seemed able to make a beginning.

I have always hated beginning a story. When I get the first paragraph written I feel as though it were half done. The rest comes easily. To begin a book, therefore, seemed quite a stupendous task. Besides, I did not see just how I could get time for it. I could not afford to take the time from my regular writing hours. And, in the end, I never deliberately sat down and said "Go to! Here are pens, paper, ink and plot. Let me write a book." It really all just "happened."

I had always kept a notebook in which I jotted down, as they occurred to me, ideas for plots, incidents, characters, and descriptions. In the spring of 1904 I was looking over this notebook in search of some idea for a short serial I wanted to write for a certain Sunday School paper. I found a faded entry, written many years before: "Elderly couple apply to orphan asylum for a boy. By mistake a girl is sent them." I thought this would do. I began to block out the chapters, devise and select incidents and "brood up" my heroine. Anne – she was not so named of malice aforethought, but flashed into my fancy already christened, even to the all-important "e" – began to expand in such a fashion that she soon seemed very real to me and took possession of me to an unusual extent. She appealed to me, and I thought it rather a shame to waste her on an ephemeral little serial. Then the thought came, "Write a book. You have the central idea. All you need do is to spread it out over enough chapters to amount to a book."

The result was *Anne of Green Gables*. I wrote it in the evenings after my regular day's work was done, wrote most of it at the window of the little gable room which had been mine for many years. I began it, as I have said, in the spring of 1904. I finished it in the October of 1905.[192]

Ever since my first book was published I have been persecuted by the question "Was so-and-so the original of such-and-such in your book?" And behind my back they don't put it in the interrogative form, but in the affirmative. I know many people who have asserted that they are well acquainted with the "originals" of my characters. Now, for my own part, I have never, during all the years I have studied human nature, met one human being who could, as a whole, be put into a book without injuring it. Any artist knows that to paint *exactly* from life is to give a false impression of the subject. *Study* from life he must, copying suitable heads or arms, appropriating bits of character, personal or mental idiosyncracies, "making use of the real to perfect the ideal."[193]

But the ideal, his ideal, must be behind and beyond it all. The writer must *create* his characters, or they will not be life-like.

With but one exception I have never drawn any of my book people from life. That exception was *Peg Bowen* in *The Story Girl*. And even then I painted the lily very freely.[194] I have used real places in my books and many real incidents. But hitherto I have depended wholly on the creative power of my own imagination for my characters.

Cavendish was "Avonlea" to a certain extent.[195] "Lover's Lane" was a very beautiful lane through the woods on a neighbour's farm.[196] It was a beloved haunt of mine from my earliest

FIGURE 23 *A view of Lover's Lane, which I have written about in one of my books. It was a beautiful lane through the woods on a neighbour's farm.* Undated photograph. (Courtesy of the L.M. Montgomery Collection, Archival and Special Collections, University of Guelph Library.)

days. The "Shore Road" has a real existence, between Cavendish and Rustico. But the "White Way of Delight," "Wiltonmere," and "Violet Vale" were transplanted from the estates of my castles in Spain. "The Lake of Shining Waters" is generally supposed to be Cavendish Pond. This is not so. The pond I had in mind is the one at Park Corner, below Uncle John Campbell's house. But I suppose that a good many of the effects of light and shadow I had seen on the Cavendish pond figured unconsciously in my descriptions. Anne's habit of naming places was an old one of my own. I named all the pretty nooks and corners about the old farm. I had, I remember, a "Fairyland," a "Dreamland," a "Pussy-Willow Palace," and "No-Man's-Land," a "Queen's Bower," and many others. The "Dryads Bubble" was purely imaginary, but the "Old Log Bridge," was a real thing. It was formed by a single large tree that had blown down and lay across the brook. It had served as a bridge to the generation before my time, and was hollowed out like a shell by the tread of hundreds of passing feet. Earth had blown into the crevices, and ferns and grasses had found root and fringed it luxuriantly. Velvet moss covered its sides and below was a deep, clear, sun-flecked stream.

Anne's *Katie Maurice* was mine.[197] In our sitting-room there had always stood a big book-case used as a china cabinet. In each door was a large oval glass, dimly reflecting the room. When I was very small each of my reflections in these glass doors were "real folk" to my imagination. The one in the left-hand door was *Katie Maurice*, the one in the right, *Lucy Gray*. Why I named them thus I cannot say. Wordsworth's ballad had no connection with the latter, for I had never read it at that time.[198] Indeed, I have no recollection of deliberately naming them at all. As far back as consciousness runs, *Katie Maurice* and *Lucy Gray* lived in the fairy room behind the bookcase. *Katie Maurice* was a little girl like myself, and I loved her dearly. I would stand before that door and prattle to Katie for hours, giving and receiving confidences. In especial, I liked to do this at twilight, when the fire had been lit and the room and its reflections were a glamour of light and shadow.

Lucy Gray was grown-up and a widow! I did not like her as well as *Katie*. She was always sad, and always had dismal stories of her troubles to relate to me; nevertheless, I visited her

FIGURE 24 *When* Anne of Green Gables *was published, I had a very good reason for smiling. And even this smile did not express my feelings.* Undated photograph. (Courtesy of the L.M. Montgomery Collection, Archival and Special Collections, University of Guelph Library.)

scrupulously in turn, lest her feelings should be hurt, because she was jealous of *Katie*, who also disliked her. All this sounds like the veriest nonsense, but I cannot describe how real it was to me. I never passed through the room without a wave of my hand to Katie in the glass door at the other end.[199]

The notable incident of the liniment cake happened when I was teaching school in Bideford and boarding at the Methodist parsonage there. Its charming mistress flavoured a layer cake with anodyne liniment one day. Never shall I forget the taste of that cake and the fun we had over it, for the mistake was not discovered until tea-time. A strange minister was there to tea that night. He ate every crumb of his piece of cake. What he thought of it we never discovered. Possibly he imagined it was simply some new-fangled flavouring.[200]

Many people have told me that they regretted *Matthew's* death in *Green Gables*. I regret it myself. If I had the book to write over again I would spare *Matthew* for several years. But when I wrote it I thought he must die, that there might be a necessity for self-sacrifice on *Anne's* part, so poor *Matthew* joined the long procession of ghosts that haunt my literary past.

Well, my book was finally written.[201] The next thing was to find a publisher. I typewrote it myself, on my old second-hand typewriter that never made the capitals plain and wouldn't print "w" at all, and I sent it to a new American firm that had recently come to the front with several "best sellers."[202] I thought I might stand a better chance with a new firm than with an old established one that had already a preferred list of writers. But the new firm very promptly sent it back. Next I sent it to one of the "old, established firms," and the old established firm sent it back.[203] Then I sent it, in turn, to three "betwixt-and-between" firms, and they all sent it back. Four of them returned it with a cold, printed note of rejection; one of them "damned with faint praise."[204] They wrote that "Our readers report that they find some merit in your story, but not enough to warrant its acceptance."[205]

That finished me. I put *Anne* away in an old hat-box in the clothes room, resolving that some day when I had time I would take her and reduce her to the original seven chapters of her first incarnation. In that case I was tolerably sure of getting thirty-five dollars for her at least, and perhaps even forty.

The manuscript lay in the hatbox until I came across it one winter day while rummaging. I began turning over the leaves, reading a bit here and there. It didn't seem so very bad. "I'll try once more," I thought. The result was that a couple of months later an entry appeared in my journal to the effect that my book had been accepted. After some natural jubilation I wrote: "The book may or may not succeed. I wrote it for love, not money, but very often such books are the most successful, just as everything in the world that is born of true love has life in it, as nothing constructed for mercenary ends can ever have.[206]

"Well, I've written my book! The dream dreamed years ago at that old brown desk in school has come true at last after years of toil and struggle. And the realization is sweet, almost as sweet as the dream."

When I wrote of the book succeeding or not succeeding, I had in mind only a very moderate success indeed, compared to that which it did attain. I never dreamed that it would appeal to young and old. I thought girls in their teens might like to read it, that was the only audience I hoped to reach. But men and women who are grandparents have written to tell me how they loved *Anne*, and boys at college have done the same.[207] The very day on which these words are written has come a letter to me from an English lad of nineteen, totally unknown to me, who writes that he is leaving for "the front" and wants to tell me "before he goes" how much my books and especially *Anne* have meant to him.[208] It is in such letters that a writer finds meet reward for all sacrifice and labor.

Well, *Anne* was accepted; but I had to wait yet another year before the book was published. Then on June 20th, 1908, I wrote in my journal:

"To-day has been, as *Anne* herself would say, 'an epoch in my life.' My book came to-day, 'spleet-new' from the publishers. I candidly confess that it was to me a proud and wonderful and thrilling moment. There, in my hand, lay the material realization of all the dreams and hopes and ambitions and struggles of my whole conscious existence – my first book. Not a great book, but mine, mine, mine, something which I had created."[209]

I have received hundreds of letters from all over the world about *Anne*.[210] Some odd dozen of them were addressed, not to me, but to "Miss Anne Shirley, Green Gables, Avonlea, Prince Edward Island." They were written by little girls who had such a touching faith in the real flesh and blood existence of *Anne* that I always hated to destroy it. Some of my letters were decidedly amusing. One began impressingly, "My dear long-lost uncle," and the writer went on to claim me as *Uncle Lionel*, who seemed to have disappeared years ago. She wound up by entreating me to write to my "affectionate niece" and explain the reason of my long silence. Several people wrote me that their lives would make very interesting stories, and if I would write them and give them half the proceeds they would give me "the facts!" I answered only one of these letters, that of a young man who had enclosed stamps for a reply. In order to let him down as gently as possible, I told him that I was not in any need of material, as I had books already planned out which would require at least ten years to write. He wrote back that he had a great deal of patience and would cheerfully wait until ten years had expired; then he would write again. So, if my own invention gives out, I can always fall back on what that young man assured me was "a thrilling life-history!"

Green Gables has been translated into Swedish and Dutch.[211] My copy of the Swedish edition always gives me the inestimable boon of a laugh. The cover design is a full length figure of Anne, wearing a sunbonnet, carrying the famous carpet-bag, and with hair that is literally of an intense scarlet!

With the publication of *Green Gables* my struggle was over. I have published six novels since then. *Anne of Avonlea* came out in 1909, followed in 1910 by *Kilmeny of the Orchard*. This latter story was really written several years before *Green Gables*, and ran as a serial in an American magazine, under another title.[212] Therefore some sage reviewers amused me not a little by saying that the book showed "the insidious influence of popularity and success" in its style and plot!

The Story Girl was written in 1910 and published in 1911.[213] It was the last book I wrote in my old home by the gable window where I had spent so many happy hours of creation. It is my own favourite among my books, the one that gave me the greatest pleasure to write, the one whose characters and landscape seem to me most real. All the children in the book are purely imaginary. The old "King Orchard" was a compound of our old orchard in Cavendish and the orchard at Park Corner. *Peg Bowen* was suggested by a half-witted, gypsy-like personage who roamed at large for many years over the Island and was the terror of my childhood. We children were always being threatened that if we were not good Peg would catch us. The threat did not make us good, it only made us miserable.

Poor Peg was really very harmless, when she was not teased or annoyed. If she were, she could be vicious and revengeful enough. In winter she lived in a little hut in the woods, but as soon as the spring came the lure of the open road proved too much for her, and she started on a tramp which lasted until the return of winter snows. She was known over most of the Island. She went bareheaded and barefooted, smoked a pipe, and told extraordinary tales of her adventures in various places. Occasionally she would come to church, stalking unconcernedly up the aisle to a prominent seat. She never put on hat or shoes on such occasions, but when she wanted to be especially grand she powdered face, arms and legs with *flour*![214]

As I have already said, the story of *Nancy* and *Betty Sherman* was founded on fact. The story of the captain of the *Fanny* is also literally true. The heroine is still living, or was a few years ago, and still retains much of the beauty which won the Captain's heart.[215] The "*Blue Chest of Rachel Ward*" was another "owertrue tale."[216] *Rachel Ward* was Eliza Montgomery, a cousin of my father's, who died in Toronto a few years ago. The blue chest was in the kitchen of Uncle John Campbell's house at Park Corner from 1849 until her death.[217] We children heard its story many a time and speculated and dreamed over its contents, as we sat on it to study our lessons or eat our bed-time snacks.[218]

In the winter of 1911, Grandmother Macneill died at the age of eighty-seven, and the old home was broken up. I stayed at Park Corner until July; and on July 5th was married. Two days later my husband and I sailed from Montreal on the *Megantic* for a trip through the British Isles, another "dream come true," for I had always wished to visit the old land of my forefathers. A few extracts from the journal of my trip, may be of interest:

FIGURE 25 *The house of Uncle John Campbell at Park Corner, where I was married.* Undated photograph. (Courtesy of the L.M. Montgomery Collection, Archival and Special Collections, University of Guelph Library.)

"GLASGOW, July 20, 1911.[219]

"Thursday afternoon we left for an excursion to Oban, Staffa, and Iona.[220] We went by rail to Oban and the scenery was very beautiful, especially along Loch Awe, with its ruined castle.[221] Beautiful, yes! And yet neither there nor elsewhere in England or Scotland, did I behold a scene more beautiful than can be seen any evening at home, standing on the 'old church hill' and looking afar over New London Harbour.[222] But then – we have no ruined castles there, nor the centuries of romance they stand for!

"Oban is a picturesque little town, a fringe of houses built along the shore of a land-locked harbour, with wooded mountains rising steeply behind them. Next morning we took the boat to Iona. It was a typical, Scottish day, bright and sunny one hour, showery or misty the next. For a few hours I enjoyed the sail very much. The wild, rugged scenery of cape and bay and island and bleak mountain – the whole of course, peppered with ruined, ivy-hung castles – was an ever changing panorama of interest, peopled with the shades of the past.

"Then, too, we had a Cook's party of French tourists on board.[223] They jabbered incessantly. There was one nice old fellow in particular, with a pleasant, bronzed face and twinkling black eyes, who seemed to be the expounder-in-chief of the party. They got into repeated discussions, and when the arguments reached a certain pitch of intensity, he would spring to his feet, confront the party, wave his arms, umbrella, and guide book wildly in the air, and lay down the law in a most authoritative tone and fashion.

"As the forenoon wore away I began to lose interest in everything. Ruined castle, towering mountain, white torrent, ghosts, and French tourists lost their charm. In the morning I had been much worried because I heard that it might be too rough to stop at Staffa, and I wanted so badly to see Fingal's Cave.[224] But now I did not care in the least for Fingal's Cave, or for any other earthly thing. For the first time in my life I was horribly seasick.

"The steamer did stop at Staffa, however, and two boat-loads went ashore. I let them go. What cared I? The waves would not have daunted me, the pouring rain would not have appalled me, but seasickness!

"However, the steamer was now still and I began to feel better. By the time the boats came back for the second load I was quite well and once more it seemed a thing of first importance to see Fingal's Cave. I joyfully scrambled down into the boat and was rowed ashore with the others to the Clamshell cave. From there we had to scramble over what seemed an interminably long distance – but really I suppose it was no more than a quarter of a mile – over the wet, slippery, basalt columns that fringe the shore, hanging in the worst places to a rope strung along the surface of the cliff. Owing to my much scrambling over the rocks of Cavendish shore in early life, I got on very well and even extorted a compliment from the tour guide;[225] but some of the tourists slipped to an alarming degree. Never shall I forget the yelps and sprawls of the old Frenchman aforesaid.

SEEING FINGAL'S CAVE

"Nobody fell off, however, and eventually we found ourselves in Fingal's Cave, and felt repaid for all our exertions.

"'Tis a most wonderful and majestic place, like an immense Gothic cathedral. It is hard to believe that it could have been fashioned merely by a freak of nature. I think every one there felt awed; even those irrepressible French tourists were silent for a little time. As I stood there and listened to the deep, solemn echo of the waves the memory of a verse of Scripture came to me 'He inhabiteth the halls of eternity.'[226] And it seemed to me that I stood in very truth in a temple of the Almighty that had not been builded by hands.

"We went on to Iona and landed there for a brief, hurried, scrambling exploration. Iona is interesting as the scene of St. Columba's ministry.[227] His ancient cathedral is still there. Of greater interest to me was the burial place of the earliest Scottish kings, about sixty of them, it is said, finishing with that Duncan who was murdered by Macbeth.[228] They were buried very simply, those warriors of ancient days. There they lie, in their island cemetery, beneath the gray sky. Neither 'storied urn nor animated bust'[229] mark their resting place. Each grave is covered simply by a slab of worn, carved stone. But they sleep none the less soundly for that, lulled by the eternal murmur of the waves around them.

"I would have liked to have spent several days in Iona, prowling by myself around its haunted ruins and getting acquainted with its quaint inhabitants. There is really little pleasure in a hurried scramble around such places, in the midst of a chattering, exclaiming mob of tourists. For me, at least, solitude is necessary to real enjoyment of such places. I must be alone, or with a few 'kindred souls' before I can dream and muse, and bring back to life the men and women who once dwelt there and made the places famous.[230]

WELCOME LETTERS FROM HOME

"We returned to Glasgow yesterday by water and were glutted with scenery. I was very tired when we reached our hotel. But weariness fell away from me when I found letters from home.[231] How good they tasted in a foreign land! They bridged the gulf of ocean, and I saw the Cavendish hills and the green gloom of the maple wood at Park Corner. Ah! beautiful as the old world is, the homeland is the best."

"July 30, 1911.
ROYAL HOTEL,
Prince St.,
Edinburgh.

"Monday we went out to Ayr with a Cook guide.[232] As a rule we dislike the Cook parties and go alone wherever we can. But this expedition was pleasant, as there were only two besides ourselves and they were Canadians, Mr. and Mrs. T. from Ontario.[233] We had also a very nice guide. Two things subtracted from the pleasure of the day, it poured rain most of the time and I had a grumbling facial neuralgia. But in spite of both drawbacks I enjoyed myself 'where'er we trod 'twas haunted, holy ground.'[234] We saw the room – the low-ceilinged, humble little room where once a cotter's son was 'royal born by right divine,'[235] and we explored the ruins of the old Alloway Kirk made classic forever by Tam O'Shanter's adventures.[236]

POOR, SWEET HIGHLAND MARY!

"Then we went to the Burns monument just because it was on the list of 'sights' and the guide was bound to do his duty by us.[237] I have no interest whatever in monuments. They bore me horribly. But two things in the monument did interest me, a lock of Highland Mary's fair hair and the Bible upon which she and Burns swore their troth in their parting tryst.[238] Poor, sweet Highland Mary! I don't suppose she was anything more than a winsome little country lass, no sweeter or prettier than thousands of other maidens who have lived and died, if not unwept, at least unhonored and unsung.[239] But a great genius flung over her the halo of his love and lo! she is one of the immortals, one of the fair ladies of old romance who will be forever remembered because of the man who loved her. She is of the company of *Laura* and *Beatrice*, and *Stella*, of *Lucasta* and *Julia*, and of the unknown lady of Arvers' sonnet.[240]

"Wednesday we went to the Trosachs.[241] This is one of the expeditions I have looked forward to all my life, ever since I read *The Lady of the Lake* in schooldays. Sitting behind my old desk at school I dreamed out the panorama of hill and lake and pass, where *Ellen* lived and *Fitz-James* wandered and *Roderick Dhu* brooded like a storm cloud over a Highland hill.[242] And I made a covenant with myself that when my ship came in I should go and see it.

"We sailed up Loch Lomond to Inversnaid and there took coaches for a five-mile drive across to Loch Katrine.[243] Of all the ways of locomotion I have ever tried I like coaching best. It beats motoring 'hollow.' We soon reached Stronachlachar,[244] which, in spite of its dreadful name, is an exquisite spot, and took the boat down Loch Katrine to the Trosachs pier.

BETTER THAN THE REAL

"I cannot decide whether Loch Katrine disappointed me or not. I think it did, a little. It was as beautiful as I had dreamed it, but it was not *my* Loch Katrine, not quite the Loch Katrine of my 'Chateau en Espagne.'[245] And I resented the difference, as one might resent a change made in his childhood's home on going back to it after long years.

"The lower portion of the lake is certainly much smaller than my idea of it as given by the poem. And the famous 'Silver Strand' is a poor affair now. Since the instalment of the Glasgow waterworks the lake has risen several feet and covered 'the beach of pebbles white as snow.'[246] I brought a handful of them home with me as souvenirs. But I think I shall keep the Loch Katrine of my dream in my geography of the 'Lady of the Lake.' I like it better than the real one.[247]

"We coached through the Trosachs to the Trosachs hotel. The Trosachs is beautiful and grand, and perhaps before the carriage road was made it was wild enough, especially for some benighted wanderer who had all too good reason to fear Highland plunderers.[248] But it is far from being the wild, riven, precipitous dell of my fancy. No, it is not the Trosachs where I have so often wandered with *Fitz-James*.

"The hotel is in a lovely spot, on the shore of Loch Achray.

"'Where shall we find in foreign land – So lone a lake, so sweet a strand?'[249]

"Yet Loch Achray, too, was on a smaller scale than I had expected. We walked along it that night as far as the 'Brig of Turk,'[250] gathering bell-heather and bluebells as we went. Scottish bluebells are certainly the sweetest things! They seem the very incarnation of old Scotia's romance.

A FOOLISH DISAPPOINTMENT

"Next morning we walked through the Trosachs to Loch Katrine in a pouring rain and hired one of the boatmen to row us to and around 'Ellen's Isle.'[251] I don't think I liked it because it, too, was not the islet of my dream, and I was conscious of a foolish disappointment.

"Benvenue, however, did not disappoint me.[252] It dominates the landscape. Everywhere we went, there was old Benvenue, rugged and massive, with a cloud-wreath resting on his 'summit hoar.'[253] I was very sorry that the night we spent there was wet. I should have loved to have seen a sunset effect on Benvenue."

"August 6, 1911.

"Last Monday morning we went by train to Melrose and coached over six miles of most beautiful road to Abbotsford.[254] Although we went on our own account we could not help falling in with a Cook excursion and this somewhat spoiled the day for us. But the scenery along the road is exquisite and we saw the Eildon Hills, cleft in three by the spells of wizardry.[255] Abbotsford is most interesting, crowded with relics I should have loved to have dreamed over in solitude. But that might not be. The rooms were filled by a chattering crowd, harangued by a glib guide. I wondered if Scott would have liked to think of his home being so over-run by a horde of curious sight-seers.[256]

WHERE SCOTT IS BURIED

"We drove from Abbotsford to Dryburgh where Scott is buried.[257] As we were able to escape from the 'Cookies' here we enjoyed the magnificent ruin doubly. Then we returned to Melrose and explored the ruins of the Abbey there. We could not follow Scott's advice, which I never believe he failed, as is asserted, to take himself, and view it by moonlight.[258] But in that mellow, golden-gray evening light it was beautiful enough, beautiful and sad, with the little bluebells growing in its ruined courts and over its old graves. Michael Scott is reputed to be buried there,[259] and there the heart of Robert Bruce was buried,[260] and, doubtless, rests as quietly as though it had, according to his wish, been laid in the soil of the Holy Land.

"There is some wonderful hand-carving still left in Melrose, and the little hand high up on one of the arches is as suggestive as it is beautiful. What fair lady's hand was chiselled there in lasting stone? One cannot but think it was wrought by a lover.

"On Wednesday we left for Inverness,[261] but stopped off *en route* to visit Kirriemuir, the 'Thrums' of Barrie's stories. In particular, I wanted to see the 'Den' where *Sentimental Tommy* and his cronies held their delightful revels.[262] It is a lovely spot. One thing about it made me feel at home, its paths, which Barrie calls 'pink,'[263] are the very red of our own island roads. I could have fancied that I was prowling in the woods around Lovers' Lane.[264]

LIKE INVERNESS BEST

"Of all the places we have visited in Scotland thus far I like Inverness best. In itself it is only a small gray town but the surrounding scenery is magnificent.

"We drove out to Culloden[265] the evening of our arrival and it is one of the drives that, for sheer pleasure, will always stand out in my memory. The road was exceedingly lovely and we were fortunate enough to have a nice old driver who knew all the history and legend of everything, and was very willing to tell it in delightful broad Scotch.

"The next day we visited Tomnahurich, the famous cemetery of Inverness. It deserves its fame; I am sure it must be the most beautiful cemetery in the world. It is a large hill outside the city, rising in a perfect cone, and thickly covered with trees. The name is a Gaelic word meaning 'the hill of the fairies,' and surely it must once have been a spot meet for a fairy kingdom and the revels of Titania.[266] Seen at eventide, against a sunset sky, it seems a veritable outpost of the Land of Old Romance.

"We returned by way of the Caledonian Canal to Fort William,[267] and thence by train. The sunset effects on the mountains along our way were wonderful. If I were to live near mountains for any length of time I should learn to love them *almost* as much as I love the sea."

"August 13, 1911.

"Last Monday we visited Roslin Chapel,[268] a wonderful

specimen of Gothic work in perfect preservation. This is the chapel of Scott's ballad, 'Fair Rosabelle':

> 'Seemed all on fire that chapel proud
> Where Roslin's chiefs uncoffined lie.'[269]

"Wednesday we left Edinburgh and went to Alloa to visit friends.[270] Thursday we 'did' Dollar Glen.[271] I had never heard of this place until Mr. M.[272] of Alloa told us of it, yet it is one of the wildest, grandest spots we have seen in all Scotland. If Scott had touched it with his genius it would be as widely known as the Trosachs. Indeed, it is much like what I had imagined the Trosachs to be. Dollar Glen is like a deep gash cleft down through the heart of the mountain.

"Stirling and Abbey Craig on Friday, places steeped with romance.[273] Yesterday we came to Berwick to spend a week in the Marmion country.[274] Mr. M. and Miss A. came with us.[275] Berwick is a most quaint, antiquated old town. As we live on the Spittal side,[276] when we want to go anywhere we have to be rowed over the river mouth by one of the half-dozen quaint old ferrymen who have boats for hire. Last night we all went for a walk along the Spittal shore by moonlight. It was beautiful, but so like the Cavendish shore that it made me bitterly homesick."

"Carlisle, August 20.[277]

"We are spending Sunday in Carlisle perforce, since we could not get any farther last night, owing to the big railway strike which has been paralysing Britain this past week. At Berwick we did not suffer from it, nor heed it. We let the outer world go by and lived in realms of romance where ferry boats and shank's mare[278] were the only desired means of locomotion.

"Last Monday we went to Holy Island and explored the ruins of the old Abbey which was the scene of *Constance de Beverley's* death in 'Marmion.'[279] We had an enjoyable sail down to Holy Island but the return home was sadly different. It was quite rough and how that wretched little steamer pitched and rolled! Both our gentlemen became so overcome that they had to retire temporarily from the scene, while Miss A. and I fought off surrender only by a tremendous effort of will and would have suffered less I think if we had just allowed ourselves to go!

"Luckily seasickness is never fatal and next day we were all ready for an excursion to Norham Castle,[280] a very ruinous ruin.

"Growing all over the grounds was a little blue flower which I never saw anywhere else save in the front orchard of the old home in Cavendish. Great-grandmother Woolner had brought it out from England with her. It gave me an odd feeling of pain and pleasure mingled, to find it growing there around that old ruined Scottish castle which seemed to belong so utterly to another time and another order of things. We walked from Norham to Ladykirk and then back by the Tweed.[281] When we grew tired we sat down on its bank and dreamed dreams. What meeter place could there be for dreaming than the twilit banks of Tweed?[282]

"Next day we went to Flodden Field.[283] It disappointed me unreasonably, it was all so peaceful, and harvest-hued, and agricultural. I felt as aggrieved as though I had had any right to expect to see a mediæval battle being fought under my eyes.

"Thursday afternoon we had a delightful little expedition to Homecliffe Glen and its deserted old mill.[284] It might serve as a scene for a ghost story. In the midst of the ravine we came upon a clump of spruce trees literally loaded with gum, the first I had seen since leaving home. Spruce gum and the delights of picking it seem quite unknown in Scotland. We spent a half-hour picking it. To me and my husband the gum tasted delicious, but neither Mr. M. nor Miss A. liked its flavor declaring it was 'bitter.'"

"York, England.[285]
August 27, 1911.

"Last Monday we went to Keswick and stayed there until Thursday. It is impossible to exaggerate the beauty of the Lake District:[286]

'The haughtiest heart its wish might bound
Through life to dwell delighted here.'[287]

"And then it is so interwoven with much of the best in English literature. The very spirit of Wordsworth seems to haunt those enchanted valleys, those wild passes, those fairy-like lakes.

"Monday afternoon we took a coach-drive around Lake

Derwentwater. All was beautiful. An interesting sight was the Castle Rock, which figures as the magic castle of St. John in Scott's 'Bridal of Triermain.'[288] There is only one point where the resemblance to a castle – said to be very striking – can be seen, and we were not fortunate enough to see it from that particular point.

"Tuesday we went to Buttermere Lake; Wednesday we motored for eighty miles around Lake Windermere.[289] Some of the huge rocks on the mountain tops are of very peculiar shape. One of them is named, 'The Lady Playing on the Organ.' It is on the very top of a majestic mountain and certainly does, from one point of view, look exactly like a woman seated at a huge organ. Somehow, it captivated my imagination and I wove a hundred fancies round it. Who was the player, sitting forever at her mighty instrument? And what wonderful melodies did she play on it when the winds of heaven blew about her and the mountain tempest thundered and the great stars stayed to listen?

"That evening we walked out to the 'Druid Circle,' a ring of large stones on a hill-top, supposed to have been in old time a temple of the sun.

"Nothing I have seen thus far made such a vivid impression on me as this. The situation is magnificent. The hill is completely encircled by a ring of the most famous mountains in the Lake District, Helwellyn and Skiddaw among them, and the sense of majesty produced was overwhelming. Certainly those old sun-worshippers knew how to choose their sites. To stand there, at sunset, in that temple of a departed creed, surrounded by that assembly of everlasting hills and picture the rites, perchance dark and bloody, which must once have been celebrated there, was an experience never to be forgotten.

"Friday we came to York, mainly to see the magnificent cathedral. It *is* magnificent, a dream of beauty made lasting in stone.

"Yesterday afternoon I became the proud and happy possessor of a pair of china dogs![290]

"I have been pursuing china dogs all over England and Scotland. When I was a little girl, visiting at Grandfather Montgomery's, I think the thing that most enthralled me was a pair of china dogs which always sat on the sitting-room mantel. They were white with green spots all over them; and Father told me that whenever they heard the clock strike twelve at midnight they bounded down on to the hearth-rug and barked. It was, therefore, the desire of my heart to stay up until twelve some night and witness this performance, and hard indeed did I think the hearts of my elders when this was denied me. Eventually I found out, I forget how, that the dogs did nothing of the sort. I was much disappointed over this but more grieved still over the discovery that Father had told me something that wasn't true. However, he restored my faith in him by pointing out that he had only said the dogs would jump down when they *heard* the clock strike. China dogs, of course, could not hear.

"I have always hankered to possess a pair of similar dogs, and, as those had been purchased in London, I hoped when I came over here, I would find something like them. Accordingly I have haunted the antique shops in every place I have been but, until yesterday, without success. Dogs, to be sure, there were in plenty but not the dogs of my quest. There was an abundance of dogs with black spots and dogs with red spots; but nowhere the aristocratic dogs with green spots.

"Yesterday in a little antique shop near the great Minster I found a pair of lovely dogs and snapped them up on the spot.[291] To be sure they had no green spots. The race of dogs with green spots seems to have become extinct. But my pair have lovely gold spots and are much larger than the old Park Corner dogs. They are over a hundred years old and I hope they will preside over my Lares and Penates with due dignity and aplomb."[292]

"Russell Hotel,[293] London.
September 18, 1911.

"So much has been crammed into this past fortnight that I have a rather overfed feeling mentally. But when time is limited and sights unlimited what are harassed travellers to do? The British Museum, the Tower, Westminster Abbey, Crystal Palace, Kenilworth Castle, the Shakespeare Land, Hampton Court, Salisbury and Stonehenge, Windsor and Parks and Gardens galore![294]

"Our hotel is in Russell Square, the haunt of so many of the characters in *Vanity Fair*. One expects to see *Amelia* peering out of a window looking for *George*, or perhaps *Becky* watching for *Jos*.[295]

"Our afternoon at Kenilworth Castle was a delight. Of course, we had to be pestered with a guide; but I succeeded in forgetting him, and roamed the byways of romance alone. I saw Kenilworth in its pride, when aspiring Leicester entertained haughty Elizabeth.[296] I pictured poor *Amy Robsart* creeping humbly into the halls where she should have reigned as Mistress.[297] Back they thronged from the past, those gay figures of olden days, living, loving, hating, plotting as of yore.

"Last Thursday we went to see the Temple Church, in the grounds of which Oliver Goldsmith is buried.[298] The church is a quaint old place, set in a leafy square which, despite the fact that Fleet Street is roaring just outside it,[299] is as peaceful and silent as a Cavendish road. But when I recall that square it is not of the quaint old church and *Poor Noll's* grave that I shall think.[300] No, it will be of a most charming and gentlemanly pussy cat, of exquisite manners, who came out of one of the houses and walked across the square to meet us. He was large and handsome and dignified, and any one could see with half an eye that he belonged to the caste of *Vere de Vere*.[301] He purred most mellifluously as I patted him, and rubbed himself against my boots as though we were old acquaintances, as perchance we were in some other incarnation. Nine out of ten cats would have insisted on accompanying us over to *Oliver's* grave, and perhaps been too hard to get rid of. Not so this Marquis of Carabas.[302] He sat gravely down and waited until we had gone on, seen the grave and returned to where he sat. Then he stood up, received our farewell pats, waved his tail amiably, and walked gravely back to the door from which he had emerged, having done the honor of his demesne in most irreproachable fashion. Truly he did give the world assurance of a cat!

"We sail for home next Thursday on the *Adriatic*.[303] I am glad, for I am replete with sight-seeing. I want now to get back to Canada and gather my scattered household gods around me for a new consecration."[304]

As my husband was pastor of an Ontario congregation,[305] I had

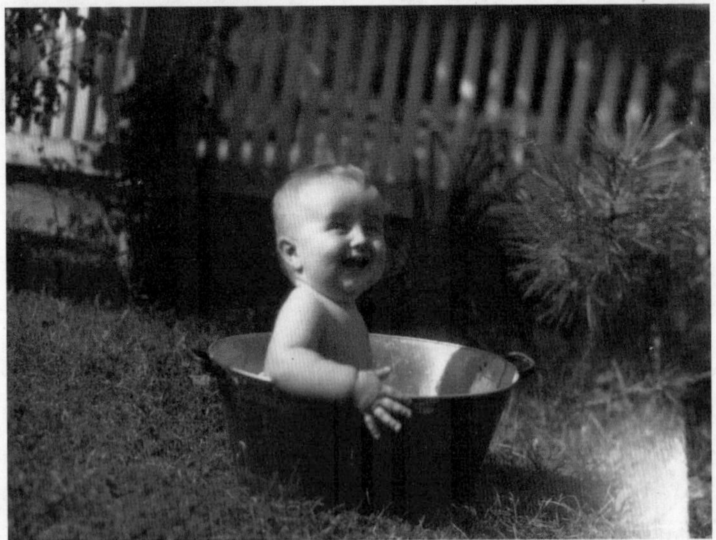

FIGURES 26–27 *Chester* (top); *Stuart* (bottom). Undated photographs, ca. 1916. (Courtesy of the L.M. Montgomery Collection, Archival and Special Collections, University of Guelph Library.)

now to leave Prince Edward Island and move to Ontario. Since my marriage I have published four books, *Chronicles of Avonlea*, *The Golden Road*, *Anne of the Island*, and *The Watchman*, the latter being a volume of collected verse.

The "Alpine Path" has been climbed, after many years of toil and endeavor. It was not an easy ascent, but even in the struggle at its hardest there was a delight and a zest known only to those who aspire to the heights.

> "He ne'er is crowned
> With immortality, who fears to follow
> Where airy voices lead."[306]

True, most true! We must follow our "airy voices," follow them through bitter suffering and discouragement and darkness, through doubt and disbelief, through valleys of humiliation and over delectable hills where sweet things would lure us from our quest, ever and always must we follow, if we would reach the "far-off divine event" and look out thence to the aerial spires of our City of Fulfilment.[307]

(1917)

Afterword

We did not like to declare ourselves women, because – without at that time suspecting that our mode of writing and thinking was not what is called "feminine" – we had a vague impression that authoresses are liable to be looked on with prejudice ...

– CHARLOTTE BRONTË, WRITING AS "CURRER BELL" IN 1850[1]

Oh, I wonder if I shall ever be able to do anything worth while in the way of writing. It is my dearest ambition.

– L.M. MONTGOMERY, JOURNAL ENTRY DATED 28 SEPTEMBER 1893[2]

IN AN ARTICLE PUBLISHED IN *BOOKSELLER AND STATIONER* (Toronto) in 1916, L.M. Montgomery participated on a panel of six well-known Canadian authors – three male, three female – to answer the question "What Are the Greatest Books in the English Language?"[3] Her selection of six texts that she claimed she would attempt "to save from complete extinction" if compelled to do so – Charles Dickens's *David Copperfield* (1850) and *The Pickwick Papers* (1837), George Eliot's *The Mill on the Floss* (1860), William Makepeace Thackeray's *Vanity Fair* (1847–1848), Charlotte Brontë's *Jane Eyre* (1847), and Sir Walter Scott's *Rob Roy* (1817) – is fairly consistent with the favourite prose authors she had named in a journal entry dated two years before this publication, a list that included "Scott, Dickens, Thackeray, Collins, Trollope and fifty others."[4] The unidentified compiler of the article drew attention to the fact that none of the six Canadian authors included in the piece had listed a Canadian book in his or her response; what escaped notice was that Montgomery was the only one of the six to select a text written by a woman – and, in fact, she listed two of them.

Montgomery's choices are noteworthy not only because no women are included on the list of favourite authors in her 1914 journal entry (except for those implied in the phrase "and fifty others") but also because the two female authors mentioned on the list meant for public consumption – George Eliot and Charlotte Brontë – are examples of a specific form of female authorship in nineteenth-century Britain.[5] In *The Madwoman in the Attic: The Woman Writer and the Nineteenth-Century Literary Imagination* (1979), Sandra M. Gilbert and Susan Gubar link British author George Eliot, pseudonym of Mary Ann Evans (1819–1880), to French author George Sand, pseudonym of Amandine Lucile-Aurore Dupin (1804–1876), claiming that these authors "most famously used a kind of male-impersonation to gain male acceptance of their intellectual seriousness" and were among a group of women authors who "protested not that they were 'as good as' men but that, as writers, they *were* men." The works of Eliot and Sand continue to be published under the male pseudonyms they chose for their careers; by contrast, the publishers of posthumous editions of the work of Charlotte (1816–1855), Emily (1818–1848), and Anne (1820–1849) Brontë have ignored the androgynous pseudonyms and identities these authors had cultivated during their lifetimes, opting instead for their legal names and unambiguous gender identities as women. This reversal effectively undoes what Gilbert and Gubar see as the Brontë sisters' strategy to "conceal[] their troublesome femaleness behind the masks of Currer, Ellis, and Acton Bell, names which Charlotte Brontë disingenuously insisted they had chosen for their androgynous neutrality but which most of their earliest readers assumed were male." Moreover, what they call "the cloak of maleness" allowed these women authors an opportunity to "move vigorously away from the 'lesser subjects' and 'lesser lives' which had constrained [their] foremothers."[6] The authorship of Charlotte Brontë's breakout first novel was cloaked even further in the designation of Currer Bell not as author but as editor of a book published initially as *Jane Eyre: An Autobiography*.

But while Montgomery declined to include Brontë and Eliot in her private account of favourite authors, the influence of Brontë in particular is unmistakable, to the point that, in a chapter on Montgomery and "the conflictedness of a woman writer," Carole Gerson declares that "at one level, Montgomery is always rewriting *Jane Eyre*."[7] I would extend that line of thinking by speculating that Montgomery perhaps named her major protagonists Anne and Emily after two of the Brontë sisters and refrained from creating a heroine named Charlotte in order to make such a connection less definitive (although characters named Charlotte or Charlotta appear in *Anne of Avonlea*, *Further Chronicles of Avonlea*, and two stories in *Akin to Anne: Tales of Other Orphans*). The fact that her novel *Emily of New Moon* has so many echoes of *Jane Eyre* adds weight to this speculation, as does the title of *Shirley* (1849), Charlotte Brontë's second novel, and the fact that Emily Brontë's middle name, Jane, would be gifted to the protagonist of *Jane of Lantern Hill*, whereas Patricia "Pat" Gardiner, protagonist of *Pat of Silver Bush* and *Mistress Pat*, calls to mind the father of the Brontë sisters, Patrick (1777–1861), and their brother, Patrick Branwell (1817–1848), as do two sensitive boy characters in *The Blythes Are Quoted*. Given the extent to which Montgomery peppered her fiction and her non-fiction with literary allusions – a practice that extends to the texts in this volume, as my notes attest – such a theory is far more plausible than the one that would see Montgomery naming these characters after her late mother's three sisters, Annie Macneill Campbell, Jane Macneill McKenzie, and Emily Macneill Montgomery. In a journal entry dated 1925, writing against the claim that Charlotte Brontë had "creative genius," Montgomery retorted that "her genius was one of amazing ability to describe and interpret the people and surroundings she *knew*. All the people in her books who impress us with such a wonderful sense of reality were drawn from life."[8] By the 1920s, readers were making the same assumptions about Montgomery's work, even though she always denied that her characters were based on real people.[9]

Montgomery's inclusion of Eliot and Brontë on her public 1916 list and her exclusion of them and of any other woman author from her private 1914 list provide a starting point for my discussion of Montgomery's "arrival" as an author, not only of twenty-four books published between 1908 and 1939 but also of eleven hundred periodical pieces published across an even broader span of time, from 1890 to 1942. Although critics have frequently discussed Montgomery's books as part of a North American context within the pre–First World War and interwar periods (when they consider historical context at all),[10] it seems plausible that she looked to Eliot and the Brontës as models of female authorship when she was starting her writing career in the last decade of the nineteenth century. Indeed, as I mentioned in the headnote to Montgomery's essay on Shakespeare's Portia earlier in this volume, an unsigned editorial in the *Island Guardian and Christian Chronicle* of Charlottetown declared that her essay "might have come from George Eliott [*sic*] in her 'teens."[11] Moreover, in a journal entry dated 1915 in which she told of hearing of a young fan whose daily reading included a chapter from *Anne of Green Gables* and a chapter from the Bible, she admitted that "in my salad days I may have dreamed of rivalling Brontë and Eliot. I certainly never in my wildest flights dreamed of competing with the Bible!!!"[12] Montgomery did more than attempt to "rival" these nineteenth-century British novelists, however; although she lived in the isolated community of Cavendish, "eleven miles from a railroad and twenty-five from a town,"[13] she had ample access to the literary cultures of North American metropolises thanks to her unfettered access, as the town postmistress, to literary magazines from all over the continent.[14]

Moreover, Montgomery's experiences as an author – "My ambitions were laughed at or sneered at. The sneerers are very quiet now. The *dollars* have silenced them" – were typical for women of her era, not only in Canada but internationally.[15] As Alexis Easley notes in her contribution to *The Cambridge Companion to Victorian Women's Writing* (2015), "Women who chose the literary life often faced social censure, received substandard pay, and fell subject to a critical double standard." While periodicals were crucial to the development of the careers of many women writers, providing venues that "were often more accessible than the conventional book trade," many women opted to publish their work anonymously or through the use of one or multiple pseudonyms, including Elizabeth Barrett Browning (1806–1861) and Christina Rossetti (1830–1894) early in their careers and Jane Austen (1775–1817) until her death. Publishing their work in this way, according to Easley, "enabled many women to begin writing careers without having to assume 'feminine' identities" and "to situate their work outside a narrowly defined feminine literary tradition."[16]

Several reference books on pseudonyms reveal some of the motivations behind the adoption of a name for a career, although, perhaps because the compilers of these volumes are men, the specific factors at play in women's careers are rarely considered in detail. In *Handbook of Pseudonyms and Personal Nicknames* (1972), which cross-references "L.M. Montgomery" to the author's "real" name, "Macdonald, Lucy Maude [*sic*] Montgomery," Harold S. Sharp suggests that some authors and actors choose to adopt a pseudonym because "a given name may be unwieldy" or because "an author may wish to conceal his [or her] identity."[17] In *Pseudonyms* (1977), Joseph F. Clarke adds to this list by taking into account a wider set of possible circumstances: "a need to conceal one's identity because of persecution or discrimination," or else "to differentiate between the kinds of books they write, to preserve their anonymity or to keep separate their vocation and avocation." And, in the case of women writing under men's names, a pseudonym may have been a strategy resorted to "before the freedom and tolerance of the twentieth century."[18] In *Dictionary of Literary Pseudonyms* (1982), Frank Atkinson posits that name changes can also occur when there is a perceived need for the authorial name to match the genre to which the text belongs, listing romances and westerns as examples, "on the grounds that any product sells better under a familiar label."[19] Far earlier than these volumes, in *Pseudonyms of Authors* (1882), John Edward Haynes provided even more compelling reasons to adopt a fictitious name:

> a genuine modesty with those who decline to place their true name before the public until their work has passed through the terrible crucible of the merciless critic, so that if it should not succeed and be generally condemned, the real author would be known to only a few friends; fears of personal injury if their name is disclosed, where direct attacks are made upon motive or character; many times the real name would serve to limit the sale of a work, notably, where the private character of the writer has been tainted, or when

> totally unknown to the public, the idea is often entertained, that a work published anonymously, or over a pseudonym, will have a larger sale on account of the universal desire to ascertain the author's real name, and that the investigation will bring out a large amount of gratuitous advertising.

Furthermore, Haynes added, "Literary titles are frequently changed when ill success attends previous efforts, or when an entire change is made in the character of the works."[20] In other words, authors resort to pseudonyms to protect their privacy and to make their work conform to convention – including, at an extreme, the prejudice that women cannot write or should not write at all.

Montgomery settled ultimately on "L.M. Montgomery," a name she also used in her private life,[21] for the vast majority of her publications. This gender-neutral authorial identity would allow her to maximize her audience – and, by extension, her sales – for it meant she could persuasively write stories aimed at boys as well as poems with male speakers in a way that "Lucy Maud Montgomery" could not. That decision places her within a long tradition of English-speaking women writers who sought to avoid gender inequality within male-dominated publishing industries by changing or eliminating parts of their names in order to appear more gender neutral (and hence be perceived as male). One common approach was for writers to use their initials, a strategy that persists in this age of social media;[22] another was to follow the Brontë sisters and choose androgynous or conspicuously male authorial names and identities.[23] Nearly a century after Montgomery fought with her first publisher over what version of her name would appear on the cover of *Anne of Green Gables* (he wanted "Lucy Maud Montgomery," which she says she "loathe[d]"),[24] Joanne Rowling agreed to her publisher's request that they issue *Harry Potter and the Philosopher's Stone* under the name "J.K. Rowling" due to the assumption that boy readers would be turned off the book if they knew it had been written by a woman.[25] More recently, YA author A.J. Walkley explained in a 2012 *Huffington Post* article why she had opted for double-initials even in the Web 2.0 era despite the fact that a quick Google search would immediately solve the mystery of her gender: "Women writers have used initials and male pen names for centuries to cover up their gender while publishing their writing, knowing that for some readers (namely male), simply seeing a female's name on the cover of a book would dissuade them from even cracking the spine … I still believe I may have more male readers with the use of 'A.J.' instead of 'Alison' under my titles and bylines – and this is troublesome."[26] But in an entry on pseudonyms in *The Oxford Companion to Women's Writing in the United States* (1995), Susan Coultrap-McQuin reminds us that anonymity and pseudonymity allowed eighteenth- and nineteenth-century women writers the option of maintaining respectability and that "they have also been used as assertive strategies in women's literary careers," namely "to name oneself outside of patriarchal, racist, and heterosexist limits."[27] In other words, a practice that began as a strategy for women authors to negotiate sexist attitudes within the public sphere is now "troublesome," to use Walkley's term, in the twenty-first century.

Given the ongoing tradition of women authors masking their names or their genders in order to avoid what Charlotte Brontë referred to in one of the epigraphs to this afterword as "prejudice," and given that the convention of publishing work "anonymously or under pseudonyms or initials" extended to Canada's early newspapers, as Gerson notes in her book *Canadian Women in Print 1750–1918* (2010),[28] it might seem reasonable to expect Montgomery to emulate this pattern, especially given that she published in newspapers and magazines for nearly two decades prior to the publication of *Anne of Green Gables*. Yet she did the exact opposite of this. Many of her earliest publications appeared under her full legal name, "Lucy Maud Montgomery," including her poem "On Cape Le Force," which is significant for several reasons: first, "Lucy Maud Montgomery" was a name combination that by her own account she had never liked and that no one had ever called her;[29] second, for this initial publication, which appeared in the Charlottetown *Daily Patriot* while the adolescent Montgomery was living with her father in Saskatchewan, she drew heavily on the oral repertoire of her difficult maternal grandfather, to the point that biographer Mary Henley Rubio refers to this publication as an act of poaching, something that everyone in her Cavendish community would have gleaned upon reading the poem because her grandfather's stories were so well known;[30] and third, far from being relegated to a corner or to

TABLE 1 Work published as "Lucy Maud Montgomery," 1890–1899

TITLE/TYPE	PERIODICAL/LOCATION/DATE
"On Cape Le Force" (poem)	*Daily Patriot* (Charlottetown), 26 November 1890
"The Wreck of the 'Marco Polo'" (essay)*	*Montreal Daily Witness*, 5 March 1891
"June!" (poem)	*Daily Patriot* (Charlottetown), 12 June 1891
"A Western Eden" (essay)*	*Prince Albert Times and Saskatchewan Review*, 17 June 1891
"Farewell" (poem)	*Saskatchewan* (Prince Albert), 2 September 1891
"The Wreck of the 'Marcopolo,' 1883" (poem)	*Daily Patriot* (Charlottetown), 29 August 1892
"The Last Prayer" (poem)	*The College Record* (Charlottetown), 1894 (exact date unknown)
"Portia" (essay)*	*Daily Patriot* (Charlottetown), 11 June 1894
"The Violet's Spell" (poem)	*The Ladies' World* (New York), July 1894
"Blueberry Hill" (poem)	*The Ladies' World* (New York), August 1899

* Appearing in this volume.

the women's page, the entire poem appeared prominently on the front page of the newspaper for that day.

Montgomery continued to use her legal name on several of her subsequent publications through 1899 (see table 1),[31] including her poem "The Violet's Spell," published in *The Ladies' World* (New York) – a venue so prominent that in several retrospective accounts of her early career she referred to this poem as the first she ever published[32] – and whose acceptance prompted her earliest declaration of her ambition to be a writer, shown as the second epigraph to this afterword. By 1894, however, she had already started publishing work using her initials, including several items appearing in this volume (see table 2): an early essay describing her cross-Canada journey home to Prince Edward Island from Saskatchewan and three pieces published in the student periodical of Prince of Wales College, *The College Record*. While this transition from "Lucy Maud Montgomery" to "L.M. Montgomery" would suggest that she had settled on her preferred

TABLE 2 Early work published as "L.M. Montgomery," 1891–1897

TITLE/TYPE	PERIODICAL/LOCATION/DATE
"From Prince Albert to P.E. Island" (essay)*	*Daily Patriot* (Charlottetown), 31 October 1891
"The Usual Way" (playlet)*	*The College Record* (Charlottetown), March 1894
"Extracts from the Diary of a Second Class Mouse" (sketch)*	*The College Record* (Charlottetown), April 1894
"High School Life in Saskatchewan" (essay)*	*The College Record* (Charlottetown), May 1894
"Our Practical Joke" (story)	*Golden Days for Boys and Girls* (Philadelphia), 8 August 1896
"I Wonder" (poem)	*The Ladies' Journal* (Toronto), September 1896
"The Missing Pony" (story)	*Golden Days for Boys and Girls* (Philadelphia), 17 October 1896
"Home from Town" (poem)	*American Agriculturist* (Springfield, MA), 28 November 1896
"The New Moon" (poem)	*The Ladies' Journal* (Toronto), January 1897
"Riding to Church" (poem)	*American Agriculturist* (Springfield, MA), 20 February 1897
"The Prize in Elocution" (story)†	*Times* (Philadelphia), 7 March 1897
"The Gable Window" (poem)	*The Ladies' Journal* (Toronto), April 1897
"Love and Lacework" (poem)	*The Ladies' Journal* (Toronto), May 1897
"Apple-Blossoms" (poem)	*The Ladies' World* (New York), May 1897
"The Extra French Examination" (story)	*Times* (Philadelphia), 16 May 1897
"Detected by the Camera" (story)	*Times* (Philadelphia), 27 June 1897
"In Haying Time" (poem)	*The Ladies' Journal* (Toronto), July 1897
"A Case of Trespass" (story)	*Golden Days for Boys and Girls* (Philadelphia), 24 July 1897
"The Marked Door" (poem)	*The Ladies' Journal* (Toronto), August 1897
"The Violet Challie Dress" (story)	*Times* (Philadelphia), 15 August 1897

"At the Dance" (poem)	*The Ladies' Journal* (Toronto), September 1897
"The Gold-Link Bracelet" (story)	*Times* (Philadelphia), 26 September 1897
"When I Go Home" (poem)	*The Congregationalist* (Boston), 11 November 1897
"If Love Should Come" (poem)	*Munsey's Magazine* (New York), December 1897
"Wanted – A Little Girl" (poem)	*Portland (ME) Transcript*, 15 December 1897

* Appearing in this volume.

† Attributed erroneously to "L.W. Montgomery."

authorial identity once the novelty of being published had ebbed, such an assumption tells only part of the story. Beginning in 1895, as she started to establish herself as a contributor to popular magazines and newspapers in Canada and the United States, she published under a wide variety of signatures (see table 3).[33] In 1896, for instance, she published work as "Maud Cavendish," "Belinda Bluegrass," "Enid," and "M.L. Cavendish," as well as "L.M. Montgomery" and a variety of initialisms, some of them used likely to conceal her identity in the case of essays about her teaching experience. Given that she had been publishing poems only since 1890 and short stories only since 1895, her reliance that year on so many signatures dovetails with what Gerson refers to as "a common practice of authors or editors who felt it strategic to dilute their presence."[34] Arguably, however, such a strategy would go against the understandable attempt of an emerging author to build a literary reputation under a consistent byline: in *The Ladies' Journal*, for instance, Montgomery published as "Maud Eglinton" in February 1895, twice as "Maud Cavendish" only a few months later, and eight more times as "L.M. Montgomery" in 1896 and 1897, whereas in *Golden Days for Boys and Girls*, she published three short stories and a poem as "L.M. Montgomery," "Maud Cavendish," and "M.L. Cavendish" within a span of five months.

In this list of names used during her first dozen years as a professional writer, there is a mix of gender-neutral names involving

TABLE 3 L.M. Montgomery's pseudonyms, 1895–1906

NAME	TITLE/TYPE	PERIODICAL/LOCATION/DATE
Maud Eglinton†	"On the Gulf Shore" (poem)	*The Ladies' Journal* (Toronto), February 1895
Maud Cavendish	"When the Apple-Blossoms Blow" (poem)	*The Ladies' Journal* (Toronto), June 1895
	"A Baking of Gingersnaps" (story)	*The Ladies' Journal* (Toronto), July 1895
	"Our Charivari" (story)	*Arthur's Home Magazine* (Philadelphia), April 1897; *Philadelphia Inquirer*, 21 January 1923
Maud Cavindish	"A Strayed Allegiance" (story)	*Arthur's Home Magazine* (Philadelphia), July 1897
	"Buttercups" (poem)	*The Mayflower* (Floral Park, NY), July 1899
Belinda Bluegrass	"Which Has the Most Patience under the Ordinary Cares and Trials of Life – Man or Woman?" (poem)*	*Evening Mail* (Halifax), February 1896 (exact date unknown)
Enid	"Which Has the Most Patience under the Ordinary Cares and Trials of Life – Man or Woman?" (sketch)*	*Evening Mail* (Halifax), February 1896 (exact date unknown)
L.	"James Henry, Truant" (essay)*	*The Prince of Wales College Observer* (Charlottetown), April 1896
L.M.	"The Land of Some Day" (poem)	*The Prince of Wales College Observer* (Charlottetown), April 1896
L.M.M.	"Crooked Answers" (essay)*	*The Prince of Wales College Observer* (Charlottetown), March 1896
	"The Bad Boy of Blanktown School" (essay)*	*The Dalhousie Gazette* (Halifax), 4 March 1896
	"I've Something to Tell You, Sweet" (poem)	*The New York Family Story Paper*, 30 July 1898

	"Forever" (poem)	*The New York Family Story Paper*, 12 November 1898
	"Good-By" (poem)	*The New York Family Story Paper*, 10 December 1898
Lucy M. Montgomery	"A Girl's Place at Dalhousie College" (essay)*	*Halifax Herald*, 29 April 1896
	"Rain in the Woods" (poem)	*Sports Afield* (Chicago), August 1899
M.L. Cavendish	"In Spite of Myself" (story)	*Sunday Inter Ocean* (Chicago), 5 July 1896
	"Fisher Lassies" (poem)	*The Youth's Companion* (Boston), 30 July 1896
	"The Apple-Picking Time" (poem)	*Golden Days for Boys and Girls* (Philadelphia), 3 October 1896
M.M.	"When She Was Here" (poem)	*The New York Family Story Paper*, 7 October 1899
	"A Half-Hour in an Old Cemetery" (essay)*	*Halifax Daily Echo*, 26 September 1901; *Morning Chronicle* (Halifax), 27 September 1901
Cynthia	"Around the Table" [35 instalments] (newspaper column)*	*Halifax Daily Echo*, 28 September 1901–26 May 1902; 22 instalments also in *Morning Chronicle* (Halifax), 21 October 1901–27 May 1902
	"Many Admiring Glances Bestowed upon Graduates" (essay)*	*Halifax Daily Echo*, 30 April 1902
Joyce Cavendish	Various titles (poems)	See Table 4
Ella Montgomery	"Last Night in Dreams" (poem)	*American Agriculturist* (Springfield, MA), 10 November 1906

* Appearing in this volume.

† The name appears as "Eglington" in the publication, but in her scrapbook copy Montgomery crosses out the extraneous "g," indicating that her intended name was "Eglinton."

initials and gender-specific names such as "Belinda Bluegrass" and "Enid" (used to sign two entries, included in this volume, to an 1896 contest by the *Evening Mail* of Halifax on "Which Has the Most Patience under the Ordinary Cares and Trials of Life – Man or Woman?") and "Cynthia" (which she selected for both the byline and the main character in her newspaper column, "Around the Table," published in the *Halifax Daily Echo* in 1901–1902). Although she mentioned many of these early publications in her journals and in retrospective accounts of her career, she did not record her rationale either for using a pen name or for selecting particular pen names for particular contributions to the periodical market. It is therefore unclear whether Montgomery's choices of pen names were solely her own or whether they were the suggestions or requirements of editors who feared she was publishing too much or for too many markets simultaneously. It does not appear, for instance, that Montgomery decided to use separate authorial identities for her work for children and her work for adults or for work she deemed to be of a different calibre. Indeed, by the time she had settled on "L.M. Montgomery" as her consistent pen name in the early years of the twentieth century, her output had risen: she published an annual average of thirteen poems and eleven stories between 1897 and 1900, an annual average of thirty-one poems and thirty stories between 1901 and 1904, and an annual average of twenty-seven poems and thirty-seven stories between 1905 and 1908.[35]

Yet there is a curious exception to this early twentieth-century development in Montgomery's career: between March 1901 and March 1906, she published eighteen poems under the signature "Joyce Cavendish" in a single magazine, *The New York Family Story Paper* (see table 4). She also published in this periodical eight poems as "L.M. Montgomery," three as "L.M.M.," and one as "M.M.," so it seems surprising that she would start publishing in this periodical under a new name, one that she does not appear to have used anywhere else – especially since the last two poems published under the byline "L.M. Montgomery" were within the span of time during which she published as "Joyce Cavendish." These poems do not depart markedly from those she published under her own name, either in content or in form, so it does not appear as though she needed Joyce

TABLE 4 Poems in *The New York Family Story Paper*, 1898–1906

NAME	TITLE	DATE
L.M. Montgomery	"Dressing for the Ball"	26 February 1898
	"The Perfume of Roses"	7 May 1898
	"The Light in Mother's Eyes"	31 December 1898
	"Sweet Summer Days"	27 May 1899
	"Assurance"	10 March 1900
	"Night Watches"	28 July 1900
	"I Have Buried My Dead"	12 October 1901
	"The Love Potion"	20 January 1906
L.M.M.	"I've Something to Tell You, Sweet"	30 July 1898
	"Forever"	12 November 1898
	"Good-By"	10 December 1898
M.M.	"When She Was Here"	7 October 1899
Joyce Cavendish	"Your Influence"	2 March 1901
	"Come Where Violets Blow"	24 August 1901
	"A Smile"	26 October 1901
	"The Star thro' the Pines"	4 January 1902
	"Shall I Remember?"	1 November 1902
	"Farewell and Welcome"	14 February 1903
	"The Gray Silk Gown"	23 May 1903
	"The Charm"	19 September 1903
	"The Choice"	9 January 1904
	"Jealousy"	5 March 1904
	"On the Bridge"	11 June 1904
	"When the Frogs Are Singing"	2 July 1904
	"Air Castles"	24 September 1904
	"The Name Tree"	11 March 1905
	"The Water Nymph"	15 April 1905
	"I Wonder If She Knows"	10 June 1905
	"The Silent House"	19 August 1905
	"To Phyllis"	31 March 1906

Cavendish to express what she could not as L.M. Montgomery. It is also unclear why she continued to use this pseudonym several years after she had solidified her authorial identity as L.M. Montgomery.[36]

Although "Joyce Cavendish" is the last pseudonym listed in *Lucy Maud Montgomery: A Preliminary Bibliography* (1986), more recent findings add an unexpected epilogue to this aspect of Montgomery's career. In a contribution to *Storm and Dissonance: L.M. Montgomery and Conflict* (2008), Gerson revealed the contents of a letter she had found in the Archives of Ontario in which Montgomery mentioned that she had submitted her poem "At the Long Sault" to a poetry contest sponsored by the Toronto *Globe* in 1908 – under the pseudonym "J.C. Neville." Gerson added that she had also come across "Two Sides of a Life Story," an undated and unidentified short story attributed to J.C. Neville, in a scrapbook of Montgomery's otherwise not dedicated to her career, with no indication that Montgomery had claimed this piece as hers; while the shape of the clippings suggests publication in a newspaper rather than a magazine, there is no indication of the venue or the publication date.[37] When I read this story in one of Montgomery's scrapbooks housed at the University of Guelph archives, I was struck first of all by the blending of fiction and non-fiction – although it is clearly fiction, it uses the non-fiction forms of a woman's diary and a man's letter to tell the story – and second by the fact that the writing style strongly suggested that Montgomery had written it, notwithstanding the detail that the surname of the man Mrs. Fitzelroy wishes she had married is Cavendish. But how could I prove Montgomery had written it or that she had published work as "J.C. Neville"? For all I knew, Montgomery found this clipping somewhere, marvelled at the coincidence of its signature being the name she'd used once several years earlier for a poetry contest, and pasted it into her scrapbook. Even if I found other pieces attributed to "J.C. Neville," how could I prove that they were really by L.M. Montgomery?

In October 2016, once the manuscript for this volume was well under way, I searched for "J.C. Neville" in a digital database subscribed to by the University of Toronto's Robarts Library, and there, after sifting carefully through several unrelated results, I came across a poem attributed to J.C. Neville, entitled "Night in the Pastures," published in the 26 August 1908 issue of the Boston magazine *Zion's Herald*. Because I also had a working manuscript of Montgomery's five hundred poems by that point, I quickly identified this poem as one published ten years earlier, in *New England Farmer* (Boston) – by L.M. Montgomery. Further hits revealed that this poem had then been reprinted, again attributed to J.C. Neville, in the *Boston Daily Globe* in October 1908 and in the *Nebraska State Journal* and the *Postville Review* of Iowa in December 1908. Some of Montgomery's earliest pieces published under pseudonyms she had republished under her own name after the success of *Anne of Green Gables* (see table 5); this is the only known instance in which she did the reverse.

I cannot fathom why Montgomery republished this poem as J.C. Neville, especially in a periodical to which she was already a regular contributor under her own name, or, given that the poem appeared barely two months after the publication of *Anne of Green Gables*, why she apparently was not keen in this instance to use the sales success of her first book as a way to draw increased attention to her poetry. And unlike "Two Sides of a Life Story," about a woman who is secretly miserable in her marriage and who regrets bitterly having forsaken the man she loved – a story from which understandably Montgomery would have wanted to distance herself not only as a celebrity author but also as the wife of a minister – "Night in the Pastures" does not contain any material that would seem to be too scandalous to come from the pen of L.M. Montgomery. But at least I could prove that Montgomery published work as J.C. Neville, which strengthens the connection between this short story and Montgomery as its author, and for that reason I include it in this volume. And in the meantime, the search for further J.C. Neville texts continues.

The publication of *Anne of Green Gables* in 1908 catapulted Montgomery from prolific freelance author of short stories and poems to bestselling novelist, but along with the rewards came some drawbacks. Commenting in a journal entry dated 1921 on the sale of a short story for which she had received almost ten times what she would have "in other years," she noted that

TABLE 5 Work published under multiple signatures

TITLE/TYPE	SIGNATURE	PERIODICAL/LOCATION/DATE
"When the Apple-Blossoms Blow" (poem)	Maud Cavendish	*The Ladies' Journal* (Toronto), June 1895
	L.M. Montgomery	*The American Messenger* (New York), May 1910
"A Baking of Gingersnaps" (story)	Maud Cavendish	*The Ladies' Journal* (Toronto), July 1895
	Maud Cavendish	*The American Farmer* (Baltimore), September 1895
	L.M. Montgomery	*Western Christian Advocate* (Cincinnati), 5 October 1910
"The Goose Feud" (story)	Maud Cavendish	*Arthur's Home Magazine* (Philadelphia), April 1897
	L.M. Montgomery	*Western Christian Advocate* (Cincinnati), 22 July 1908
"Night in the Pastures" (poem)	L.M. Montgomery	*New England Farmer* (Boston), 22 October 1898
	J.C. Neville	*Zion's Herald* (Boston), 26 August 1908
	J.C. Neville	*Boston Daily Globe* (Boston), 13 October 1908
	J.C. Neville	*Nebraska State Journal* (Lincoln), 25 December 1908
	J.C. Neville	*Postville (IA) Review*, 25 December 1908
"Buttercups" (poem)	Maud Cavendish	*The Mayflower* (Floral Park, NY), July 1899
	L.M. Montgomery	*The Farm Journal* (Philadelphia), May 1910
"Last Night in Dreams" (poem)	Ella Montgomery	*American Agriculturist* (Springfield, MA), 10 November 1906
	L.M. Montgomery	*Holland's Magazine* (Dallas), August 1915

"after all it was not really for the story they paid the price but for the name, and that name was won by the long toil of the obscure years – a toil that blossoms now."[38] But there were several instances in which the circulation of her name and her work were decidedly out of her control, including the reprinting of her treatise "What to Teach Your Son," part of "Half an Hour with Canadian Mothers" earlier in this volume, in at least three dozen newspapers across North America. A century before the creation of memes, shared on social media, that marry brief quotations from *Anne of Green Gables* with visually attractive backgrounds,[39] four extracts from *Anne of Green Gables* and *Anne of Avonlea* circulated in North American newspapers, identifying the author's name rather than the text in question. In this case, Montgomery's name was seen to have greater recognition value than the titles of two of her bestselling books, troubling Faye Hammill's assertion that Montgomery's fame in the 1910s and the interwar years had "always been contingent on the much greater renown of her character Anne Shirley":[40]

> I think people make their names nice or ugly just by what they are themselves. Live so that you beautify your name, even if it wasn't beautiful to begin with, making it stand in people's thoughts for something so lovely and pleasant that they never think of it by itself.[41]
>
> In this world you've just got to hope for the best and prepare for the worst, and take whatever God sends.[42]
>
> After all, I believe the nicest and sweetest days are not those on which anything very splendid or wonderful or exciting happens, but just those that bring simple little pleasures, following one another softly, like pearls slipping off a string.[43]
>
> The mistakes of today are lessons for tomorrow. Isn't it nice to think that tomorrow is a new day with no mistakes in it yet?[44]

The reach of such short pieces should not be underestimated, since I have counted forty instances of the "mistakes" extract so far between 1914 and 1916, and no doubt the continued digitization of newspapers will yield many more instances in the years to come. These items are not without some mystery, however: the first known instance of the first extract here, which appeared under the title "Live So That You Beautify Your Name," is in the *Baylor County Banner* of Seymour, Texas, in May 1906 – more than three years before the publication of *Anne of Avonlea*.

In a sense, the "J.C. Neville" example could mark an attempt by Montgomery to claim control of her work at a time when the name "L.M. Montgomery" had started to circulate within the marketplace in ways she could no longer control. After all, two question-and-answer segments appearing in several American newspapers in the 1930s demonstrate one of the ways in which her ultimate choice of authorial identity was not uniformly accepted in the media of her day. "Is L.M. Montgomery a real name or a pen name?" asked an unsigned writer in mid-1934. The answer hardly clarifies the distinction between the two terms: "Lucy Maud Montgomery is the full pen name of Mrs. Evan [*sic*] Macdonald."[45] Six months later, a similar question appeared: "Is the author L.M. Montgomery a man?" The response makes a revealing statement about what can be considered an author's "real" name: "No, her real name is Lucy Maud Montgomery Macdonald."[46]

While in these instances the circulation of Montgomery's "real" name and of extracts from her books occurred outside her control (and quite possibly outside her knowledge), in "The Alpine Path," which closes this volume, she had the opportunity not only to name herself according to her preference – as the author of the piece and as the young person she creates within it through narrative – but also to present her life story in a way that was consistent with the ways she had represented herself in the press prior to this: after all, in the earliest known publication about herself in the months following the appearance of *Anne of Green Gables*, she was so successful in suppressing all details about herself, including her gender, that the piece appears under the headline "Author Tells How He Wrote His Story."[47]

As a narrative whose significance is made more explicit by its contrast to Montgomery's journal text, "The Alpine Path" has been studied by several critics in terms of both what it reveals and what it conceals. In a volume on Montgomery for Twayne's World Authors series, Genevieve Wiggins notes that the text "presents [an] optimistic viewpoint" about Montgomery's childhood and eventual literary success "without reference to personal frustrations."[48] William V. Thompson, discussing this memoir in *L.M. Montgomery's Rainbow Valleys: The Ontario Years, 1911–1942* (2015), notes that the text "demonstrates Montgomery's borrowing from her own journals in order to construct a public version of herself as precocious child and budding author," highlighting one such entry, dated 7 January 1910, apparently written immediately after Montgomery discovered a lump in her breast that she interpreted as cancerous.[49] Meanwhile, according to Helen M. Buss in her book *Mapping Our Selves: Canadian Women's Autobiography in English* (1993), Montgomery had difficulty in her lifetime "articulating her self in her public autobiographical writing. To read her public autobiography ... is to read of a person entirely different from the diaries. This autobiography is the positivist expression of a straightforward climb to success, an 'alpine path' to an uncomplicated literary stardom, one that must have confirmed the readers of the famous Anne books in the opinion that there is nothing so difficult in life that a girl of spunk and daring cannot overcome, given a fast-moving plot line and the lesser intelligence and imagination of all the powers that be." Montgomery's journals, Buss writes, "tell a different story," one that "also reveals a darker side."[50]

As not only a public autobiography but also a celebrity memoir, one that supplements Montgomery's shorter essays and interviews collected in Volume 1 of *The L.M. Montgomery Reader*, "The Alpine Path" acts, as Katja Lee puts it, as "one of the more significant and substantial interventions Montgomery made into the production and dissemination of her public image and brand in Canada." Yet for Lee, the text reveals a paradox between Montgomery's usual attempt to keep the focus of her life narrative on her career and the fact that the narrative in question appears in a domestic periodical for women: "There are no narratives of her childhood that reveal any inclination for the domestic arts; all interests, skills, and ambition are focused on anticipating her future work as a writer. Of Montgomery's adult life in domestic spaces, we are told very little, and of her considerable labour in this sphere, we hear nothing."[51] Rubio notes in a 1992 piece that Montgomery's opening strategy to frame the writing of the memoir as a reaction to an unshakeable habit always to say yes to the "whims" of editors suggests a set of gendered politics at play: "A male author of equal fame would have felt no need to begin his sketch in such a self-effacing way – he would have considered his writing a profession and his success proof of its excellence."[52] Lorraine York, calling Montgomery "a woman of such quick intelligence and pragmatism that ... she was well able to diagnose her own condition as a public commodity," notes another strategy by focusing on the end of the narrative, in which "the literary celebrity, prey to the glamorization of her literary life narrative, compensates by deglamorizing it," returning in her final paragraphs to the "idea of a slow, painful struggle" rather than a career.[53]

Returning to "The Alpine Path" now, after the publication of eleven volumes of her journals to date, offers us an opportunity to reconsider the strategies Montgomery employed in creating a version of her life available for public consumption, one that coincided with, as Thompson notes, "her growing awareness of herself as a public figure – as both author and minister's wife."[54] In particular, Montgomery's decision to end the narrative with a selected travelogue of her honeymoon merits closer examination. For Lee, the addition of these "restrained, even dull, travel entries that perform a kind of vague domesticity while evading personal detail" are some of the most curious components of the memoir, not only because Montgomery's husband "remains unnamed and unnarrated," but also because she remains "silent on the subject of how one might take a European honeymoon or run a household on a pastor's salary."[55]

One possibility is that Montgomery sought to erase her husband from the narrative in response to what Rubio refers to as his "deep underlying hostility to her success as a writer," which York suggests created further "role conflicts occasioned by Montgomery's celebrity."[56] Yet there might be another reason, too, depending on what new pieces of evidence are uncovered. In an alternate version of an interview Montgomery gave while on her honeymoon, Montgomery and the interviewer (identified in this version as Christian Richardson) veer off in a direction that they had avoided in the version included in Volume 1 of *The L.M. Montgomery Reader*:

> Mrs. Montgomery-Macdonald's new home is to be Leaskdale, Ontario. Her husband is a Presbyterian minister; indeed, she confesses, "was our minister in Cavendish for four years." But of Mr. Macdonald she quite refuses to talk – for publication. "He is my own private, personal property," she insists, "with which the public has nothing whatever to do. He is not to be bothered just because he has had the misfortune to marry a semi-celebrity." She is certain she is going to be lonesome for her old home. Prince Edward Island is in her estimation the loveliest spot in all Canada. "But then," she says, "I will have some one to talk to who knows all about it."[57]

Montgomery's memoir ends with an inspirational note from the editors of *Everywoman's World*, celebrating her arrival as L.M. Montgomery and signalling the fact that, although the memoir has ended, her career will continue: "The 'Alpine Path' has been climbed! At the summit we rest, to reflect with you that there has been great joy, great inspiration in the accomplishment, and to look forward to the continuation of the journey, with L.M. Montgomery, upon the sunlit top, at some future time when another glorious milestone has been pressed upon the roadway of her life."[58] Montgomery's life, work, and legacy, consisting of numerous such "glorious milestone[s]," continues to appeal to readers all over the world more than three-quarters of a century after her death, and thanks to the advances of the digital age, the recovery of neglected materials shows no sign of abating.

BENJAMIN LEFEBVRE

NOTES

1 Brontë, "Biographical Notice," ix.
2 Montgomery, 28 September 1893, in *CJLMM*, 1: 170.
3 Montgomery's response appeared alongside those of Arthur Stringer (1874–1950), Agnes C. Laut (1871–1936), Emily Murphy

(1868–1933), Robert J.C. Stead (1880–1959), and Stephen Leacock (1869–1944), all of whom rivalled Montgomery in popularity during this period.

4 "What Are the Greatest Books," 152; Montgomery, 15 April 1914, in *LMMCJ*, 1: 154. See also Lefebvre, Headnote to "What Are the Greatest Books," 151. Montgomery would mention Wilkie Collins (1824–1889), English novelist best known for *The Woman in White* (1859), in her contribution to *Fiction Writers on Fiction Writing* (1923), included in Volume 1 of *The L.M. Montgomery Reader*. Anthony Trollope (1815–1882), English novelist best known for *The Way We Live Now* (1875).

5 It is worth noting that the recent CBC/Netflix series *Anne with an "E"* continues the links between Montgomery, Brontë, and Eliot. The titles of all seven first-season episodes allude to Brontë's *Jane Eyre*, whereas the titles of all ten second-season episodes allude to Eliot's *Middlemarch*.

6 Gilbert and Gubar, *The Madwoman in the Attic*, 65.

7 Gerson, "L.M. Montgomery," 68.

8 Montgomery, 22 September 1925, in *LMMCJ*, 3: 408.

9 Two notable exceptions were Peg Bowen in *The Story Girl* and *The Golden Road* and Miss Brownell in *Emily of New Moon*. But whereas Montgomery provided the genesis of the former character in "The Alpine Path," she kept the inspiration for the latter character private. See Montgomery, 19 October 1927, in *LMMCJ*, 4: 186.

10 For a comprehensive overview of the development of Montgomery's critical reception since the publication of *Anne of Green Gables*, see the pieces and supplementary materials included in all three volumes of *The L.M. Montgomery Reader*. For an exhaustive bibliography of scholarship devoted to Montgomery's life, work, and legacy, see the website for L.M. Montgomery Online at https://lmmonline.org.

11 *Island Guardian and Christian Chronicle* (Charlottetown), "P. of W. Convocation," 2. In Montgomery's journals, references to Eliot or the Brontës or to female authorial role models more generally are infrequent. She recorded reading a biography of Eliot two months before her twenty-first birthday (Montgomery, 30 September 1895, in *CJLMM*, 1: 289) and Eliot's novels *Adam Bede* in spring 1903 (Montgomery, 12 April 1903, in *CJLMM*, 2: 68) and *Romola* in late 1910 (Montgomery, 26 December 1910,

in *CJLMM*, 2: 335); in a journal entry dated January 1911, she recorded her wish, upon rereading Elizabeth Gaskell's *The Life of Charlotte Brontë* (1857), to make one day a "pilgrimage" to the Brontë house in West Yorkshire (Montgomery, 22 January 1911, in *CJLMM*, 2: 339), which she and her husband did on their honeymoon six months later, but she omitted that part of her trip from her account of it in "The Alpine Path." In a journal entry dated 1925, however, Montgomery stated that she would not have liked Brontë as a woman: "I could never find a kindred spirit in a woman without a sense of humor" (Montgomery, 22 September 1925, in *LMMCJ*, 3: 408). For more on Eliot's evolution as an author, see Bodenheimer, "A Woman of Many Names"; Dillane, *Before George Eliot*.

12 Montgomery, 21 March 1916, in *LMMCJ*, 1: 221.

13 Montgomery, "Novel Writing Notes," 197. These distances are slightly different in "The Alpine Path."

14 As Montgomery claimed about the magazine *The Editor: The Journal of Information for Literary Workers* in an essay published in 1923, Cavendish "was one of the loveliest spots in the world – but it was absolutely out of the world in a literary sense, and *The Editor* was indispensable to me" (Montgomery, "Novel Writing Notes," 197).

15 Montgomery, 3 December 1903, in *CJLMM*, 2: 89.

16 Easley, "Making a Debut," 15, 17, 18.

17 Sharp, *Handbook of Pseudonyms*, 713, 642, vi.

18 Clarke, *Pseudonyms*, xii.

19 Atkinson, *Dictionary of Literary Pseudonyms*, 8.

20 Haynes, *Pseudonyms of Authors*, iii–iv.

21 A transcription of a letter that the fifteen-year-old Montgomery received from her classmate Nate Lockhart refers to her as "L.M. Montgomery" (Montgomery, 18 February 1890, in *CJLMM*, 1: 20). Her letters to Ephraim Weber and G.B. MacMillan are all signed "L.M. Montgomery" until her marriage in 1911 and either "L.M. Montgomery Macdonald" or "L.M. Macdonald" thereafter.

22 English-speaking women authors besides L.M. Montgomery who published under initials have included E.D.E.N. Southworth (1819–1899), American author of sixty novels, including *The Hidden Hand* (1888); Louisa May Alcott (1832–1888), American author of *Little Women* (1868–1869) and several other novels, including some published under the names L.M. Alcott and A.M.

Barnard; L.T. Meade (1844–1914), Irish author of girls' novels, including *A World of Girls* (1886); E. Nesbit (1858–1924), English author of several novels, including *The Railway Children* (1906); E.H. Young (1880–1949), bestselling English novelist; H.D. (1886–1961), American author; P.L. Travers (1899–1996), Australian-born British author of *Mary Poppins* (1934) and its sequels; P.K. Page (1916–2000), Canadian author of fiction, poetry, and children's writing; A.L. Barker (1918–2002), English author best known for *John Brown's Body* (1970); P.D. James (1920–2014), British crime novelist; V.C. Andrews (1923–1986), American author of several novels, most famously *Flowers in the Attic* (1979); E.L. Konigsburg (1930–2013), American author and illustrator of books for young people; A.S. Byatt (1936–), Booker Prize–winning British novelist; S.E. Hinton (1948–), American author of young adult fiction, most notably *The Outsiders* (1967); J.D. Robb, pseudonym of Nora Roberts (1950–), American crime novelist; K.A. Applegate (1956–), American author of the Animorphs series; A.M. Homes (1961–), American author whose books include *The Safety of Objects* (1990); E.L. James, pseudonym of Erika Mitchell (1963–), British author of *Fifty Shades of Grey* (2011) and its sequels; A.L. Kennedy (1965–), Scottish novelist and stand-up comic; J.K. Rowling (1965–), British author of *Harry Potter and the Philosopher's Stone* (1997) and its sequels, who has since published as Robert Galbraith; E. Lockhart, pseudonym of Emily Jenkins (1967–), American children's writer; K.A. Tucker (1978–), Canadian author of suspense fiction; and A.J. Walkley (1985–), American author of young adult fiction. Consider, too, women authors who omitted parts of their names to make them seem more gender neutral, including (Margaret) Marshall Saunders (1861–1947), Gene (Geneva) Stratton-Porter (1863–1924), and (Nelle) Harper Lee (1926–2016), children's writers.

23 Women who used male pseudonyms include (in addition to authors already mentioned) Olive Schreiner (1855–1920), South African author whose book *The Story of an African Farm* (1883) was published under the name Ralph Iron; Sara Jeannette Duncan (1861–1922), Canadian author whose newspaper column "Other People and I" appeared in the Toronto *Globe* under the by-line "Garth Grafton" in 1885; Madge MacBeth (1878–1965), Canadian author who wrote *The Land of Afternoon* (1924) as Gilbert Knox, a secret that was not discovered until after her

death; Karen Blixen (1885–1962), Danish author who published the memoir *Out of Africa* and the story "Babette's Feast" under the signature Isak Dinesen; Alice Bradley Sheldon (1915–1987), American author who wrote science fiction novels as James Tiptree Jr.; and Margaret Laurence (1926–1987), who submitted her earliest short stories as Steve Lancaster.

24 Montgomery to MacMillan, 8 January 1908, in *MDMM*, 37.

25 As Connie Ann Kirk notes in a biography of Rowling published in 2003, "Years later feminists would cry foul and lament that once again a woman had succumbed to the commercial pressures of publishers to sublimate her true identity and disguise her gender, as was the case with George Eliot and many other women in literary history" (Kirk, *J.K. Rowling*, 76).

26 A.J. Walkley, "Androgynous Pen Names," *Huffington Post*, 10 June 2012, http://www.huffingtonpost.com/aj-walkley/androgynous-pen-names_b_1413563.html.

27 Coultrap-McQuin, "Pseudonyms," 716, 717.

28 Gerson, *Canadian Women in Print*, 31.

29 See Montgomery, 2 July 1911, in *CJLMM*, 2: 418; Montgomery to MacMillan, 6 February 1928, in *MDMM*, 131. Montgomery stated that family members and friends called her "Maud" (and, in her journals, she referred to herself as Maud). In "The Alpine Path," an adult refers to her as a child as "little Miss Maud."

30 Rubio, *Lucy Maud Montgomery*, 63.

31 The bibliographical details in these tables draw on the list prepared by Rea Wilmshurst and included in *Lucy Maud Montgomery: A Preliminary Bibliography* (1986), co-authored with Ruth Weber Russell and D.W. Russell, and supplemented by my own extensive research on Montgomery's periodical publications, which has benefited considerably from the findings of Donna J. Campbell, Carolyn Strom Collins, Joanne Lebold, and the late Christy Woster. Many more of her periodical pieces remain unidentified or their bibliographical details unconfirmed.

32 See Montgomery, "How I Began to Write," 71; Montgomery, "How I Began," 145; "The Author of *Anne of Avonlea*," 38.

33 Not included in this list is the Prince of Wales valedictory speech that Montgomery ghostwrote for her classmate James H. Stevenson in 1894 (included in this volume) or the few pieces published (most likely erroneously) under the names "S.M. Montgomery," "L.W. Montgomery," or "Lucy Ward Montgomery."

34 Gerson, *Canadian Women in Print*, 35.

35 The numbers used to calculate these averages are limited to periodicals whose publication details are known. Several more poems and short stories appear in Montgomery's scrapbooks or are mentioned in her earnings ledger, but their publication details are unknown, so these numbers should actually be slightly higher.

36 Alternative names used for later personal essays – "Lucy Maud Montgomery" for "Four Questions Answered," "L.M. Montgomery MacDonald" [*sic*] for "The Day before Yesterday," "Lucy M. Montgomery" for a reprint of "'I Dwell among My Own People,'" and "Mrs. L.M. Macdonald (L.M. Montgomery)" for "Life Has Been Interesting" – may have been the choices of the editors of the publications in which these pieces appeared.

37 Gerson, "L.M. Montgomery," 78n8. "At the Long Sault," appearing in Scrapbook 8 with a handwritten note identifying the source of publication simply as "The Standard," also appeared in *The Watchman and Other Poems* (see *WOP*, 116–19).

38 Montgomery, 21 October 1921, in *LMMCJ*, 2: 344.

39 It is worth mentioning that many of these inspirational quotations from the twenty-first century attribute to L.M. Montgomery extracts from Kevin Sullivan's miniseries versions of *Anne of Green Gables*, including "Good Friends Are Always Together in Spirit," which was even woven into the opening credits of the recent television series *Anne with an "E."*

40 Hammill, *Women, Celebrity, and Literary Culture*, 100.

41 See Montgomery, "Live So That You Beautify Your Name." These sentences were originally a dialogue between Diana and Anne in *Anne of Avonlea*. When Diana observes that "I think people make their names nice or ugly just by what they are themselves," mentioning Josie and Gertie Pye as examples of the latter, Anne declares this to be "a lovely idea": "Living so that you beautify your name, even if it wasn't beautiful to begin with ... making it stand in people's thoughts for something so lovely and pleasant that they never think of it by itself" (*AA*, 252–53; ellipsis in original).

42 See Montgomery, untitled extract. This sentence from *Anne of Avonlea* is spoken by adolescent handmaiden Charlotta the Fourth (see *AA*, 361).

43 See Montgomery, "The Sweetest Days." This sentence is spoken by Anne in *Anne of Avonlea* (see *AA*, 210).

44 See Montgomery, "Our Mistakes." Properly, "Marilla, isn't it nice

to think that to-morrow is a new day with no mistakes in it yet?" This sentence is spoken by Anne in *Anne of Green Gables* (see *AGG*, 247), but the preceding sentence does not appear in the book.

45 *Daily Pantagraph* (Bloomington, IL), "The Daily Pantagraph's" (28 June 1934), 4; *Elmira (NY) Star-Gazette*, "Your Questions Answered" (28 June 1934), 6; *Harrisburg (PA) Telegraph*, "Ask the Telegraph," 10; *Courier-News* (Bridgewater, NJ), "Your Questions Answered," 10; *Pittsburgh Press*, "Questions – Answers" (3 July 1934), 4; *North Adams (MA) Evening Transcript*, "Ask the Transcript," 14.

46 *Daily Pantagraph* (Bloomington, IL), "The Daily Pantagraph's" (18 January 1935), 4; *Elmira (NY) Star-Gazette*, "Your Questions Answered" (18 January 1935), 6; *Kingsport (TN) Times*, "Questions and Answers," 4; *Middletown (NY) Times-Herald*, "Questions and Answers," 4; *Pittsburgh Press*, "Questions – Answers" (18 January 1935), 14; *Ithaca Journal*, "Answers from Washington," 6. I mentioned these two questions – but not their corresponding answers – in my headnote to "Something about L.M. Montgomery" in Volume 1 of *The L.M. Montgomery Reader*.

47 See "Author Tells How."

48 Wiggins, *L.M. Montgomery*, 183.

49 Thompson, "The Shadow on the House of Dreams," 116. See Montgomery, 7 January 1910, in *CJLMM*, 2: 249–81; Montgomery, 7 February 1910, in *CJLMM*, 2: 281–83; Montgomery, 25 February 1918, in *LMMCJ*, 2: 5–8.

50 Buss, *Mapping Our Selves*, 164, 165.

51 Lee, "Protecting Her Brand," 184, 189.

52 Rubio, "Subverting the Trite," 122.

53 York, *Literary Celebrity in Canada*, 78, 80.

54 Thompson, "The Shadow on the House of Dreams," 116.

55 Lee, "Protecting Her Brand," 193, 190, 191.

56 Rubio, Introduction, 8; York, *Literary Celebrity in Canada*, 87.

57 Richardson, "'Anne of Green Gables,'" 354; see also "A Canadian Novelist." My thanks to Mary Beth Cavert for bringing this version of Montgomery's interview with Richardson to my attention.

58 *Everywoman's World*, "The Summit Is Reached," 25.

Notes

THE WRECK OF THE "MARCO POLO"

By Lucy Maud Montgomery. *Montreal Daily Witness*, 5 March 1891, 2. Also in Scrapbook 7 ("Written March 1890 / Published February 1891 / In Montreal Witness").

Also with minor variations as "The Wreck of the Marco Polo" in *Daily Patriot* (Charlottetown), 11 March 1891, 1. Also in Bolger, *The Years Before "Anne,"* 33–36. Also excerpted in McCabe, *The Lucy Maud Montgomery Album*, 61–62.

1 "Noted Author Dies Suddenly," 360.

2 This error about Montgomery's age seems to coincide with an error about her birthdate. See "The Alpine Path," note 17, below.

3 See Montgomery, 19 February 1890, in *CJLMM*, 1: 21. Montgomery stated in this journal entry that she had received "honorable mention" for her 1889 submission. George Alley, the judge for Prince Edward Island, does not use this term in his report published on 1 June 1889; instead, he names the "best essay" for Queens County and adds three more stories "in the order of merit among the contributions of this county," the second of which is "a legend graphically told of a tragedy said to have occurred about the time of the establishment of British rule in the island on a spot which has perpetuated the memory of one of the principal actors in the occurrence by deriving from him its name." This report does not identify any of the contributions by title or author. In her copy of this clipping in her Blue Scrapbook, housed at the Confederation Centre Art Gallery in Charlottetown, Montgomery drew in pencil a box surrounding this text, indicating

that she recognized this vague description as a reference to her essay. Although the judge included Montgomery's entry in those he "recommend[ed] for publication," this piece does not appear to have been published. *Montreal Daily Witness*, "Dominion Prize Competition," 3.

4 This event also formed the basis of Lynn Manuel's picture book *The Summer of the "Marco Polo"* (2007).

5 *Montreal Daily Witness*, "Canada Prize Competition," 3. A clipping of this comment about Montgomery's essay (omitting the remainder of the report) appears in Scrapbook 7, on the same page as the clipping of the published essay along with the unsigned editorial comments ("The End of a Famous Ship, Well Known to Song and Story") used to introduce Montgomery's essay. Winning second prize for Queens County was "Master Nathan J. Lockhart," whose essay on "The American Gale" – referring to "an October 1851 storm [that] destroyed more than 70 schooners near Cavendish" (Rubio and Waterston, in Montgomery, *CJLMM*, 1: 21n3) – was deemed by the judge to be "a favorite sketch selected by many of the competitors." The rivalry between Montgomery and Lockhart "anticipated the Gilbert and Anne rivalry" in *Anne of Green Gables* (Gammel, *Looking for Anne of Green Gables*, 119) and was dramatized in Melanie J. Fishbane's *Maud: A Novel Inspired by the Life of L.M. Montgomery* (2017).

6 See Montgomery, 7 December 1890, in *CJLMM*, 1: 53.

7 See Montgomery, 10 July 1931, in *SJLMM*, 4: 138–39; *Globe* (Toronto), "Canadian Photos."

8 Montgomery's essay "How I Began to Write," first published in the Circle of Young Canada column in 1911, appears in Volume 1 of *The L.M. Montgomery Reader*. This *Globe* contest, which ran from 1929 to 1937, involved drawings, poems, stories, essays, or letters submitted by readers between the ages of fourteen and twenty-one; it memorialized Agnes Delamoure, who had edited the column as "Nancy Durham" from 1915 until her death in 1928. See *Globe* (Toronto), "Nancy Durham Memorial Contest"; *Globe* (Toronto), "'Nancy Durham' Dies."

9 Montgomery begins her report by outlining her evaluation criteria: first, the presence of "a well-defined and original plot," with the reminder that "a 'story,' no matter how well written, is not a story unless it has a central plot"; second, whether "the plot is worked

out well and logically"; and third, "the literary style of the story" (Montgomery, "Kindly Criticisms," 20).

10 A rural Prince Edward Island village founded in 1790, the home primarily of Canadian settlers of Scottish ancestry. Montgomery had been living with her maternal grandparents since shortly after the death of her mother when she was twenty-one months old. Although this essay locates Cavendish as "bordering on the Gulf of St. Lawrence," it does not identify the province of Prince Edward Island except in Montgomery's signature.

11 According to Martin J. Hollenberg, the Black Ball line of packets was founded by James Baines (who bought the *Marco Polo* in Liverpool in 1852) and his partners, even though the name coincided with that of two rival companies. See Hollenberg, *Marco Polo*, 27–29.

12 A deal blank is "a slice sawn from a log of timber (now always of fir or pine), and usually understood to be more than seven inches wide, and not more than three thick; a plank or board of pine or fir-wood" (*OED*).

13 Captain Bull of Christiania (now Oslo), Norway, had bought the *Marco Polo* in 1882.

14 As Montgomery explains in "The Alpine Path," later in this volume, this fishing station was named after the Siege of Cawnpore (now Kanpur), India, part of the Indian Mutiny of 1857.

15 Possibly a reference to *The Seamans Secrets* (1594), a navigation manual by John Davis (ca. 1550–1605), English explorer.

16 In her journal, Montgomery recorded that while she had heard the sound of the crash from the schoolhouse, the sight of the crash was one she would "always regret not having seen." Montgomery, 3 June 1909, in *CJLMM*, 2: 230.

17 While the word "tar" has been used figuratively "in derogatory reference to someone of mixed black (or Indian, etc.) and white origin," Montgomery seems to be using it here as "a familiar appellation for a sailor" (*OED*). She would repeat this term in "The Alpine Path," *A Tangled Web* (see *TW*, 52), and *Mistress Pat* (see *MP*, 161), always in reference to sailors.

18 The *Marco Polo* had also been launched from Saint John, now the largest city in New Brunswick, in 1851.

19 "A fine day in the middle of a period of bad weather" (*OED*).

20 From the verb "to stave," referring to something broken in pieces.

21 Several hired hands named Buote appear in Montgomery's book-length fiction: Jerry Buote in *Anne of Green Gables*, Leon Buote in *Chronicles of Avonlea*, and Pacifique Buote in *Anne of the Island*.

22 A boat that sports "a fishing net designed to hang vertically in the water, the ends being drawn together to enclose the fish" (*OED*).

23 Properly, "One touch of nature makes the whole world kin." From *Troilus and Cressida* (1609), a play by William Shakespeare (ca. 1564–1616), English playwright and poet.

A WESTERN EDEN

By Lucy Maud Montgomery. *Prince Albert Times and Saskatchewan Review*, 17 June 1891, 4. Also in Scrapbook 7. Also in Bolger, *The Years Before "Anne,"* 37–40, 47.

Also, by Lucy Ward Montgomery, in *Manitoba Daily Free Press* (Winnipeg), 4 July 1891, 3.

1 Montgomery, 6 June 1891, in *CJLMM*, 1: 72; Montgomery, 18 June 1891, in *CJLMM*, 1: 74.

2 Properly, Alexander McLachlan (1818–1896), Scottish-born Canadian poet who has been dubbed "The Robbie Burns of Canada." The extract reproduced here is from his poem "Hurrah for the New Dominion," with several minor variations in terms of punctuation, capitalization, and spelling, indicating that even by age sixteen, Montgomery had started referencing literary allusions from memory, a habit she would continue throughout her life.

3 From *Evangeline: A Tale of Acadie*, an epic poem by Henry Wadsworth Longfellow (1807–1882), American poet. The original publication prints the term "forest primeval" without quotation marks, but Montgomery adds these in ink in her scrapbook.

4 From "The Lay of the Last Minstrel," a poem by Sir Walter Scott (1771–1832), Scottish novelist and poet.

5 The name Saskatchewan is derived from the Cree term *kisiskâciwanisîpiy*, meaning "swift-flowing river." The Saskatchewan River, almost 2,000 kilometres long, begins approximately 50 kilometres east of Prince Albert. See Brandi Newton, "Saskatchewan River," The Canadian Encyclopedia, Historica Canada, last modified 4 May 2017, https://www.thecanadianencyclopedia.ca/en/article/saskatchewan-river/.

6 In her scrapbook copy, Montgomery includes an asterisk here, along with a handwritten note that is undecipherable at times: "as

it is said that whoever drinks of the waters of this river can never afterwards stay away from [illegible] always return no matter where they go."

7 Properly, "And one, a full-fed river winding slow." From "The Palace of Art," a poem by Alfred, Lord Tennyson (1809–1892), English poet.

8 I have corrected the original, in which "does not" is jumbled as "dot," as per the *Manitoba Daily Free Press* version of the text.

9 A historical novel by James Fenimore Cooper (1789–1851), published in 1826 and set during the French and Indian War of 1754–1763.

10 See Genesis 37:3 (*KJV*): "Now Israel loved Joseph more than all his children, because he *was* the son of his old age: and he *made* him a coat of many colours."

11 Saskatchewan would become a province of the Dominion of Canada in 1905.

12 Slight misquotation from "To the West! To the West!," a poem by Charles Mackay (1814–1889), Scottish author.

13 From "The Maple Leaf Forever," a song by Alexander Muir (1830–1906), Scottish-born Canadian poet and songwriter, written in 1867 in honour of Confederation.

14 In the version of this publication in the *Manitoba Daily Free Press*, this date is changed to "July 1, 1891."

FROM PRINCE ALBERT TO P.E. ISLAND

By L.M. Montgomery. *Daily Patriot* (Charlottetown), 31 October 1891, 1–2. Also in Scrapbook 7. Also in Bolger, *The Years Before "Anne,"* 52–59.

1 Montgomery did not specify in her journal which of her grandfathers had made this suggestion, but presumably it was her paternal grandfather, Donald Montgomery (1808–1893), who encouraged her writing ambitions, rather than her maternal grandfather, Alexander Macneill (1820–1898), who opposed her quest for higher education and who likely resented her appropriation of some of his oral stories as the basis of her first publications. See Montgomery, 22 October 1891, in *CJLMM*, 1: 104; Rubio, *Lucy Maud Montgomery*, 39.

2 Rubio, *Lucy Maud Montgomery*, 66; Montgomery, 5 September 1891, in *CJLMM*, 1: 97–98.

3 The original publication reads "pressing of finger tips," but Montgomery crosses out "pressing" and adds "kissing" in ink in her scrapbook copy.

4 Saskatoon, located approximately 150 kilometres southwest of Prince Albert, had been founded in 1882.

5 In her scrapbook, Montgomery adds a handwritten note at this point: "A Saskatchewan is an Indian word meaning 'mighty waters.'" See "A Western Eden," note 5, above.

6 Regina, located approximately 250 kilometres southeast of Saskatoon, had been known as Wascana until 1882 and became the capital when Saskatchewan became a province in 1905.

7 "Displaying or characterized by initiative and energy" (*OED*).

8 Pullmans were railway sleeping cars manufactured by the Pullman Company, beginning in the 1860s.

9 From the French "en déshabillé," meaning "undressed."

10 Now Kenora, located about 200 kilometres east of Winnipeg in northwestern Ontario.

11 A town in southwestern Manitoba, almost 300 kilometres west of Winnipeg.

12 A city 210 kilometres west of Winnipeg. Montgomery does not mention Rat Portage, Virden, and Brandon in the order in which she would have encountered them travelling from west to east.

13 To "boodle" is to practise bribery. Montgomery refers here likely to the Baie des Chaleurs Scandal, involving a railway line through eastern Québec whose construction had been underwritten by the Governments of Québec and Canada. A Senate inquiry launched on 4 August 1891 revealed that "the Québec government had been bribed with its own railway subsidy, the money probably having been used to pay off election expenses." P.B. Waite, "Baie des Chaleurs Scandal," The Canadian Encyclopedia, Historica Canada, last modified 12 December 2013, https://www.thecanadianencyclopedia.ca/en/article/baie-des-chaleurs-scandal/.

14 The word "waste" is used here in the sense of "uninhabited (or sparsely inhabited) and uncultivated country; a wild and desolate region, a desert, wilderness" (*OED*).

15 From "In October," by Archibald Lampman (1861–1899), Canadian poet.

16 Now the city of Thunder Bay, Ontario, since its merger with Port Arthur and the townships of McIntyre and Neebing in 1970.

17 The *Manitoba*, a luxury steamship built in 1871.

18 Presumably, this refers to the Kaministiquia River, which empties into Lake Superior at Thunder Bay.
19 The original publication reads "friend," but Montgomery corrects this in ink to "fiend" in her scrapbook copy.
20 From *The Lady of the Lake*, a poem by Scott.
21 These two couplets appear non-consecutively in "The Lighthouse," a poem by Longfellow.
22 Sault Ste. Marie, Ontario, a city located across the St. Marys River from Sault Ste. Marie, Michigan.
23 Italian for "in a subdued or low voice" (*OED*). I have corrected the original, which reads "*solto voce*."
24 Properly, "At Queenston Heights and Lundy's Lane," the opening line of "The Maple Leaf Forever," a song that Montgomery quotes in her essay "A Western Eden," above. The Battles of Queenston Heights (near Queenston, Ontario) and Lundy's Lane (fought in what is now Niagara Falls) were major events in the War of 1812.
25 This river, which flows from Lake Superior to Lake Huron, acts as an international border between Michigan and Ontario.
26 A city in southwestern Ontario, off Georgian Bay.
27 The term "Queen City" refers to "the pre-eminent or most admired city (of a particular region)" (*OED*).
28 Montgomery refers here to her paternal grandfather, Senator Donald Montgomery, who represented PEI in Ottawa from 1874 until his death in 1893 (Rubio and Waterston, introduction to *SJLMM*, 1: xiii).
29 Lord Stanley of Preston (1841–1908) served as the sixth Governor General of Canada from 1888 to 1893.
30 Sir Richard Cartwright (1835–1912), a Canadian politician, known as a talented debater and speaker.
31 The Chaudière Falls separate Ottawa from Gatineau, Québec. The 1891 Census collected statistics from 4.8 million people across Canada for a third time since Confederation.
32 This bridge, which spans 3 kilometres and which opened in 1860, links Montreal to Québec's south shore.
33 Located in the Montmorency River, outside Quebec City.
34 Pointe-Lévy, a settlement on the south shore of the St. Lawrence River, opposite Quebec City.
35 Located in Quebec City, the site of the Battle of the Plains of Abraham on 13 September 1759, during which the invasion of British troops led to the French surrendering Québec to the British.

36 Town on the Restigouche River in northern New Brunswick.
37 Located in eastern New Brunswick, off the Petitcodiac River; incorporated as a city in 1890.
38 Pointe-du-Chêne, a New Brunswick community on Shediac Bay near the Northumberland Strait; the SS *Northumberland*, built earlier in 1891 in Newcastle upon Tyne, UK, and owned by the Charlottetown Steam Navigation Company.
39 Montgomery would reuse this legend in her 1939 article "Prince Edward Island," which she contributed to the Canadian Pacific Railway publication *The Spirit of Canada* (1939) and which is included in Volume 1 of *The L.M. Montgomery Reader*.
40 Montgomery quotes this line from Scott's "The Lay of the Last Minstrel" in "A Western Eden," above.

THE USUAL WAY

By L.M. Montgomery. *The College Record* (Charlottetown), March 1894, 5–8. Also in Scrapbook 7 ("Written March 1894 / Published March 1894 / In 'College Record'"). Also in Blue Scrapbook.

1 Montgomery, "The Day before Yesterday," 233. As Marian Bruce notes, *The College Record* did not appear in 1895 and was revamped early in 1896 as *The Prince of Wales College Observer* (see Bruce, *A Century of Excellence*, 72), to which Montgomery would contribute while a student at Dalhousie.
2 Montgomery, 11 April 1894, in *CJLMM*, 1: 202.
3 Rubio and Waterston, in *CJLMM*, 1: 167n4.
4 I have corrected the original, which reads "Cierco." Marcus Tullius Cicero (106–43 BCE) was a Roman philosopher whose writings had an enormous influence on the Latin language and on European literatures. Nineteenth-century texts such as Henry P. Linton's *Select Orations of Marcus Tullius Cicero, for the Hilary Term Examination of the Junior Sophister Year, from the Text of Jo. Case. Trellis, with a Literal Translation and Notes* (1845) featured the Latin text on the verso pages and a literal English translation on facing recto pages; other editions, like the one described here, included notes in the end matter.
5 The phrase "Quæres a nobis, Grati – " is from "The Oration of M. Tullius Cicero for the Poet A. Licinio Archais" and is translated literally as "You will ask then of me, Gratius" (Linton, *Select Orations*, 76, 77).

6 "A loose-fitting coat the back of which is not shaped to the figure, but hangs more or less straight from the shoulders" (*OED*).
7 I have corrected the original, which reads "Disgustingly," following Montgomery's handwritten corrections in her scrapbook copy.
8 Rubio and Waterston identify this instructor as Herbert Shaw, a graduate of McGill who "had been appointed in September to teach mathematics and drawing" (*CJLMM*, 1: 168n2).
9 Like the characters in this playlet, Montgomery found Roman History to be "one of the most interesting classes we have" (Montgomery, 14 November 1893, in *CJLMM*, 1: 175).
10 Julius Caesar (100–44 BCE), Roman politician and prose writer.
11 Eriphile and Iphigenia are characters in *Iphigénie* (1674), a dramatic tragedy by Jean Racine (1639–1699), French playwright, that Montgomery had studied that year. See Montgomery, 14 November 1893, in *CJLMM*, 1: 176.

EXTRACTS FROM THE DIARY OF A SECOND CLASS MOUSE

By L.M. Montgomery. *The College Record* (Charlottetown), April 1894, 2–4. Also in Scrapbook 7 ("Written April 1894 / Published April 1894 / In College Record"). Also in Red Scrapbook, Confederation Centre Art Gallery.

1 Montgomery's journal indicates that she wrote the piece on 11 April, two days after recording her hesitation to commit to another contribution for the paper since "I haven't the faintest idea what to write about" (Montgomery, 11 April 1894, in *CJLMM*, 1: 202; Montgomery, 9 April 1894, in *CJLMM*, 1: 202).
2 Rubio and Waterston, in *CJLMM*, 1: 167n4.
3 The Prince of Wales College shared a campus with the Normal School for student teachers; Montgomery had some of her classes in that building.
4 Presumably, Professor John Caven (1826–1914), who taught English and school management.
5 The year 1894 was not a leap year, so February had only twenty-eight days. See also "Around the Table," note 195, below.
6 This "pea-nut" party actually occurred, according to a journal entry dated the same day as the Second-Class Mouse's entry, but Montgomery later regretted her involvement in it. See Montgomery, 8 March 1894, in *CJLMM*, 1: 193; Montgomery, 2 September 1919, in *LMMCJ*, 2: 179–80.

HIGH SCHOOL LIFE IN SASKATCHEWAN

By L.M. Montgomery. [*The College Record* (Charlottetown, PE), May 1894.] Scrapbook 7 ("Written May 1894 / Published May 1894 / In College Record"). Also in Bolger, *The Years Before "Anne,"* 68–69.

1 Montgomery, 19 September 1890, in *CJLMM*, 1: 46–47; Montgomery, 7 January 1910, in *CJLMM*, 2: 274; Montgomery, 20 February 1896, in *CJLMM*, 1: 314.

2 "The North-West Mounted Police was a paramilitary police force established in 1873 to maintain law and order, and to be a visible symbol of Canadian sovereignty, in the newly acquired North-West Territories (including present-day Alberta and Saskatchewan)." Edward Butts, "North-West Mounted Police," The Canadian Encyclopedia, Historica Canada, last modified 12 June 2016, https://www.thecanadianencyclopedia.ca/en/article/north-west-mounted-police/. As Rubio and Waterston note, "Prince Albert was the district centre for the North West Mounted Police" (Rubio and Waterston, in *CJLMM*, 1: 61n2).

3 The Book of Proverbs, part of the Judeo-Christian Bible, includes several chapters attributed to Solomon, who, according to the sacred writings of Abrahamic religions, reigned as King of Israel during the tenth century BCE. The statement in Proverbs 13:24 (*KJV*) – "He that spareth his rod hateth his son: but he that loveth him chasteneth him betimes" – has been debated as the origin of the more modern proverb "Spare the rod and spoil the child," which advocates discipline (physical or otherwise) to ensure the proper development of young people.

4 This slur against Montgomery's Metis classmates is even more derogatory in the slightly different version in her journal: "Mr. Mustard has a pretty hot temper and as several of the boys have a fair share of 'nitchie' in them, we have lively times occasionally" (Montgomery, 19 September 1890, in *CJLMM*, 1: 47).

5 The North Saskatchewan River. See Brandi Newton, "North Saskatchewan River," The Canadian Encyclopedia, Historica Canada, last modified 5 February 2017, https://www.thecanadianencyclopedia.ca/en/article/north-saskatchewan-river/.

6 Within a system of ethics, "moral law" refers to a set of behavioural guidelines. In the Bible, this would include the Ten Commandments (see Exodus 20:1–17 and Deuteronomy 5:6–21) as well as additional laws found the Old Testament.

7 *The Great Lone Land: A Narrative of Travel and Adventure in the North-West of America* (1872), by William Francis Butler (1838–1910), English Army officer.

VALEDICTORY

By James H. Stevenson. Excerpted from "Prince of Wales College," *Daily Examiner* (Charlottetown), 9 June 1894, 2. Also in Scrapbook 7 ("Written June 1894 / Published June 1894 / In 'Examiner'").

1 *Daily Examiner* (Charlottetown), "Prince of Wales College" (9 June 1894), 2; *Daily Examiner* (Charlottetown), "Prince of Wales College" (8 June 1894), 2.

2 Montgomery, 5 June 1894, in *CJLMM*, 1: 215; Montgomery, 6 June 1894, in *CJLMM*, 1: 215; *Island Guardian and Christian Chronicle* (Charlottetown), "P. of W. Convocation," 2.

3 Rubio and Waterston note that Montgomery's 1893–1894 class "consisted of seventy-seven women and ninety-nine men"; Prince of Wales College had been co-educational since 1879 (Rubio and Waterston, in *CJLMM*, 1: 167n3).

4 Here, Montgomery refers to *The College Record*, in which she had published three pieces included in this volume as well as a poem.

5 This German phrase appears on the badge of the Prince of Wales.

6 Properly, "And judge that they who counsel strife / Would bid us smite – a brother." From "The Triumphs of Our Language," a hymn lyric by James Gilborne Lyons (1800–1868), Irish-born American hymn lyricist, appearing in his book *Christian Songs, Translations, and Other Poems* (1861).

"PORTIA" – A STUDY

By Lucy Maud Montgomery. *Island Guardian and Christian Chronicle* (Charlottetown), 14 June 1894, 3. Also in Scrapbook 7 ("Written June 1894 / Published June 1894 / In Ch'Town 'Guardian'"). Also in Bolger, *The Years Before "Anne,"* 140–42.

Also, with minor variations and as "Portia," in *Daily Patriot* (Charlottetown), 11 June 1894, 2.

Also, with minor variations, excerpted from "Prince of Wales College," in *Daily Examiner* (Charlottetown), 11 June 1894, 2.

1 *Daily Examiner* (Charlottetown), "Prince of Wales College" (8 June 1894), 2. Montgomery also received the highest score in

second-year Agriculture and first-year School Management as well as first-year honours in essay writing and teaching.

2 *Daily Examiner* (Charlottetown), "Prince of Wales College" (9 June 1894), 2; *Island Guardian and Christian Chronicle* (Charlottetown), "P. of W. Convocation," 2; Montgomery, 9 June 1894, in *CJLMM*, 1: 217. George Eliot, pseudonym of Mary Ann Evans (1819–1880), English author best-known for the novels *The Mill on the Floss* (1860) and *Middlemarch* (1871–1872).

3 The original reads "No titled lover with princely retinue," but Montgomery adds the word "he" and the comma in ink in her scrapbook copy.

4 The original reads "solely," but Montgomery corrects this as "sorely" in her scrapbook copy.

5 The original reads "succeeds," but Montgomery crosses out the final *s* in her scrapbook copy.

6 The original reads "grandeur," but Montgomery crosses out this word and replaces it with "gardens" in her scrapbook copy.

"WHICH HAS THE MOST PATIENCE UNDER THE ORDINARY CARES AND TRIALS OF LIFE – MAN OR WOMAN?"

Untitled contributions by Belinda Bluegrass and Enid. [*Evening Mail* (Halifax), February 1896.] Scrapbook 7 ("Written January 1896 / Published February 1896 / In 'Halifax Evening Mail'"). Also partly in Bolger, *The Years Before "Anne,"* 159.

1 Montgomery, 15 February 1896, in *CJLMM*, 1: 311.

2 For commentary on the rhetoric Montgomery used in her journal to describe her submissions to this contest, see Rubio, *Lucy Maud Montgomery*, 84.

3 "The Prize Awarded," *Evening Mail* (Halifax), undated clipping, in Scrapbook 7; Montgomery to Weber, 2 September 1909, in *GGL*, 91.

4 "Personals," unidentified and undated clipping, in Scrapbook 7; Montgomery, 25 September 1895, in *CJLMM*, 1: 145. See also Lefebvre, "Introduction: A Life in Print," 18–19.

5 For the creation stories of Adam and Eve, see Genesis 1–5 (*KJV*).

6 I have corrected the original, which reads "That's he sure."

7 In the Book of Job in the Old Testament, Job undergoes a series of trials that dramatizes the philosophical question of why bad things happen to good people. Job's story has been alluded to

innumerable times throughout Western history in literature, film, music, and visual art.

8 The original reads "That where one was really found," but Montgomery corrects "where" as "when" in her scrapbook.

CROOKED ANSWERS

By L.M.M. [*The Prince of Wales College Observer* (Charlottetown), March 1896.] Scrapbook 7 ("Written February 1896 / Published March 1896 / In 'College Observer'").

1 See Montgomery, 7 November 1896, in *CJLMM*, 1: 334–35; Montgomery, 18 August 1896, in *CJLMM*, 1: 325–26; Montgomery, 2 February 1897, in *CJLMM*, 1: 352–53; Montgomery, 30 June 1897, in *CJLMM*, 1: 368–78; Montgomery, 22 January 1898, in *CJLMM*, 1: 385–87; Montgomery, 8 April 1898, in *CJLMM*, 1: 391–95.

2 I have not been able to locate copies of the earliest issues of *The Prince of Wales College Observer*. A clipping with the masthead of an 1896 issue appears in Montgomery's Blue Scrapbook.

3 The original publication reads "All the evoked answers," but following Montgomery's handwritten corrections in her scrapbook copy I have replaced "evoked" with "crooked."

4 The original reads "certain visitor," but in Montgomery's scrapbook copy she underlines "certain," adds an asterisk immediately before this word, and writes "critical" in the margin.

5 Properly, "*bons mots*," the plural form of a French term referring to "a clever or witty saying" (*OED*).

6 Properly, Thomas à Becket (ca. 1120–1170), Archbishop of Canterbury from 1162 to his death, who was canonized as a saint by Pope Alexander III after he was murdered.

7 William Tyndale (ca. 1494–1536) completed the first English translation of the New Testament and selections of the Old Testament.

8 The Battle of Dunbar was fought in Dunbar, Scotland, on 3 September 1650. A legend states that King Charles II (1630–1685), who had been King of England, Scotland, and Ireland since February 1649, hid from his pursuers in an oak tree until he was able to escape to France.

9 This artificial waterway in Egypt connects the Mediterranean Sea and the Red Sea.

10 This strip of land joins North America and South America.

11 Montgomery would use the "Birds" essay again in the penultimate instalment of "Around the Table" below. Chapter 11 of *Anne of Avonlea* contains this essay in full (see *AA*, 112–13).

12 One of Anne's students signs his "Birds" essay in a similar way in *Anne of Avonlea* (see *AA*, 113).

THE BAD BOY OF BLANKTOWN SCHOOL

By L.M.M. *The Dalhousie Gazette* (Halifax), 4 March 1896, 220–23. Also in Scrapbook 7 ("Written February 1896 / Published March 1896 / In 'Dalhousie Gazette'").

1 Montgomery, 18 September 1894, in *CJLMM*, 1: 240.

2 One of the definitions of "smelt" in the *OED* is "a small fish ... allied to the salmon, and emitting a peculiar odour."

3 An allusion to Luke 11:25 (*KJV*): "And when he cometh, he findeth *it* swept and garnished." See also Matthew 12:44 (*KJV*).

JAMES HENRY, TRUANT

By L. [*The Prince of Wales College Observer* (Charlottetown), April 1896.] Scrapbook 7 ("Written March 1896 / Published April 1896 / In 'College Observer'").

1 I have corrected the original, which reads "as they said," from Montgomery's handwritten corrections in her scrapbook copy.

2 The word "longer" is pronounced "long-ger." Montgomery would note later that she had never heard that word for fence rails used outside Prince Edward Island or seen it in any form of literature. See Montgomery, in *DCMF*, 91; Montgomery, 1 March 1925, in *LMMCJ*, 3: 337; Montgomery, "Come Back with Me," 335–36.

A GIRL'S PLACE AT DALHOUSIE COLLEGE

By Lucy M. Montgomery. *Halifax Herald*, 29 April 1896, 12. Also in Scrapbook 7 ("Written April 1896 / Published April 1896 / In 'Halifax Herald'").

Also in Bolger, *The Years Before "Anne,"* 161–68.

Also in *Atlantis: A Women's Studies Journal / Journal d'études sur la femme* 5 (Fall 1979): 146–53.

Also as "The Thirty Sweet Girl Graduates of Dalhousie University" in Montgomery, *Anne of Green Gables*, edited by Devereux, 371–79.

Also excerpted in Montgomery, *Anne of Green Gables*, edited by Rubio and Waterston, 272–75.

1 Devereux, in Montgomery, *Anne of Green Gables*, edited by Devereux, 371.

2 Montgomery, 14 March 1896, in *CJLMM*, 1: 316. Two articles ("Dalhousie College Gazette" and "Dalhousie College Students' Societies") are signed "R.M.H.," but the remaining ("Fossilized Oxford and Cambridge," "The Officers of the Various Societies," and "Names of Students Who Got Through") are unsigned. In the last of these pieces, "Montgomery, Lucy" is listed under "English" / "Second Year," even though she was a first-year student.

3 Devereux, in Montgomery, *Anne of Green Gables*, edited by Devereux, 371.

4 Headnote to "A Girl's Place at Dalhousie College," 147, 146, 147.

5 The first two extracts appear in canto 2, the third in the prologue of "The Princess: A Medley," a poem by Tennyson.

6 Reading, writing, and arithmetic, the fundamentals of skills-based education.

7 I have corrected the original, which reads "to think that the attainments."

8 Hypatia of Alexandria (ca. 370–415 CE), an Egyptian philosopher and mathematician who had been tutored by her father in astronomy, mathematics, and science. According to Joshua J. Mark, Hypatia was "seen as a 'stumbling block' to those who would have accepted the 'truth' of Christianity were it not for her charisma, charm, and excellence in making difficult mathematical and philosophical concepts understandable to her students." She was killed by a Christian mob because her teachings "contradicted the teachings of the relatively new church." See Joshua J. Mark, "Hypatia of Alexandria," Ancient History Encyclopedia, 2 September 2009, https://www.ancient.eu/Hypatia_of_Alexandria/.

9 Euclid of Alexandria (lived ca. 300 BCE) "systematized ancient Greek and Near Eastern mathematics and geometry"; he was the author of *The Elements*, "the most widely used mathematics and geometry textbook in history." See N.S. Palmer, "Euclid," Ancient History Encyclopedia, 23 October 2015, https://www.ancient.eu/Euclid/. In *Anne of Green Gables*, Anne refers to her geometry textbook by Euclid's name (see *AGG*, 362).

10 I have corrected the original, which reads "they would persist," as per Montgomery's handwritten corrections in her scrapbook copy.

11 Cecily Devereux, annotating this piece as an appendix to her critical edition of *Anne of Green Gables*, states that this phrase means "to remain a virgin," referring to Longfellow's poem *Evangeline: A Tale of Acadie* (Devereux, in Montgomery, *Anne of Green Gables*, edited by Devereux, 373n1).

12 One of the definitions of "bluestocking" offered by the *Oxford English Dictionary* was popular throughout the nineteenth century: "A woman devoted to literary, scholarly, or intellectual activities," and later, "with derogatory connotations, applied to intellectual women in general."

13 Philippa Fawcett (1868–1948), English mathematician and lecturer. The title "senior wrangler" was given by the student at Cambridge who received the highest score in mathematics; because women at the time were not permitted to receive a B.A. at Cambridge, Fawcett could not earn this title even though her score in 1890 was much higher than that of her male classmate with the highest score. I have corrected the original, which reads "wranglee."

14 Agneta Frances Ramsay (1867–1931) received the highest marks in the classical tripos, Cambridge's program in classics, in 1887.

15 Margaret Florence Newcombe (1857–1937) and Lillie B. Calkin (1862–1952) were first cousins. Newcombe married James Starr Trueman in 1890 and would become principal of Halifax Ladies' College. Calkin married George S. Carson in 1886, and their daughter, Annie, would graduate from Halifax Ladies' College.

16 Established in 1887, the Halifax Ladies' College is where Montgomery boarded while a Dalhousie student.

17 Bachelor of Laws degree. Eliza Ritchie (1856–1933), who taught at Wellesley until 1899.

18 Cornell University, located in Ithaca, New York, began admitting women as students in 1870, the same year as the founding of Wellesley College, a women's liberal arts college in Massachusetts.

19 Master of Laws degree.

20 Bryn Mawr College, a women's liberal arts college in Pennsylvania that was founded in 1885, was the first American college to offer women advanced degrees, including the Ph.D.

21 Annie Isabella Hamilton (1866–1941), the first woman to graduate with a medical degree from Dalhousie University, set up a practice in Halifax after graduation and, in 1903, moved to China, where she worked as a medical missionary for the rest of her life.

22 I have corrected the original, which reads "into reading room."

23 I have corrected the original, which reads "that will – certainly not."

24 I have corrected the original, which reads "which as frequently discussed" and "time above."

25 Properly, "Her children arise up, and call her blessed." Proverbs 31:28 (*KJV*).

TO THE EDITOR

By L.M. Montgomery. Excerpted from "Gleanings from Our Mail Bag," *The Editor: A Journal of Information for Literary Workers* (Franklin, OH), March 1899, 125–27.

A HALF-HOUR IN AN OLD CEMETERY

By M.M. *Halifax Daily Echo*, 26 September 1901, 1. Also in Scrapbook 3.

Also in *Morning Chronicle* (Halifax), 27 September 1901, 3.

1 Gerson, "L.M. Montgomery," 69; Montgomery, 13 November 1901, in *CJLMM*, 2: 23–24. See also Lang, *Women Who Made the News*, 47–51.

2 From "The Solitary Reaper," a poem by William Wordsworth (1770–1850), English poet.

3 The original reads "34 years," but Montgomery changes the 3 to an 8 in ink in her scrapbook copy.

4 The phrase "scope for the imagination" would eventually become one of Anne Shirley's signature expressions, beginning in *Anne of Green Gables*.

5 From "Ye Mariners of England," a poem by Thomas Campbell (1777–1844), Scottish poet.

6 The Stars and Stripes, otherwise known as the flag of the United States of America, had forty-five stars until 1908. St. George's Cross, a red cross against a white background, forms part of the basis of the flag of England.

7 The Battle of Boston Harbor took place on 1 June 1813, during the War of 1812, between the HMS *Shannon* and the USS *Chesapeake*, resulting in a British victory.

8 The Battle of Inkerman, the Battle of the Alma, and the Battle of Balaclava were all fought as part of the Crimean War, on 5 November, 20 September, and 25 October 1854.

9 Properly, "those bleak heights henceforth shall be famous in story." From *Lucile* (1860), a book-length poem by Owen Meredith, pseudonym of Edward Bulwer-Lytton (1831–1891), English poet.
10 Properly, "After life's fitful fever he sleeps well." From *Macbeth* (1606), a tragic play by Shakespeare.

AROUND THE TABLE

This entire column is arranged to appear as one continuous text in Scrapbook 3, with the instalments appearing in the following order: 1–14, 16–17, 22, 20–21, 23, 18, 15, 19, 24–27, 29–35; instalment 28 is absent from this copy.

1 Montgomery, 14 November 1901, in *CJLMM*, 2: 26.
2 Montgomery, 28 November 1901, in *CJLMM*, 2: 36.
3 Montgomery, 14 November 1901, in *CJLMM*, 2: 26.

OVER THE TEA CUPS

"Over the Tea Cups." By Cynthia. *Halifax Daily Echo*, 28 September 1901, 10.

4 These descriptive phrases, referred to in newspaper terms as a "deck," are omitted from the copy of this column in Scrapbook 3.
5 Dating back to the eighteenth century and sporting a variety of styles, an elaborate hat for women with a wide brim.
6 Possibly an allusion to "The Frequented Village," a poem by Thomas Dermody (1775–1802), Irish poet.
7 From "A Dream of Fair Women," a poem by Tennyson.
8 American graphic artist Charles Dana Gibson (1867–1944) created a visual icon of white feminine physical attractiveness that became known as the Gibson girl.
9 Properly, "a delusion, a mockery, and a snare." From Thomas Denman, English judge and politician, in his judgment on the 1844 case of *Daniel O'Connel vs. The Queen*. This phrase appears also in chapter 1 of *Rilla of Ingleside* (see *RI*, 3) and in Montgomery, "The Importance of Beauty in Everything," 296.
10 This phrase is included in a letter from George Gordon, Lord Byron (1788–1824), English poet, to Augusta Leigh (1783–1851), 18 September 1816, in Byron, *Byron's Letters and Journals*, 232.
11 The Halifax Public Gardens were started by the Nova Scotia Horticultural Society in 1836 and merged with a civic garden in 1875; they remain open today.

12 From "The Lotus-Eaters," a poem by Tennyson.

13 The title of a speech given in Chicago in April 1899 by then-future U.S. President Theodore Roosevelt (1858–1919), in which he argued that great effort and labour were necessary for success.

14 "Clove Pinks" (*Dianthus caryophyllus*), a type of carnation; "Adam and Eve" (*Aplectrum hyemale*), a type of orchid; "Bouncing Bess" (*Saponaria officinalis*), also called "soapwort," a plant with clusters of pink or white flowers used as an alternative to soap; "Scarlet Lightning" (*Lychnis chalcedonica*), a plant with scarlet or white flowers whose petals are shaped in a way that resembles a Maltese cross; "Sweet Balm" (*Melissa officinalis*), a perennial plant with hermaphrodite flowers and tremendous medicinal value; "Butter and Eggs" (*Linaria vulgaris*), a species of toadflax whose flowers are similar to those of a snapdragon; "Bride's Bouquet" (*Poranopsis paniculata*), also known as "Christmas Vine" and "Snow Creeper," a climbing vine of green leaves with thick clusters of white flowers; "Prince's Feather" (*Amaranthus hypochondriacus*), an ornamental plant with plumes of reddish-purple flowers; "Bleeding Heart" (*Lamprocapnos spectabilis*), a plant with heart-shaped flowers. For a journal entry on old-fashioned gardens written only a few months before this column, see Montgomery, 28 August 1901, in *CJLMM*, 2: 20. See also Montgomery, *The Annotated Anne of Green Gables*, 437.

15 An infectious (and often deadly) disease with no proven treatment. In *Anne of Green Gables*, Anne ruins a cake while fantasizing that she nurses Diana from smallpox only to succumb to the disease herself (*AGG*, 174). Smallpox is a major plot point in "The Quarantine at Alexander Abraham's" (in *Chronicles of Avonlea*) and "In Her Selfless Mood" (in *Further Chronicles of Avonlea*).

16 A serious infection caused by the pathogenic bacterium *Corynebacterium diphtheriae*. In *Rilla of Ingleside*, Mary Vance saves the day when Rilla's ward, Jims, becomes gravely ill with "dipthery croup" (*RI*, 270), referring to a type of diphtheria that leads to serious respiratory problems that are similar to those of croup, even though the diseases are unrelated.

17 This expression, which refers to someone who sleeps with a clear conscience, can be traced back to *Abrégé de l'histoire de Port-Royal*, a non-fiction work by Racine: "Elle s'endormit du sommeil des justes." It also appears in *Vanity Fair*, by Thackeray.

18 This hairstyle, named after Jeanne Antoinette Poisson, Marquise

de Pompadour (1721–1764), mistress of King Louis XV of France, involves sweeping the hair away from the face and wearing it high over the forehead. This hairstyle returned to fashion for women as part of the Gibson Girl look in the 1890s.

[LETTERS, BOOKS, AND NECKWEAR]

"Around the Table." By Cynthia. *Halifax Daily Echo*, 5 October 1901, 3.

19 A main street in Halifax and the location of Halifax City Hall. As indicated in Montgomery's advertisements for the Christmas season included later in this volume, many of the major shops in Halifax were located on this street.

20 A fichu is "a triangular piece of some light fabric, worn by ladies, now as a covering for the neck, throat, and shoulders, formerly also for the head" (*OED*).

21 The term "substance" refers to "maintenance, (means of) subsistence" (*OED*). In "[Seeing and Perceiving]" below, Polly mentions receiving a monthly allowance from her father.

22 The phrase "all sorts and conditions of neckwear" is an allusion to *All Sorts and Conditions of Men* (1882), a novel by Walter Besant (1836–1901), English author. Chapter 6 of *Anne of Avonlea* is entitled "All Sorts and Conditions of Men ... and Women."

23 *The Love Letters of Honoré de Balzac, 1833–1842* and *The Love Letters of Dorothy Osborne to Sir William Temple, 1652–54* had been published in 1901.

24 Robert Browning (1812–1889) and Elizabeth Barrett Browning (1806–1861), English poets. *The Letters of Elizabeth Barrett Browning* had been published in 1897, *The Letters of Robert Browning and Elizabeth Barrett Browning, 1845–1846* in 1899.

25 Otto von Bismarck (1815–1898), first Chancellor of Germany between 1871 and 1890. *The Love Letters of Prince Bismarck* had been published in 1901.

26 Victor Hugo (1802–1855), French novelist, poet, and playwright. *The Love Letters of Victor Hugo* had been published in 1901.

27 Properly, "Charity suffereth long, and is kind." From 1 Corinthians 13:4 (*KJV*).

28 *Love-Letters from King Henry VIII to Anne Boleyn* had been published in 1714; *The Life Romantic: Including the Love-Letters of the King*, by Richard Le Gallienne (1866–1947), English author, had been published in 1901.

29 *The Love-Letters of a Worldly Woman* by Lucy Clifford (1846–1929), English journalist and novelist, had been published in 1892 under the name Mrs. W.K. Clifford.

30 *An Englishwoman's Love-Letters*, a novel published anonymously in 1900, was deemed scandalous due to its content, but the scandal dissipated after the revelation that the book had been written by Laurence Housman (1865–1959), English playwright.

31 Popular catchphrase form of "Advice to persons about to marry – Don't!," attributed to Henry Mayhew (1812–1887), English social researcher, journalist, and co-founder (in 1841) of the London magazine *Punch*, which took as its masthead the character of Mr. Punch in the traditional puppet play "Punch and Judy."

32 The term "parlous" is referred to here in the sense of "perilous, dangerous, precarious" (*OED*).

33 "Ye olden tyme" and "ye olde tyme" are Old English phrases referring to times past. *Ye Amherst Girl of Ye Olden Tyme*, a non-fiction book by Alice M. Walker (1855–1928), American author, had been published in 1901.

34 A Nova Scotia town 85 kilometres northwest of Halifax.

[CHARITABLE FITS AND DESPERATE MEASURES]
"Around the Table." By Cynthia. *Halifax Daily Echo*, 12 October 1901, 1.

Also in *Morning Chronicle* (Halifax), 14 October 1901, 7.

35 Founded in 1802 and located at the corner of South and Robie Streets, the Halifax Poor's Asylum was a workhouse for orphans, the elderly, and the unemployed that would close in 1947. This anecdote was excerpted and appears with minor variations as "Polly and the Poor's Asylum," in McCabe, "Lucy Maud Montgomery's Table Talk," 162.

36 From the colloquial phrase "to beg, borrow, or steal." The earliest usage of a version of this phrase listed in the *Oxford English Dictionary* is from *Tristram Shandy* (1759–1767), a nine-volume novel by Laurence Sterne (1713–1768), Irish novelist.

37 See "'Portia' – A Study," note 2, above.

38 Plural form of a variant of "knick-knack."

39 An expression derived from one of the titular characters in traditional Punch and Judy puppet shows.

40 The Duke of York (who would reign as King George V between 1910 and his death in 1936) and the Duchess of York (later known

as Queen Mary) visited Halifax as part of an extended tour of the British Empire in 1901, an event that received considerable coverage in both the *Halifax Daily Echo* and the *Morning Chronicle*. See, for instance, *Halifax Daily Echo*, "A Royal Welcome"; *Morning Chronicle* (Halifax), "Grand Welcome"; *Morning Chronicle* (Halifax), "Nova Scotia Welcomes."

41 The first contingent of soldiers who had fought in the Second Boer War returned to Canada in December 1900. That event was celebrated in Halifax with parades and concerts.

42 This phrase appears in *Roxy* (1878), a novel by Edward Eggleston (1837–1902), American novelist, and in *Samantha among the Brethren* (1890), signed "Josiah Allen's Wife," a humorous novel by Marietta Holley (1836–1926), American novelist.

43 From "Lochinvar," a poem by Scott.

44 In the United Kingdom, this gold coin has a nominal value of one pound sterling.

[COLLISIONS AND CROSSED WIRES]

"Around the Table." By Synthia [*sic*]. *Halifax Daily Echo*, 19 October 1901, 4.

Also, by Cynthia, in *Morning Chronicle* (Halifax), 21 October 1901, 2.

45 Properly, "Fools and children should never look at unfinished work," American proverb.

46 Built in the 1860s and located at 1723 Hollis Street; possibly was undergoing renovation at the time Montgomery was writing.

47 Term for October found in a number of Indigenous nations, including Abenaki, Cree, Ojibwe, and Sioux. Montgomery would use this term again in *The Golden Road* (see *GR*, 321).

48 In *The Pilgrim's Progress* (1678), by John Bunyan (1628–1688), English writer and Baptist preacher, the protagonist, Christian, falls into a bog called the Slough of Despond due to the weight of his sins.

49 Montgomery later reused this anecdote in chapter 6 of *Anne of the Island*, involving Philippa Gordon (*AIs*, 58). This anecdote was excerpted and appears with minor variations as "Polly's Postscripts" in McCabe, "Lucy Maud Montgomery's Table Talk," 162–63.

50 Both original versions read "properly furnished," but Montgomery crosses out "furnished" and replaces it in ink with "punished" in her scrapbook copy.

51 Laura Jean Libbey (1862–1924), American author of popular romance novels.

52 I have corrected the original, which reads "ood for it is to pin up hair!"

53 One definition of signet is "a seal, usually set in a ring, regarded as an item of jewellery and featuring distinctive lettering or design. Also: a ring to which such a seal is fixed" (*OED*).

54 Properly, "What therefore God hath joined together let not man put asunder," a saying traditionally stated at the end of a wedding ceremony to indicate that a marriage can never be dissolved. See Matthew 19:6 (*KJV*).

["AFTER THE BALL"]
"Around the Table." By Cynthia. *Halifax Daily Echo*, 26 October 1901, 1, 12.

Also in *Morning Chronicle* (Halifax), 28 October 1901, 3.

55 Title of a popular song by Charles K. Harris (1867–1930), American songwriter, written in 1891.

56 Compare this to Montgomery's assessment of the Duke and the Duchess in her journal: "Our future king is an insignificant man with a red nose. The duchess looks to be the best man of the two. She was a big, rather fine-looking woman dressed rather dowdily in black" (Montgomery, 23 November 1901, in *CJLMM*, 2: 34).

57 "Beaux yeux" is French for "beautiful eyes" and is also a possible pun on "bijoux," French for "jewels." I have corrected the original, which reads "Dolly admires."

58 I have corrected the original, which reads "tear down street!"

59 A literal translation of the French phrase "Revenons à nos moutons," from the anonymous play *La Farce de Maistre Pierre Pathelin* (ca. 1460), referring to a return to the subject at hand. The expression occurs again in *Rilla of Ingleside* (see *RI*, 11, 116). See also Montgomery, 6 April 1894, in *CJLMM*, 1: 201.

60 This anecdote was excerpted and appears in shorter form as "A Hallowe'en Charm," in McCabe, "Lucy Maud Montgomery's Table Talk," 163.

61 A partner in marriage, "weal and woe" being an idiomatic expression referring to good and bad days, happiness and sorrow, prosperity and adversity, and so forth.

62 The expression "the eternal fitness of things" refers to the congruity between an action and its agent. This expression originated in

The History of Tom Jones, Foundling (1749), a novel by Henry Fielding (1707–1754), English novelist and dramatist. In *The Story Girl*, the narrator posits that "a cat in a hayloft is a beautiful example of the eternal fitness of things" (*SG*, 103). The phrase also appears in *Anne of Green Gables* (see *AGG*, 72–73).

63 The origin of this expression is unknown, but it appears to refer to "stern parents."

64 Montgomery's Blue Scrapbook includes an unidentified clipping, "A Humane Pater," containing the source of this story:

> One reads so frequently of the paternal boot as applied to the undesirable youthful suitor that it is a pleasure to chronicle the more humane method adopted by a wealthy Glasgow merchant for choking off a "follower" of his daughter. The girl was very young, so was the follower, but nevertheless he called formally on the object of his affections. The merchant and his wife entered the room, the latter bearing a glass of milk and a huge slice of bread spread with butter and jam.
>
> "Now dear, run away to bed," said the kindly mother to her daughter; "it's time that all good girls should be in bed."
>
> Then the Glasgow merchant addressed the astonished young man, –
>
> "Now, youngster, you drink that glass of milk, and take that slice of bread and jam to eat on the road home – and hurry, for your mother must be anxious about your being out so late by yourself."
>
> The young man did not call again.

65 Orris root consists of "the fragrant rhizome of any of several irises of the *Iris germanica* group; a powdered preparation of such rhizomes, used in perfumery and formerly in medicine" (*OED*).

[DISMAL NOVEMBER]

"Around the Table." By Cynthia. *Halifax Daily Echo*, 2 November 1901, 1.

Also in *Morning Chronicle* (Halifax), 4 November 1901, 7.

66 See "Around the Table," note 270, below.

67 Thanksgiving Day, an official Canadian holiday since 1879, was celebrated at various points in the autumn months until 1957, since when it has been celebrated consistently the second Monday

in October. See Montgomery, 28 November 1901, in *CJLMM*, 2: 35–36; David Mills, Laura Neilson Bonikowsky, and Andrew McIntosh, "Thanksgiving in Canada," The Canadian Encyclopedia, Historica Canada, last modified 11 March 2016, https://www.thecanadianencyclopedia.ca/en/article/thanksgiving-day/.

68 Pseudonym of Léon Paul Blouet (1847–1903), French author.

69 This misunderstanding is reused in *Anne of Avonlea* (*AA*, 150).

70 Margaret Wolfe Hungerford (1855–1897), Irish author of light romantic novels appearing under the pseudonym "The Duchess."

71 Allusion to "The Fox without a Tail," from *Aesop's Fables*, which ends with the following moral: "Distrust interested advice."

72 Medium; in the middle. This expression appears in *Samantha and the Race Problem* (1892), a humorous novel by Marietta Holley, signed "Josiah Allen's Wife." The expression occurs again in *Anne of Green Gables* (see *AGG*, 424).

73 Ireland, first referred to as "Emerald Isle" in "When Erin First Rose," a poem by William Drennan (1754–1820), Irish poet.

[WEDDING BELLS]

"Around the Table." By Synthia [*sic*]. *Halifax Daily Echo*, 11 November 1901, 1.

Also in *Morning Chronicle* (Halifax), 12 November 1901, 6.

74 This phrase is attributed to Ralph Waldo Emerson (1803–1882), American essayist and poet, but it reads as "All mankind love a lover" in his essay "Love," in *Essays: First Series* (1841).

75 Popular nineteenth-century saying.

76 The article in question, which claims that "about a century has passed since woman's fondness began to spoil the English novel," was actually written by a woman: Neith Boyce (1872–1951), American novelist and playwright. The quoted phrase "for the deterioration of heroes" does not appear in the article.

77 To make a bad situation worse, an idiom popularized in the widely circulated 1848 speech "Slaveholding Insolence" by Cassius Marcellus Clay (1810–1903), American politician and anti-slavery activist.

78 This quoted phrase does not appear in the article itself. Boyce claims that "as she has prevented the hero of the novel from soaring to the lonely peaks which she can't reach herself, so also she forbids him to ramp through the pleasant meadows, witlessly enjoying himself" (Boyce, "The Novelist's Deadliest Friend," 27).

79 Properly, *Tommy and Grizel*, a 1900 sequel to *Sentimental Tommy* (1896), by J.M. Barrie (1860–1937), Scottish novelist and playwright best known for *Peter Pan*.

80 Properly, "weariness of the flesh." From Ecclesiastes 12:12 (*KJV*).

81 Genesis, the first book in the Old Testament, describing the origins of the earth and of humankind.

[BAD LUCK AND BAD ADVICE]

"Around the Table." By Cynthia. *Halifax Daily Echo*, 16 November 1901, 1.

Also in *Morning Chronicle* (Halifax), 18 November 1901, 3.

82 From "Young Benjie," a ballad by Scott.

83 A meteor shower that peaks in November.

84 The original reads "there is known way," but Montgomery adds the "no" in ink in her scrapbook copy.

85 See "[Dismal November]," published just two weeks prior to this instalment.

86 Unveiled in 1860, the Welsford-Parker Monument, which commemorates the British involvement in the Crimean War and which is found in Halifax's Old Burying Ground, depicts a lion above a tall arch. Montgomery (as "Cynthia") first wrote about this location in "A Half-Hour in an Old Cemetery," reprinted earlier in this volume.

[A WALK IN THE PARK]

"Around the Table." By Cynthia. *Halifax Daily Echo*, 23 November 1901, 1.

Also in *Morning Chronicle* (Halifax), 25 November 1901, 7.

87 Point Pleasant Park, at the south end of the Halifax peninsula.

88 The Northwest Arm, an inlet, part of Halifax Harbour.

89 Properly, "the Warden of the Honour of the North." From the "Halifax" portion of "The Song of the Cities," a poem by Rudyard Kipling (1865–1936), English poet and novelist.

90 Properly, "And thank God that it ain't no wuss!" From "Give Thanks for What?," a poem by William Augustus Croffut (1836–1915), American journalist and author.

91 A phrase found fifteen times throughout the Old and New Testaments, referring to the afterlife.

92 Properly, "beauty is its own excuse for Being." From "The Rhodora," a poem by Emerson.

93 Allusion to "Give me liberty, or give me death!," attributed to Patrick Henry (1736–1799), American attorney who championed the movement for independence in Virginia in the 1770s.

94 The *OED* defines "ethyl" as "an alkyl group – C_2H_5, which occurs in ethanol and its derivatives (and of which there are two in ether), derived from ethane by loss of a hydrogen atom."

95 In "[Collisions and Crossed Wires]" and "[Wedding Bells]," Cynthia's byline appears (likely erroneously) as "Synthia."

[CAKES AND DRESSES]

"Around the Table." By Cynthia. *Halifax Daily Echo*, 2 December 1901, 1.

Also in *Morning Chronicle* (Halifax), 3 December 1901, 3.

96 The term "presto, change" echoes the phrase "presto changeo," an early twentieth-century American expression "announcing the climax of a conjuring trick or a sudden transformation" (*OED*).

97 The Halifax Conservatory of Music, founded in 1887, had been offering licences and diplomas in partnership with Dalhousie University since 1898.

98 I have corrected the original, which reads "he says intends."

99 Flour ("And Solomon's provision for one day was thirty measures of fine flour, and threescore measures of meal").

100 Butter ("she brought forth butter in a lordly dish").

101 Sugar ("To what purpose cometh there to me incense from Sheba, and the sweet cane from a far country? Your burnt offerings are not acceptable, nor your sacrifices sweet unto me").

102 Raisins ("And they gave him a piece of a cake of figs, and two clusters of raisins: and when he had eaten, his spirit came again to him: for he had eaten no bread, nor drunk any water, three days and three nights").

103 See Nahum 3:12 (*KJV*), which suggests figs ("All thy strong holds shall be like fig trees with the firstripe figs: if they be shaken, they shall even fall into the mouth of the eater").

104 See Numbers 17:8 (*KJV*), which suggests almonds ("And it came to pass, that on the morrow Moses went into the tabernacle of witness; and, behold, the rod of Aaron for the house of Levi was budded, and brought forth buds, and bloomed blossoms, and yielded almonds").

105 Honey ("And all they of the land came to a wood; and there was honey upon the ground").

106 Eggs ("As the partridge sitteth on eggs, and hatcheth them not; so he that getteth riches, and not by right, shall leave them in the midst of his days, and at his end shall be a fool").

107 Spice ("And she gave the king an hundred and twenty talents of gold, and of spices great abundance, and precious stones: neither was there any such spice as the queen of Sheba gave king Solomon").

108 Milk ("And she opened a bottle of milk, and gave him drink, and covered him").

109 Salt ("And every oblation of thy meat offering shalt thou season with salt; neither shalt thou suffer the salt of the covenant of thy God to be lacking from thy meat offering: with all thine offerings thou shalt offer salt").

110 This verse reads "And offer a sacrifice of thanksgiving with leaven, and proclaim and publish the free offerings: for this liketh you, O ye children of Israel, saith the Lord God."

111 This verse reads "Thou shalt beat him with the rod, and shalt deliver his soul from hell." See also "High School Life in Saskatchewan," note 3, above.

112 In this context, the verb "to squeeze" is used colloquially to refer to a loverly embrace.

[PRESENTS AND SECRETS]

"Around the Table." By Cynthia. *Halifax Daily Echo*, 7 December 1901, 1.

Also in *Morning Chronicle* (Halifax), 9 December 1901, 3.

113 "Little old woman up in the sky, / See how she makes the feathers fly! / She sits in the twilight overhead / And picks her geese for a feather-bed." Nineteenth-century rhyme. In *Anne of the Island*, Davy Keith asks if this woman in the sky is God's wife (*AIs*, 169).

114 Properly, "A thing of beauty is a joy for ever." From "Endymion," a poem by John Keats (1795–1821), English poet.

115 Properly, Thomas à Kempis (ca. 1380–1471), Dutch priest and author of the influential devotional book *The Imitation of Christ*.

116 *The Visits of Elizabeth* (1900), an epistolary novel satirizing high society by Elinor Glyn (1864–1943), English author.

117 Persian poet and philosopher (1048–1131) whose poems first appeared in English as *Rubaiyat of Omar Khayyam* (1859), translated by Edward FitzGerald (1809–1883), English poet.

118 This 1887 book, subtitled *Being a Handbook to Marriage* and signed "A Graduate in the University of Matrimony," has been attributed to Edward John Hardy (1849–1920), Irish clergyman and writer.

119 Reference to the Royal Society for the Prevention of Cruelty to Animals, founded in the United Kingdom in 1824 and followed by a number of not-for-profit organizations around the world.

120 "He that will steal a pin will steal a better thing," an American proverb.

121 One of the definitions of "prostration" in the *OED* refers to "extreme physical weakness or exhaustion; (also) extreme mental depression or dejection; an instance of this." One of the examples in the *OED* definition is from *Anne of the Island* (see *AIs*, 15).

[PREACHMENTS ON CHRISTMASTIDE]

"Around the Table." By Cynthia. *Halifax Daily Echo*, 14 December 1901, 1.

Also in *Morning Chronicle* (Halifax), 16 December 1901, 7.

122 From "The Vision of Sir Launfal" (1848), a long poem by James Russell Lowell (1819–1891), American author.

123 Louis XIII, Louis XIV, Louis XV, and Louis XVI reigned as Kings of France between 1610 and 1792.

124 "The absolute truth; esp. used to emphasize that something, esp. a statement, is or should be true in every particular, with no facts omitted or untrue elements added" (*OED*), an expression that can be traced to the sixteenth century.

125 Allusion to "Variety is the spice of life," a proverb that originates in the six-book poem *The Task* (1785) by William Cowper (1731–1800), English poet: "Variety's the very spice of life, / That gives it all its flavour."

[ILLUSIONS OF CHRISTMAS]

"Around the Table." By Cynthia. *Halifax Daily Echo*, 23 December 1901, 1, 12.

Also in *Morning Chronicle* (Halifax), 26 December 1901, 5.

126 Properly, "one of those things that no fellow can find out." From *Lord Dundreary and His Brother Sam: The Strange Story of Their Adventures and Family History* (1863). The character originated in the play *Our American Cousin* (1858), by Tom Taylor

(1817–1880), English playwright. Montgomery's version of the quotation was also used in *Anne of the Island* (see *AIs*, 74), and in Montgomery, "The 'Teen-Age Girl," 273.

127 Archaic expression meaning "if it pleases you," referring to a second plural possessive pronoun.

128 This expression appears in *Anne of Green Gables* (see *AGG*, 5), in "The Alpine Path" below, and in Montgomery's journal entry dated 18 November 1901, in *CJLMM*, 2: 31. It is a type of Wellerism, an expression involving a proverb or saying misapplied to humorous effect, named after a character in *The Pickwick Papers*, a novel by Dickens that Montgomery later selected as one of six "Greatest Books in the English Language" for a piece published in the *Bookseller and Stationer*. The editors of *The Annotated Anne of Green Gables* note that "the source of this particular proverb is not known, but it bears relation to many proverbial statements about immunity to pain based upon proximity to it"; they add that the expression is evidence of xenophobia against the Irish (Barry, Doody, and Jones, in Montgomery, *The Annotated Anne of Green Gables*, 42–43n11).

129 Montgomery returns to this childhood illusion in *The Story Girl* (see *SG*, 56–57).

130 A character in *Alice's Adventures in Wonderland* (1865), a children's book by Lewis Carroll, pseudonym of Charles Lutwidge Dodgson (1832–1898), English author and photographer. In chapter 8 of *Anne of Green Gables*, the narrator mentions that "Marilla was as fond of morals as the Duchess in Wonderland, and was firmly convinced that one should be tacked on to every remark made to a child who was being brought up" (*AGG*, 83).

131 From *Trilby* (1895), a popular novel by George du Maurier (1834–1896), French-English author and cartoonist.

132 Montgomery was unable to go home to Cavendish for Christmas that year. For her Christmas plans in Halifax, see "The Alpine Path," note 182, below.

133 The phrase is used figuratively to mean "to relax one's efforts, take things easy" (*OED*), an expression that can be traced to the eighteenth century.

134 "A crystalline terpenoid alcohol found in peppermint and other natural oils, whose odour and taste produce a characteristic cooling sensation, used medicinally in decongestants and analgesics, and as a flavouring" (*OED*).

[RETROSPECTION AND RESOLUTIONS]
"Around the Table." By Cynthia. *Halifax Daily Echo*, 30 December 1901, 8.

Also in *Morning Chronicle* (Halifax), 31 December 1901, 7.

135 "On Our Way Rejoicing," title of a nineteenth-century hymn with lyrics by John Samuel Bewley Monsell (1811–1875), Irish poet.

136 This phrase was popularized as a storytelling device in the collection of short stories *Plain Tales from the Hills* (1888), by Kipling.

137 This malapropism mistakes Herculaneum, the Ancient Roman city destroyed in 79 CE, for the word "Herculean," referring to the strength of Hercules, a figure of Roman classical mythology who has been represented innumerable times in fiction, art, and popular culture. This phrase also appears in *Anne of Avonlea* (see *AA*, 128).

138 The expression "Tom, Dick, and Harry," referring to "any three (or more) representatives of the populace taken at random," originates in the mid-eighteenth century (*OED*). These generic characters return in "Many Admiring Glances Bestowed upon Graduates" later in this volume.

139 "Old Father Time," a personification of time who is "conventionally represented as an aged man carrying a scythe and freq. an hourglass," originates in the mid-sixteenth century (*OED*).

140 Traditional proclamation made at the death of a sovereign ruler, referring here to Edward VII (1841–1910), who had succeeded to the throne after the death of his mother, Queen Victoria (1819–1901), earlier that year; its origins are in fifteenth-century France.

[MISTAKES AND BLUNDERS]
"Around the Table." By Cynthia. *Halifax Daily Echo*, 6 January 1902, 8.

141 Possibly an allusion to *Discourses* (1868), by John Riddell (1818–1868), Scottish preacher.

142 The origin of this "old rhyme" is unknown.

143 Bridgetown, a town in Nova Scotia's Annapolis County, west of Halifax; North Mountain is located on the northern edge of the Annapolis Valley.

144 Sixteenth-century proverb referring to the obligation to accept even a poor offer when it is the only one available.

145 In *Anne of Green Gables*, when Anne tumbles off the roof at Diana's house and Diana panics that Anne has been killed, Anne

replies, "No, Diana, I am not killed, but I think I am rendered unconscious" (*AGG*, 258).

146 Montgomery had experienced this herself when reading the ten-year letter of her adolescent friend Will Pritchard, who had died in 1897, only six years after he had written it. "The letter seemed like a message from the dead – from the world of spirits" (Montgomery, 15 April 1897, in *CJLMM*, 1: 361).

147 "A vessel to hold burning charcoal or other fuel, for heating anything placed upon it; a portable grate" (*OED*).

148 Properly, "and he went forth conquering, and to conquer." From Revelation 6:2 (*KJV*).

[UNLIKEABLE PEOPLE]
"Around the Table." By Cynthia. *Halifax Daily Echo*, 13 January 1902, 8.

149 This paragraph and the six that follow appear with minor variations as "'Preserve Me from the Candid Friend,'" in McCabe, "Lucy Maud Montgomery's Table Talk," 163–64.

150 The quotation "Save, save, oh save me from the candid friend!" is attributed to George Canning (1770–1827), English politician for the Tory party who served as British prime minister during the last four months of his life.

151 "Like to cure like" ("similia similibus curentur," or "let similar things take care of similar things"), the doctrine behind homeopathy, a form of alternative medicine invented in the late eighteenth century by Samuel Hahnemann (1755–1843), German physician.

152 "A sin or weakness which dominates a person's moral character" (*OED*).

153 The definition of "a bore" as "a man who will persist in talking about himself, when you want to talk about yourself," is attributed to George Augustus Selwyn (1809–1878), first Anglican Bishop of New Zealand.

154 "If the cap fits, wear it," an expression that originated in the early eighteenth century. The cap in question possibly refers to a fool's cap.

155 The Battle of Paardeberg, a major battle in the Second Boer War, took place in the second half of February 1900. "Bobs" presumably refers to Frederick Sleigh Roberts, 1st Earl Roberts (1832–1914), who had been commanding the British forces in South Africa since the preceding December. According to Rubio

and Waterston, Montgomery had named her own cat Bobs after Lord Roberts (Rubio and Waterston, in *CJLMM*, 2: 265n1).

156 Properly, "in season, out of season." From 2 Timothy 4:2 (*KJV*).

157 *Inferno*, the first of three parts of the fourteenth-century poem *Divine Comedy*, by Dante Alighieri (c. 1265–1321), Italian poet.

158 This phrase has been used commonly in legal documents since the fifteenth century; "these presents" refers to such documents.

159 This anecdote appears again in *Anne of Avonlea* (see *AA*, 31).

[THE FIERCE WHITE LIGHT OF PERFECT TRUTH]

"Around the Table." By Cynthia. *Halifax Daily Echo*, 18 January 1902, 12.

160 Possibly an allusion to the popular song "Daisy Bell (Bicycle Built for Two)," released in 1892.

161 This well-known sixteenth-century melody has been attached to a wide variety of lyrics within Christian traditions.

162 Properly, "Hark! from the Tombs a Doleful Sound," with lyrics by Isaac Watts (1674–1748), English lyricist; this hymn was sung at the funeral of George Washington (1732–1799), first president of the United States of America.

163 See "Around the Table," note 124, above.

164 Evidently, Jen did not take Cynthia's advice, from the first installment of this column, not to trim her own hat.

165 Properly, "The woman that deliberates is lost." From *Cato* (1712), a play by Joseph Addison (1672–1719), English politician and author.

166 A snuggery is "a cosy or comfortable room, esp. one of small size, into which a person retires for seclusion or quiet" (*OED*).

[SEEING AND PERCEIVING]

"Around the Table." By Cynthia. *Halifax Daily Echo*, 27 January 1902, 1, 8.

167 Guglielmo Marconi (1874–1937), Italian electrical engineer who made significant technological advances in radio and wireless telegraphy. In order to experiment with wireless messages between North America and the United Kingdom, he set up a receiver in St. John's, Newfoundland, in December 1901. An article about him entitled "The Wireless Way: A Chat with Marconi" had appeared in the *Morning Chronicle* less than a month before the publication of this column.

168 The Portuguese term “auto da fé,” meaning “act of faith,” refers to the public execution of persons deemed heretics in a variety of religious inquisitions, sometimes by being burned at the stake.
169 See “Around the Table,” note 131, above.
170 Two of Montgomery’s most fascinating literary characters are Sara Stanley (in *The Story Girl* and *The Golden Road*) and Katherine Brooke (in *Anne of Windy Poplars*).
171 This definition of humour would be reused in almost identical form in *Anne of the Island* (see *AIs*, 290).
172 Martha Washington (1731–1802), wife of George Washington, inherited this cookbook, likely handwritten in England in the seventeenth century, from her first mother-in-law; it is now in the collection of the Historical Society of Pennsylvania.
173 Undated idiom meaning someone who is in extreme poverty.
174 “A soft, lustrous silk or rayon fabric with a flattened pile, resembling velvet” (*OED*).

[GARRETS AND CHEERFUL PEOPLE]
“Around the Table.” By Cynthia. *Halifax Daily Echo*, 3 February 1902, 1, 8.

175 Denizens of Halifax. The etymological relationship between “Halifax” and “Haligonian” is subject to debate.
176 Missionary hymn, dated 1819, with lyrics by Reginald Heber (1783–1826), English hymn writer and parson.
177 Properly, “weep with them that weep.” Romans 12:15 (*KJV*).
178 The Orpheus Music Hall, on Granville Street, opened in 1886.
179 “Having the ethereal qualities associated with a fairy; delicate, light; graceful; immaterial,” as opposed to the term’s more “pejorative sense: insubstantial; superficial; impractical and foolishly idealistic” (*OED*).

[A WALK IN THE WOODS]
“Around the Table.” By Cynthia. *Halifax Daily Echo*, 10 February 1902, 4.

180 “Rembrandtesque” refers to the work of Rembrandt Harmenszoon van Rijn (1606–1669), Dutch etcher and painter.
181 Properly, “And so in mountain solitudes – o’ertaken / As by some spell divine – / Their cares dropped from them like the needles shaken / From out the gusty pine.” From “Dickens in Camp,” a poem by Bret Harte (1836–1902), American author.

182 In "Trying the 'Rose Act,'" an 1893 short story attributed to "Josiah Allen's Wife," the narrator addresses her husband: "I would be willin' to charm you, Josiah Allen, but I don't see how I could allure and do housework at the same time." For more on this author, see "Around the Table," note 42, above. In *Anne of the Island*, Philippa Gordon claims this expression as "*my* mission" (see *AIs*, 185).

183 Samuel Porter Jones (1847–1906), Methodist revivalist preacher in the southern United States.

184 One definition of the transitive verb "to prink" is "to make tidy, spruce, or smart; to dress up, deck out, adorn" (*OED*).

[DOUBLE STANDARDS]

"Around the Table." By Cynthia. *Halifax Daily Echo*, 17 February 1902, 4.

Also in *Morning Chronicle* (Halifax), 18 February 1902, 5.

185 See "Around the Table," note 154, above.

186 Ellen M. Stone (1846–1927), an American missionary, had been kidnapped in Macedonia by revolutionaries on 3 September 1901 and would be held for ransom until her release on 23 February 1902, a week after the publication of this column. Stone is the subject of Teresa Carpenter's Pulitzer Prize–winning biography, *The Miss Stone Affair: America's First Modern Hostage Crisis* (2003). These two paragraphs introducing the "anti-slang society" as well as Theodosia's struggles to avoid slang and Cynthia's final comment about slang appear as "The Anti-Slang Society," in McCabe, "Lucy Maud Montgomery's Table Talk," 164.

187 See "Around the Table," note 59, above.

188 Possibly a misprinted allusion to "damned with faint praise." See "The Alpine Path," note 204, below.

[TALL TALES AND CLOSE CALLS]

"Around the Table." By Cynthia. *Halifax Daily Echo*, 24 February 1902, 6.

Also in *Morning Chronicle* (Halifax), 25 February 1902, 9.

189 "Little Red Riding Hood," a European fairy tale that can be traced back to the tenth century, has appeared in a number of forms, most prevalent of which are by Charles Perrault (1628–1703) of France and Jacob (1785–1863) and Wilhelm (1786–1859) Grimm of Germany.

190 Evidently a variant of tales by Eleanor Mure (1779–1885), Robert Southey (1774–1843), and Joseph Cundall (1818–1895) that featured a female protagonist (eventually named Goldilocks) opposite three bears.

191 "The Old Woman and Her Pig," a cumulative tale that was collected in *English Folk Tales* (1890), by Joseph Jacobs (1854–1916), Australian folklorist.

192 "Jack and the Beanstalk," an early nineteenth-century English folk tale best known as its late nineteenth-century version by Jacobs; "Bluebeard," popularized by Perrault; "Cinderella" and "Sleeping Beauty," which have appeared in countless versions all around the world, including well-known versions by Perrault and the Brothers Grimm; "Puss in Boots," an Italian folk tale whose earliest known version, from the mid-sixteenth century, is attributed to Giovanni Francesco Straparola (ca. 1485–1558), Italian author, and was subsequently rewritten by Giambattista Basile (1566–1632), Italian author, and by Perrault.

193 Montgomery reused this anecdote in *Anne of the Island* (see *AIs*, 74–75).

194 A similar exchange appears between Susan Baker and Miss Cornelia in *Anne's House of Dreams* (see *AHD*, 170).

[GRAVES OF THE PAST]

"Around the Table." By Cynthia. *Halifax Daily Echo*, 3 March 1902, 1, 8.

Also in *Morning Chronicle* (Halifax), 4 March 1902, 3.

195 A twenty-ninth day in February is added to the Gregorian calendar every four years, with some exceptions, such as the year 1900 (hence the eight-year gap between Ted's birthdays); also known as a leap year.

196 A silvertip bear is a grizzly bear.

197 The phrase "gold of Ophir" is used frequently in the Old Testament as a reference to fine gold.

198 "Billet-doux," French for "sweet note," refers to a love letter.

199 Presumably, Theodosia is referring here to her dance card, on which women in the nineteenth and early twentieth centuries recorded the names of prospective dance partners.

200 Properly, "Lord, what fools these mortals be!" From *A Midsummer Night's Dream*, a comic play by Shakespeare.

201 In Christian traditions, Lent refers to a solemn religious observance in the forty days preceding Easter Sunday, the day that commemorates the resurrection of Christ. In *Jane of Lantern Hill*, Aunt Gertrude omits sugar in her tea during Lent (see *JLH*, 218).

[SPRING AND SMILES AND OLD MAIDS]
"Around the Table." By Cynthia. *Halifax Daily Echo*, 10 March 1902, 8.

Also in *Morning Chronicle* (Halifax), 11 March 1902, 6.

202 I have corrected the original, which reads "comraday."

203 Wilhelm II (1859–1941), German Emperor (*Kaiser*), ruled the German Empire and the Kingdom of Prussia from 1888 to 1918; he is mentioned frequently in *Rilla of Ingleside*.

204 Charles Darwin (1809–1882), English biologist, made this point in his book *On the Origin of Species* (1859).

205 Joseph-Elzéar Bernier (1852–1934), a French Canadian mariner who gave lectures to raise funds for his Arctic explorations; he would not reach the North Pole until 1904.

206 Although several sources attribute this quotation to Brer Rabbit, it appears in slightly different form in *Uncle Remus* (1881), a volume of African American folk tales adapted by Joel Chandler Harris (1848–1908), American author. In this text, it is "Brer Fox" who "lay low," while it is the "Tar-Baby" who "ain't sayin' nuthin'."

[OLD HOUSES AND PARLOUR GAMES]
"Around the Table." By Cynthia. *Halifax Daily Echo*, 17 March 1902, 1, 8.

207 *The Second Primer: Being Sentences and Verses with Pictures*, based on books prepared by J.M.D. Meiklejohn (1836–1902), Scottish author, appeared in a Canadian edition in 1881.

208 "The March Winds Do Blow," an illustration by G.F. Barnes that appeared in *The Poet and the Children: Carefully Selected Poems from the Works of the Best and Most Popular Writers for Children* (1882), edited by Matthew Henry Lothrop.

209 For "The Duchess," see "Around the Table," note 70, above. Henryk Sienkiewicz (1846–1916), Polish author best known around the world for his historical novel *Quo Vadis* (1896), set in Rome under Emperor Nero in 64 CE.

210 For Rembrandt, see "Around the Table," note 180, above. John Everett Millais (1829–1896), English painter and co-founder of the Pre-Raphaelite Brotherhood.

211 Richard Wagner (1813–1883), German composer, librettist, and conductor who contributed enormously to the field of opera. John Philip Sousa (1854–1932), American composer and conductor of more than one hundred patriotic and military marches.

212 Properly, Hans Christian Andersen (1805–1875), Danish author best known for fairy tales such as "The Little Mermaid" and "The Ugly Duckling." Numerous collections of his work had been published in English by the start of the twentieth century. See Montgomery, 1 June 1909, in *CJLMM*, 2: 225–26.

213 This play by Shakespeare was the subject of Montgomery's 1894 essay "'Portia' – A Study," included in this volume.

214 Sir Wilfred Ivanhoe, protagonist of *Ivanhoe* (1820), a historical novel by Scott; Lancelot, a knight of Arthurian romance whose story is told in numerous texts, including Tennyson's poem "Lancelot and Elaine," parodied in *Anne of Green Gables*.

215 Little Eva, an angelic character who dies in childhood in *Uncle Tom's Cabin* (1852), an anti-slavery novel by Harriet Beecher Stowe (1811–1896), American author. An abridgment of Stowe's novel for children was published as *The Story of Little Eva, from "Uncle Tom's Cabin"* the same year as this column, part of the Famous Children of Literature series published by Dana Estes and Company. Estes's stepson, L.C. Page, would become Montgomery's first publisher. Becky Sharp, a social-climbing character in *Vanity Fair* (1847–1848), a satirical novel by William Makepeace Thackeray (1811–1863), English author.

216 See "Around the Table," note 155, above.

217 Clara Barton (1821–1912), American nurse and humanitarian who founded the American Red Cross.

218 Also known as Mary I of Scotland (1542–1587). She was ordered beheaded by her first cousin once removed, Queen Elizabeth I of England (1533–1603).

219 "Old Subscriber," a generic title used for unsigned contributions to magazines or newspapers by their readers; "Vox populi," Latin for "voice of the people," referring to public opinion.

220 "Anon." is a short form of "anonymous," whereas "ibid." is a short form of "ibidem," Latin for "in the same place," used primarily in bibliographic citations.

221 A play in American football in which seven players lock arms and advance in the shape of a V, apex forward, with the ball carrier inside; it originated with the Princeton football team in 1884.

222 A nurse character in *The Life and Adventures of Martin Chuzzlewit* (serialized 1843–1844), a novel by Dickens. A prig is someone who is overzealous with protocol and propriety.

223 Possibly a reference to Edward H. Hobson (1825–1901), American soldier who fought in the Civil War, or to Frederick Hobson (1873–1917), English soldier who fought in the Second Boer War and who would win a Victoria Cross for an act of bravery during the First World War.

[THE VIRTUES OF LAZINESS]

"Around the Table." By Cynthia. *Halifax Daily Echo*, 24 March 1902, 1.

224 "The Total Depravity of Inanimate Things" is the title of a satirical article, published in 1864, by Katherine Kent Child Walker (1833–1916), American author. This article was included in *Mark Twain's Library of Humor* (1888).

225 For Montgomery, a "castle in Spain" is an idealized place of the imagination, a phrase used in *Anne's House of Dreams* (see *AHD*, 6) and more centrally throughout *The Blue Castle*. For Elizabeth Rollins Epperly, this metaphor can be traced to *The Alhambra* (1832), a book of sketches and stories by Washington Irving (1783–1859), American writer, that Montgomery read frequently (Epperly, *Through Lover's Lane*, 26, 82–83). See also Montgomery to Weber, 8 April 1906, in *GGL*, 37.

226 Properly, "the pomps and vanity of this wicked world," a phrase appearing in the *Book of Common Prayer*.

227 This phrase originates in the letters of Cyrano de Bergerac (1619–1655), French writer.

228 Properly, "He jests at scars that never felt a wound." From *Romeo and Juliet* (1597), a tragic play by Shakespeare.

229 "Birds of a feather flock together," meaning "those of like character" (*OED*), an idiomatic expression originating in the mid-sixteenth century.

230 See "Around the Table," note 154, above.

231 Properly, "For Satan finds some mischief still / for idle hands to do." From "Against Idleness and Mischief," a poem by Watts.

232 Seventeenth-century English proverb emphasizing the benefits of acting without haste or of rising early.

233 An 1806 poem by Wordsworth.

234 This paragraph and the one that follows appear as "A Photographic Party" in McCabe, "Lucy Maud Montgomery's Table Talk," 165.

235 Properly, *Ainslee's Magazine*. Montgomery's poem "Harbor Sunset" had appeared in the January 1902 issue of this New York periodical.

[HOW KISSING WAS DISCOVERED]

"Around the Table." By Cynthia. *Halifax Daily Echo*, 31 March 1902, 8.

236 This holy location in the Christian tradition would be the setting for the title poem in Montgomery's *The Watchman and Other Poems* (see *WOP*, 3–7).

237 Properly, "the east wind was out of her soul." From *The Professor at the Breakfast-Table* (1860), by Oliver Wendell Holmes Sr. (1809–1894), American physician and author. Montgomery would quote Holmes's books again in Montgomery, "The 'Teen-Age Girl," 277, 281.

238 Properly, "I say the tale as 'twas said to me." From "The Lay of the Last Minstrel," a long poem by Scott. This tale appears in slightly different form in chapter 18 of *The Story Girl*, also entitled "How Kissing Was Discovered" (see *SG*, 185–90). An unidentified and undated clipping entitled "When Kissing Came into the World," signed C. Lauron Hooper (her surname is partly obscured by another clipping), appears in Montgomery's Blue Scrapbook. In this extended version, Aglaia is named Eurybia.

[CHARMS AND SUPERSTITIONS, TRICKS AND SURPRISES]

"Around the Table." By Cynthia. *Halifax Daily Echo*, 7 April 1902, 8. Also in *Morning Chronicle* (Halifax), 8 April 1902, 5.

239 "Monday's Child," a mid-nineteenth-century fortune-telling nursery rhyme for children of which there are numerous versions; chapter 4 of Montgomery's *Pat of Silver Bush* is entitled "Sunday's Child."

240 I have corrected the original, which reads "I argue with Theodosia."

[SMILES AND TEARS]

"Around the Table." By Cynthia. *Halifax Daily Echo*, 14 April 1902, 8. Also in *Morning Chronicle* (Halifax), 15 April 1902, 6.

241 "April! thou art like woman – beautiful, / Made up of smiles and tears – a glimpse of heaven / And then – a cloud." From "April," an unsigned poem published in *The New England Magazine* in 1833.

[THE GREAT ART OF LETTER-WRITING]

"Around the Table." By Cynthia. *Halifax Daily Echo*, 21 April 1902, 8. Also in *Morning Chronicle* (Halifax), 24 April 1902, 6.

242 Properly, "if eyes were made for seeing, / Then Beauty is its own excuse for being." From "The Rhodora," a poem by Emerson.

243 This brand of water-soluble cocoa, sold as a breakfast food, was manufactured in London, England, by the James Epps Company in the nineteenth and early twentieth centuries, often advertised with the slogan "Grateful – Comforting." In *Anne of Ingleside*, Jem Blythe tells his "mother dearwums," Anne, that she looks "sweet and pure ... pure as Epps' cocoa" (*AIn*, 134; ellipsis in original).

244 An allusion to Isaiah 44:3 (*KJV*): "For I will pour water upon him that is thirsty, and floods upon the dry ground."

245 This paragraph and the three that follow appear as "Advice about Writing Letters," in McCabe, "Lucy Maud Montgomery's Table Talk," 165.

246 From the Latin proverb "Verba volant, scripta manent," literally translated as "Spoken words fly away, written words remain."

247 Properly, "She'll vish there was more, and that's the great art o' letter writin'." From *The Pickwick Papers*, a novel by Dickens.

248 An allusion to Song of Solomon 2:12 (*KJV*): "The voice of the turtle is heard in our land."

[THE GREAT ART OF PACKING A TRUNK]

"Around the Table." By Cynthia. *Halifax Daily Echo*, 28 April 1902, 8.

249 A shorter version of this anecdote, attributed to Philippa Gordon, appears in *Anne of the Island* (see *AIs*, 99–100). Montgomery likewise "flitted" to a new boarding house around this time, although she gave no details about her move; see Montgomery, 1 May 1902, in *CJLMM*, 2: 52–53.

250 "The Man without a Country," a short story by Edward Everett Hale (1822–1909), American writer, published in *The Atlantic* in 1863; *Peter Schlemihl, or, The Man without a Shadow* (1874), a play by J.H. Treadwell based on a novella by Adelbert von Chamisso (1781–1838), French-born German poet.

251 Properly, "Do the corners first, and the middle will take care of itself," an American proverb.

252 This traditional marriage vow is rooted in Ephesians 5:21–24 (*KJV*).

253 French phrase denoting a social system in which men dominate or are prioritized over women.

254 The original reads "The ten ladies, / one man left behind, returned to their / merely smiling contemptuously on the / homes satisfied with the success of their / raid." Two lines of text appear in the wrong order, an error that Montgomery corrects in ink in her scrapbook.

[JONAH DAYS]

"Around the Table." By Cynthia. *Halifax Daily Echo*, 5 May 1902, 8. Also in *Morning Chronicle* (Halifax), 6 May 1902, 5.

255 See "Around the Table," note 248, above. Montgomery had also used this allusion in "Cynthia's" article "Many Admiring Glances Bestowed upon Graduates," published less than a week before this column but appearing later in this volume.

256 The phrase "Et tu, Brute?" (Latin for "And you, Brutus?") is used to question the loyalty of a friend during a moment of unexpected betrayal; it appears in *Julius Caesar* (ca. 1599), a tragic play by Shakespeare.

257 An abbreviation of "*pro tempore*," a Latin phrase meaning "for the time being."

258 "An impure bicarbonate of potash containing more carbon dioxide than pearl-ash does, much used as an ingredient in baking-powders. Now also applied to sodium bicarbonate used for the same purpose" (*OED*).

259 See "Around the Table," note 59, above.

260 In their edition of Montgomery's complete early journals, Rubio and Waterston note that Ada Estey, wife of Methodist minister John Estey, "once mixed liniment into a cake" (Rubio and Waterston, in *CJLMM*, 1: 231n1). Montgomery had already used

this incident in her 1898 story "A New-Fashioned Flavoring" and would use it again in chapter 21 of *Anne of Green Gables*, entitled "A New Departure in Flavourings." See also "Author Tells How He Wrote His Story," 34.

261 In the Book of Jonah in the Old Testament, Jonah tries to escape a divine mission given to him by God and suffers as a result. Here, a "Jonah day" refers to a day during which everything goes wrong. Chapter 12 of *Anne of Avonlea* is entitled "A Jonah Day." This paragraph and the three that follow appear as "A Jonah Day," in McCabe, "Lucy Maud Montgomery's Table Talk," 165.

262 Located at 1451 Barrington Street in Halifax, Government House is the official residence not only of the Lieutenant Governor of Nova Scotia but also of any British monarch who visited the province.

263 Euphemism for spring that originates in *The Winter's Tale* (1623), a play by Shakespeare. Montgomery would publish a short story entitled "In the Sweet o' the Year" in 1907.

[ON PHOTOGRAPHY]

"Around the Table." By Cynthia. *Halifax Daily Echo*, 12 May 1902, 4.
Also in *Morning Chronicle* (Halifax), 13 May 1902, 6.
Also as "'Cynthia's' 1902 Article on Photography," in Epperly, *Through Lover's Lane*, 179–82.

264 See Proverbs 25:4 (*KJV*): "Take away the dross from the silver, and there shall come forth a vessel for the finer." In other words, remove waste from what is valuable.

265 This paragraph and the remaining portions of this column appear with minor variations as "Photography as a Hobby: Cynthia's Advice to Beginners," in McCabe, "Lucy Maud Montgomery's Table Talk," 166–67.

266 This freestanding bell tower, completed in the late fourteenth century, is located in the Tuscan city of Pisa in central Italy.

267 This classical saying and oxymoron is sometimes translated into English as "more haste, less speed."

268 "A place for everything and everything in its place," a seventeenth-century proverb.

269 Montgomery took such a photo in Leaskdale in 1922 and inserted it in her journal; see Montgomery, 17 September 1922, in *LMMCJ*, 3: 53.

[THE MORAL OF MAY]

"Around the Table." By Cynthia. *Halifax Daily Echo*, 19 May 1902, 8. Also in *Morning Chronicle* (Halifax), 20 May 1902, 5.

270 Ralph Waldo Emerson wrote an essay entitled "Compensation," but while the phrase "There are always compensations" is frequently attributed to him, a search for this phrase in his body of work has proven inconclusive.

271 Wilhelmina (1880–1962), who reigned as Queen of the Kingdom of the Netherlands from 1890 to 1948, had given birth to a stillborn son on 4 May 1902, two weeks before the publication of this column.

272 This anecdote would be attributed to Stella Maynard in *Anne of the Island* (see *AIs*, 86–88).

273 To live in luxury, an early eighteenth-century expression.

274 Properly, "To teach the young idea how to shoot." From "Spring," part of *The Seasons* (1730), by James Thomson (1700–1748), Scottish poet and playwright.

275 The origin of this expression is unknown, but Montgomery uses it elsewhere: see Montgomery, 7 March 1903, in Montgomery and Lefurgey, "' ... Where Has My Yellow Garter Gone?,'" 54; Montgomery to Weber, 2 September 1909, in *GGL*, 90.

276 "An early form of motion-picture camera and projector combined" (*OED*), a word introduced in the mid-1890s.

277 See Deuteronomy 8:3, Matthew 4:4, and Luke 4:4 (*KJV*).

278 Properly, "Those whom the gods wish to destroy they first make mad," an ancient proverb.

279 This student composition about birds, used in "Crooked Answers" earlier in this volume, returns in *Anne of Avonlea* (see *AA*, 112–13).

[DELIGHTFUL DAYS]

"Around the Table." By Cynthia. *Halifax Daily Echo*, 26 May 1902, 1. Also in *Morning Chronicle* (Halifax), 27 May 1902, 3.

280 A community east of Halifax, now part of Halifax Regional Municipality.

281 *Godey's Lady's Book* of Philadelphia was launched in 1830, had a circulation of 150,000 by 1860, and ceased publication in 1878. As Montgomery mentions in "The Alpine Path" later in this volume, the title of her celebrity memoir came from a poem published in that magazine during her childhood.

282 A mantilla is "a large light veil or scarf, often of black lace, worn by (esp. Spanish) women over the head and covering the shoulders" (*OED*).

283 Thackeray provided illustrations for his novels, most notably *Vanity Fair*. Montgomery seems to be referring to the time period depicted in these texts rather than their aesthetic qualities.

284 "Wooed and Married and A'," a poem by Alexander Ross (1699–1784), Scottish poet.

HALF AN HOUR WITH CANADIAN MOTHERS

By L.M. Montgomery. *The Ladies' Journal* (Toronto), November 1901, 20–21. Also in Scrapbook 6.

1 The text of "What to Teach Your Son" appears with minor variants under several titles ("Mother, Teach Your Son," "Teach the Boy," "What to Teach Boys," "What to Teach the Boy," "What to Teach Your Boy," and "What to Teach Your Son"), some of them signed "L.M. Montgomery" and others unsigned. These two versions of "One Mother's Opinion" claim to reprint the piece from a magazine called *The Interior*, but that publication has not yet been located.

2 The original reads "children's,' garden," but Montgomery corrects the erroneous comma and the quotation mark in her scrapbook.

3 As a transitive verb, "to bedight" means "to equip, furnish, apparel, array, bedeck" (*OED*).

4 "Foxglove" is "the popular name of *Digitalis purpurea*, a common ornamental flowering plant," whereas "sweet William" refers to "a species of pink, *Dianthus barbatus*, cultivated in numerous varieties, bearing closely-clustered flowers of various shades of white and red, usually variegated or parti-coloured" (*OED*). For definitions of "bride's bouquet" and "bleeding hearts," see "Around the Table," note 14, above.

5 The original says "Lama," but Montgomery corrects this to "Alma" in ink in her scrapbook copy.

6 Montgomery would return to this notion of birth and commemorative trees in *The Story Girl* (see *SG*, 12–14).

7 The Second Boer War, also known as the South African War, had been fought since October 1899 and would result in a British victory in May 1902. For more on the Battle of Paardeberg, see "Around the Table," note 155, above.

8 The published text reads "serving," but Montgomery corrects this to "sewing" in ink in her scrapbook copy. Paul Irving refers to his late mother as his "little mother" throughout *Anne of Avonlea*.

9 Montgomery would return to this mother–daughter conflict in a 1931 essay (see Montgomery, "The 'Teen-Age Girl," 276).

10 Between "It" and "is" at the start of this sentence, an extraneous and apparently unrelated line of text appears in the original publication: "voice, 'won't you come up here and." Montgomery omitted this line in her scrapbook copy, so I do not include it here.

11 In "The Alpine Path," later in this volume, Montgomery writes of the humiliation she felt when forced as a child to wear "baby aprons" to school – except that her grandmother, in stark contrast to the "Little Mother" described here, did not alter these garments in an attempt to reduce her humiliation.

12 The phrase "wilderness of woe" appears in several Christian hymns from the nineteenth century.

13 This joke would appear again in *Anne of Avonlea* (see *AA*, 109).

14 This joke first appeared in "Crooked Answers" earlier in this volume and would appear again in *Anne of Avonlea* (see *AA*, 110).

15 Like the childlike misunderstanding of the definition of "glacier," this joke also appeared first in "Crooked Answers," earlier in this volume, and in *Anne of Avonlea* (see *AA*, 109–10).

16 A similar childlike misunderstanding about the surname "Lord" reappears in "Innocent Irreverence," later in this volume.

17 In 2 Kings in the Old Testament, Elijah and Elisha, two of the most prominent prophets of Israel, cross the Jordan River on dry land. After Elijah is taken to heaven on a chariot of fire, Elisha picks up Elijah's mantle (the term referring to a cloak likely made of animal skin), which has fallen, as a symbol of Elisha inheriting Elijah's wisdom. This joke about Elisha inheriting Elijah's old clothes would be repeated in *Anne of Avonlea* (see *AA*, 174).

CHRISTMAS SHOPPING IN HALIFAX STORES

Excerpted from *Halifax Daily Echo*, 9 December 1901, 1; 10 December 1901, 1; 11 December 1901, 6; 12 December 1901, 1; 13 December 1901, 1; 16 December 1901, 8; 17 December 1901, 8; 18 December 1901, 10; 19 December 1901, 10.

Also, in substantially abridged form, in *Morning Chronicle*

(Halifax), 10 December 1901, 6; 11 December 1901, 6; 13 December 1901, 3; 14 December 1901, 8; 19 December 1901, 6.

1 See Montgomery, 8 December 1901, in *CJLMM*, 2: 37; see also Montgomery, 12 December 1901, in *CJLMM*, 2: 37.

2 The Nova Scotia Furnishing Company was located at 1668 Barrington Street.

3 Reclining chair first marketed by Morris & Company in the 1860s.

4 A reefer is "a thick, close-fitting double-breasted jacket" (*OED*).

5 These shoes were manufactured by the Arnold Shoe Company of North Abington, Massachusetts, founded in 1875.

6 "Coney" refers to fur from a rabbit, whereas "electric seal" refers to rabbit fur that has been altered to simulate sealskin.

7 For the definition of "sacque," see "The Usual Way," note 6, above.

8 The original reads "a thoughtful a" followed by white space and then "most cases" on the next line, so I have added "and in" as my best guess of what wording should be there.

9 A repeater watch (or clock) chimes the time on demand, to be used in the dark or by visually impaired individuals; because of the mechanical intricacies involved, repeater watches were considered a status symbol.

10 The term "aerated" refers to carbonated beverages.

11 The Labatt Brewing Company, founded in London, Ontario, by Irish-born John Kinder in 1847; Glen Moray whiskey, distilled in Scotland since 1897.

MANY ADMIRING GLANCES BESTOWED UPON GRADUATES

By Cynthia. *Halifax Daily Echo*, 30 April 1902, 1. Also in Scrapbook 3.

1 Properly, "most potent, grave, and reverend signors." From *Othello* (ca. 1603), a tragic play by Shakespeare. The word "signors" refers to "a title of courtesy for or form of address to an Italian man," whereas "seignior" could also mean "a person high in rank or authority" (*OED*).

2 John Forrest (1842–1920), a Presbyterian minister and a professor of history and political economy, was president of Dalhousie University from 1885 to 1911. For the origins of the names "Tom," "Dick," and "Harry" as a grouping, see "Around the Table," note 138, above.

3 This phrase refers to Tennyson's "The Princess," extracts of which Montgomery used as the epigraph to her article "A Girl's Place at Dalhousie College," included earlier in this volume.
4 Jeanette Cann (1880–1956) would go on to teach English at Victoria College in British Columbia. She would serve as president of the Victoria branch of the Canadian Federation of University Women from 1912 to 1914 and again from 1928 to 1929.
5 William Bernard Wallace (1861–1928), once a writer for the *Morning Chronicle*, had been judge of the County Court of Halifax since January 1901.
6 Frederick Courtney (1837–1918), an Anglican priest, was the fifth Bishop of Nova Scotia.
7 Robert Alexander Falconer (1867–1943), born in Charlottetown, taught New Testament Greek at Pine Hill Divinity Hall in Halifax; he would later serve as president of the University of Toronto from 1907 to 1932.

NETTED DOILY

By L.M. Montgomery. *The Modern Priscilla* (Boston), April 1903, 21.
1 Montgomery, 27 January 1902, in *CJLMM*, 2: 43.

INNOCENT IRREVERENCE

By L.M. Montgomery. *Lippincott's Monthly Magazine* (Philadelphia), July 1905, A38.

TWO SIDES OF A LIFE STORY

By J.C. Neville. Unidentified and undated clipping. Red Scrapbook 1, L.M. Montgomery Collection, University of Guelph archives.
1 I have corrected the original, which reads "vowed the the future."

THE ALPINE PATH: THE STORY OF MY CAREER

By L.M. Montgomery. *Everywoman's World* (Toronto), June 1917, 38–39, 41; July 1917, 16, 32–33, 35; August 1917, 16, 32–33; September 1917, 8, 49; October 1917, 8, 58; November 1917, 25, 38, 40.
1 The short story "Akin to Love" (previously published as "The

Courtship of Josephine") appeared in May 1915, the serial "Schooled with Briars" (previously published as "The Bitterness in the Cup") from May to August 1916, the short story "The Old Mirror" (previously published in 1904) in August 1916, the poem "If I Were King" in January 1917, and the short story "The Schoolmaster's Bride" in July 1917.

2 These two pieces appear in Volume 1 of *The L.M. Montgomery Reader*.

3 I have consulted surviving copies of issues of *Everywoman's World* at Library and Archives Canada (Ottawa), on microfilm, and digitally through the Early Canadiana Online searchable database, but several gaps remain. Although I have verified that Anglin's "My Career" began in the December 1916 issue and ended in the April 1917 issue and that "Julia Arthur's Own Story of Her Career" began in May 1916 and ended in September 1916, I have been unable to locate the issues in which their respective remaining instalments appeared.

4 Farmer, "Will My Daughter Be an Author?," 8. This image and this caption appear unidentified in *SJLMM*, 1: 344, and in Montgomery, 12 October 1906, in *CJLMM*, 2: 154.

5 *Everywoman's World*, "The Ground Floor," 1.

6 Church and De Bubna, "Tam: The Story of a Woman" (March 1884), 237.

7 Montgomery, 21 October 1916, in *LMMCJ*, 1: 251. See also Montgomery, 5 January 1917, in *LMMCJ*, 1: 268–69; Montgomery, 22 November 1926, in *LMMCJ*, 4: 97–98.

8 Preface to *AP*, 6.

9 For more on the publication and reception of the 1974 book version of "The Alpine Path," see Lefebvre, "Introduction: A Critical Heritage," 4–5; Lefebvre, "Epilogue," 362–63.

10 See Rubio, "Satire, Realism, and Imagination"; Fredeman, "The Land of Lost Content"; Little, "But What about Jane?" This journal issue, minus the book reviews appearing therein, was reprinted in book form as *L.M. Montgomery: An Assessment*, edited by John Robert Sorfleet, in 1976.

11 Montgomery, 5 January 1917, in *LMMCJ*, 1: 269.

12 *Everywoman's World*, editors' note, 8.

13 Murray Simonski is credited as "superintending editor" on 1917 issues of this magazine, the only editor listed on the masthead.

Montgomery mentioned correspondence with an editor in a journal entry dated January 1917, but she does not identify that editor by name. See Montgomery, 5 January 1917, in *LMMCJ*, 1: 268.

14 Montgomery did, in fact, refer publicly to her development of her career as a writer during her lifetime, including a short autobiographical sketch she published in July 1912 in *The Editor: The Journal of Information for Literary Workers*, although she downplayed her career in a different way than she does here: "There isn't really much to say regarding my literary career. It has been made up of two elements: 'hard work' and 'stick to it'" (Montgomery, "Letters from the Literati," 4; see also Lefebvre, "Introduction: A Life in Print," 9–10).

15 In a journal entry dated 1916 but not published until 2016, Montgomery revealed part of the deal of this editor's "whim": "They want 30,000 words" (Montgomery, 21 October 2016, in *LMMCJ*, 1: 251). The published text fell somewhat short of this mark at 25,000 words, not including the captions accompanying her photographs; perhaps for this reason, but more likely due to narrow expectations about women's life narratives, Montgomery was asked for an additional thousand words on her love affairs. She refused to discuss her romances in such a public forum but took the opportunity to detail them in her journal. See Montgomery, 5 January 1917, in *LMMCJ*, 1: 269–75.

16 Properly, "The Fringed Gentian," a poem that appears in chapter 5, "Fringed Gentian," of the sixteen-chapter serial "Tam! The Story of a Woman" by Ella Rodman Church and Augusta de Bubna, in the March 1884 issue of *Godey's Lady's Book* of Philadelphia. The clipping in one of Montgomery's scrapbooks (see Epperly, *Imagining Anne*, 127) matches the *Godey's* text. The source of this poem was identified by Carol Gaboury in the late 1980s (see "In Memoriam," 1; Wiggins, *L.M. Montgomery*, 96). The poem and Montgomery's changes to its text are discussed in the headnote to this piece. *The Shining Scroll*, a periodical of the L.M. Montgomery Literary Society (Minnesota) edited by Mary Beth Cavert and Carolyn Strom Collins, takes its title from this poem.

17 Here, Montgomery omits her birthdate of 30 November 1874. A profile of Montgomery by Marjory MacMurchy published in 1914 had listed Montgomery's birth year as 1877 (MacMurchy, "L.M. Montgomery of the Island," 129), a mistake that persisted

in several obituaries after her death on 24 April 1942; an earlier profile by MacMurchy had listed Montgomery's birthdate as "some time in the seventies or eighties of the nineteenth century" (MacMurchy, "L.M. Montgomery: Story Writer," 122).

18 Properly, "compass'd by the inviolate sea." From "To the Queen," a poem by Tennyson.

19 Properly, "haunt of ancient Peace." From "The Palace of Art," a poem by Tennyson.

20 Montgomery would rework parts of this paragraph for her contribution to *The Spirit of Canada*, published in 1939 (see Montgomery, "Prince Edward Island," 353).

21 L.M. Montgomery dedicated *Anne of Green Gables*, her first book, to the memory of her father (1841–1900) and of her mother (1853–1876), who had married each other on 4 March 1874, less than nine months before her birth. See "Family Tree," 505; Rubio, *Lucy Maud Montgomery*, 27.

22 Montgomery reveals here only part of her ancestry. In a piece published in 1929 in *Ontario Library Review*, she added Irish and French ancestors to the list (Montgomery, "An Autobiographical Sketch," 255). In a journal entry also dated 1929, she considered that she was "a queer mixture racially – the Scotch Macneills, the English Woolners and Penmans, the Irish of Mary McShannon (Hugh Montgomery's wife) and that far-off French descent" (Montgomery, 27 June 1929, in *LMMCJ*, 4: 265).

23 Montgomery's great-great-grandparents, Hugh Montgomery and Mary McShannon, had arrived in Prince Edward Island in 1769 (see Rubio and Waterston, Introduction to *SJLMM*, 1: xiii). She told this anecdote with only minor variations in Montgomery, 27 May 1911, in *CJLMM*, 2: 411. Years later, she told this story to G.B. MacMillan, but with some new details: in this telling, PEI at the time of Hugh and Mary Montgomery's arrival was "all woods, except for a few French and Indian settlements around the shore," and she recorded Mary Montgomery's words used to announce her intention never to set foot on a boat again: "Here I stay" (Montgomery to MacMillan, 7 March 1939, in *MDMM*, 196–97). In *Emily of New Moon*, this story appears in similar form and features Hugh Murray and Mary Shipley, ancestors of Emily Byrd Starr – except in this version of the tale, the words "Here I Stay" appear on Mary Shipley Murray's tombstone as a form of revenge from her husband (*ENM*, 73–74).

24 The American Revolutionary War, during which the thirteen colonies in the United States fought for independence against Great Britain, concluded in 1783.

25 Bedeque, a rural community in the western part of Prince Edward Island. Montgomery taught in Lower Bedeque in 1897–1898.

26 Richmond Bay, now known as Malpeque Bay, on the north shore of PEI. Montgomery tells this story with only minor variations in her journal, but with one major difference involving what she calls "two conflicting stories as to their coming to P.E. Island." The first was that the Penmans had been "a family of United Empire Loyalists who came to Canada at the close of the American War of Independence" and that the beauty of the Penman daughters allowed them to marry well in spite of the family's poverty, and the second concerned George Penman's job as paymaster in the British army. In this account, Montgomery marries the two "conflicting" stories into one (see Montgomery, 23 May 1911, in *CJLMM*, 2: 405). She also told the story with the same details in an early letter to G.B. MacMillan; see Montgomery to MacMillan, 5 June 1905, in *MDMM*, 9–10. Prior to reworking this story into *The Story Girl* (see *SG*, 72–79), she had published a version of it as a stand-alone short story, "A Pioneer Wooing," in 1903.

27 See "From Prince Albert to P.E. Island," note 28, above.

28 The term "suffragette," the earliest known usage of which is 1906, refers to "a female supporter of the cause of women's political enfranchisement, *esp.* one of a violent or 'militant' type" (*OED*). The major goal of women's suffrage was to obtain the vote for women. Women in Manitoba, Saskatchewan, and Alberta were given the right to vote in provincial elections in 1916, with women in British Columbia and Ontario following in 1917, the year this piece was published; women were then granted the right to vote in federal elections in 1918. See Veronica Strong-Boag, "Women's Suffrage in Canada," The Canadian Encyclopedia, Historica Canada, last modified 25 August 2016, https://www.thecanadianencyclopedia.ca/en/article/suffrage/. In a 1910 interview, Montgomery is quoted as claiming that "no, I am not a suffragette … I am a quiet, plain sort of person, and while I believe a woman, if intelligent, should be allowed to vote, I would have no use for suffrage myself"; another report from this visit to Boston confirmed the impression that Montgomery "has no favor for woman suffrage" ("Says Woman's Place," 51; "Miss L.M. Montgomery," 65).

29 According to Mary Henley Rubio, "Maud's maternal great-great-grandfather, John Macneill (born circa 1750), had come to Charlottetown from the Kintyre peninsula of Argyllshire, Scotland, around 1772" (Rubio, *Lucy Maud Montgomery*, 22). In her journal, Montgomery uses similar phrasing but dates John Macneill's arrival in Canada "somewhere around the year 1780" (Montgomery, 28 January 1912, in *CJLMM*, 2: 373).

30 Hector Macneill (1746–1818), Scottish poet. This description of Montgomery's poet relative and the titles of these poems appear with minor variations in a 1913 profile by MacMurchy (see MacMurchy, "L.M. Montgomery: Story Writer," 122). See also Montgomery, 28 January 1912, in *CJLMM*, 2: 373. Robert Burns (1759–1796), Scottish poet.

31 Montgomery mentions William Macneill in her journals using similar phrasing, but omits here the fact that he "was the first white male English child – and I think the first white male child of any race – to be born in Charlottetown" (Montgomery, 28 January 1912, in *CJLMM*, 2: 373).

32 George III (1738–1820) ruled as King of Great Britain and Ireland from 1760 to 1801, then as King of the United Kingdom of Great Britain and Ireland until his death.

33 This body of water features prominently in *Anne of Green Gables*. As Montgomery states later in this memoir, it is often attributed erroneously to Cavendish Pond. See Montgomery, 27 January 1911, in *CJLMM*, 2: 350.

34 This anecdote about Elizabeth Townsend appears in slightly different form – minus the epitaph on her husband's tombstone – in Montgomery, 27 May 1911, in *CJLMM*, 2: 411.

35 Antigua is an island in the West Indies.

36 This epitaph appears in nearly identical form in Montgomery, 27 May 1911, in *CJLMM*, 2: 409–10, except that James Townsend's age at his death is listed as his "67th year," rather than his eighty-seventh.

37 Compare this with Montgomery's private assessment about Grandfather Macneill in her journal: "He had a rich, poetic mind, a keen intelligence and a refined perception. He was a good conversationalist and a lover of nature. His faults were an irritable temper, a vanity that sometimes made him a little ridiculous and at other times smarted under imaginary slights, and, worst of all, an utter disregard of the feelings of other people – or, rather, a failure

to realize that they had any feelings" (Montgomery, 7 January 1910, in *CJLMM*, 2: 269).

38 This description of her great-uncle appears in longer form in her journal, where she refers to him as "Uncle Jimmie," suggesting he was a prototype for "Cousin Jimmy" in *Emily of New Moon* and its sequels. See Montgomery, 28 January 1912, in *CJLMM*, 2: 388–89.

39 The words "mute inglorious" originate in "Elegy Written in a Country Churchyard," a poem by Thomas Gray (1716–1771), English poet.

40 It was actually *The Golden Road* (1913) that Montgomery had dedicated "to the memory of Aunt Mary Lawson who told me many of the tales repeated by the Story Girl." She had dedicated *The Story Girl* "to my cousin Frederica E. Campbell in remembrance of old days, old dreams, and old laughter." Mary Lawson had died in 1912 (see Montgomery, 10 October 1912, in *LMMCJ*, 1: 86–87).

41 In her journals, in which this description of Aunt Mary Lawson appears with only minor variations, Montgomery referred to PEI as a "colony" rather than as a "Province" (Montgomery, 8 June 1911, in *CJLMM*, 2: 413).

42 Clara Macneill Montgomery died of tuberculosis on 14 September 1876 (Rubio, *Lucy Maud Montgomery*, 27). The description here of Montgomery's memory of her mother's funeral appears with only minor variations in Montgomery, 8 April 1898, in *CJLMM*, 1: 390; see also Montgomery, 7 January 1910, in *CJLMM*, 2: 249.

43 Montgomery claimed in her journal that she had already written of her earliest memory for an audience, in the form of an English assignment at Dalhousie University for Archibald MacMechan, who gave her positive feedback on it (see Montgomery, 9 October 1895, in *CJLMM*, 1: 290). Chapter 1 of the 1974 book version of "The Alpine Path" ends here.

44 This statement attributed to Aunt Mary Lawson also appears in Montgomery, 28 January 1912, in *CJLMM*, 2: 390.

45 Montgomery repeated this saying in her journals: see Montgomery, 2 June 1931, in *SJLMM*, 4: 125. This joke appears with different surnames in *Anne's House of Dreams* (see *AHD*, 45), which was published the same year as "The Alpine Path."

46 Compare this to a journal entry dated 1910: "The first six years of my life are very hazy. I do not seem to have any *connected*

memories of them. Here and there a picture like scene stands out in vivid colours" (Montgomery, 7 January 1910, in *CJLMM*, 2: 250). Three additional early memories included in this journal entry – all of them ending in young Montgomery screaming in terror – are omitted from this public memoir.

47 Emily Macneill (1856–1927), the younger sister of Montgomery's mother, who married John Montgomery of Malpeque (Rubio and Waterston, in *CJLMM*, 1: 115n5). Commenting on this aunt in a journal entry dated 1905, Montgomery admitted, "I have never cared for her ... I can never forgive her for the sneer and slurs she used to call upon my childish ambitions and my childish faults" (Montgomery, 2 January 1905, in *CJLMM*, 2: 117).

48 Properly, "No brilliant but distant shore." From "Heaven," an unsigned mid-nineteenth-century poem.

49 Montgomery tells this anecdote about her childhood belief in heaven with only minor variations in Montgomery, 27 January 1911, in *CJLMM*, 2: 357. In *Anne of Avonlea*, young Davy Keith would gain a similar misunderstanding about the location of heaven (see *AA*, 174–75).

50 "But now 'tis little joy / To know I'm farther off from heav'n / Than when I was a boy." From "I Remember, I Remember," a poem by Thomas Hood (1799–1845), English poet. This quotation also appears in Montgomery, 27 January 1911, in *CJLMM*, 2: 357.

51 Properly, "Closer is He than breathing, and nearer than hands and feet." From "The Higher Pantheism," a poem by Tennyson.

52 See Revelation 21:21 (*KJV*): "And the twelve gates *were* twelve pearls; every several gate was of one pearl: and the street of the city *was* pure gold, as it were transparent glass."

53 Built in the 1870s, the Senator Donald Montgomery House in Park Corner, 20 kilometres from Cavendish. Also known as the Lucy Maud Montgomery Heritage Museum, it was reopened as Montgomery Inn in 2016.

54 A slightly different version of this anecdote appears in Montgomery, 7 January 1910, in *CJLMM*, 2: 250–52.

55 Montgomery here omits a sentence that appears in the version of this story told in her journal: "One of these – to hold the burned hand in a saucer of kerosene oil – made the burn far worse" (Montgomery, 7 January 1910, in *CJLMM*, 2: 251).

56 This anecdote is told with only minor variations in Montgomery, 7 January 1910, in *CJLMM*, 2: 252. Another version of this

anecdote in Montgomery's journals is told in a substantially different way, although the only detail that contradicts this version is that it was young Montgomery who read this prediction in the newspaper. See Montgomery, 23 May 1911, in *CJLMM*, 2: 407.

57 See 1 Corinthians 15:52 (*KJV*).

58 In the version of this anecdote appearing in her journals, the quotation reads "low-descending sun." Properly, "Count that day lost whose low-descending sun / Views from thy hand no worthy action done," an unsigned poem from the late seventeenth century. The quoted phrase also appears in Montgomery, "[Seasons in the Woods]," 91.

59 See Isaiah 63:3 (*KJV*): "I have trodden the winepress alone."

60 This anecdote appears with only slight variations in Montgomery's journals, in which she identified this man as "old Mr. Muirhead of Summerside" (Montgomery, 23 May 1911, in *CJLMM*, 2: 406–7).

61 See Romans 3:13 (*KJV*). The first instalment of the 1917 version of "The Alpine Path" ends here, as does chapter 2 of the 1974 book version.

62 These last two sentences appear with only minor variations in Montgomery, 7 January 1910, in *CJLMM*, 2: 254.

63 Montgomery's recollections of having to eat dinner at home and to wear buttoned boots and "baby aprons" to school first appear with minor variations in Montgomery, 7 January 1910, in *CJLMM*, 2: 261.

64 In her journals, in which this recollection of her humiliating second day of school is told with only minor variations, Montgomery identified this "big" girl as "Pensie Macneill, I think" (Montgomery, 7 January 1910, in *CJLMM*, 2: 253). Montgomery and Penzie (Pensie) Macneill (1872–1906) had been close childhood friends; a sample of letters written by the adolescent Montgomery and sent to Penzie during the former's year in Saskatchewan are included in Bolger, *The Years Before "Anne,"* 86–104, 111–33. Recollections of Penzie are included in Montgomery's 1936 article "Come Back with Me to Prince Edward Island," which centres on a farm diary that had been kept by Penzie's father, Charles Macneill.

65 The version of this anecdote in Montgomery's journals includes details about Montgomery's teachers and classmates that are omitted here (see Montgomery, 7 January 1910, in *CJLMM*, 2: 253–54).

66 Produced in Great Britain, the Royal School Primer and the six

Readers that followed this volume consisted of fiction, poetry, spelling, reading comprehension, and writing exercises. In many cases, editions were published to dovetail with the curricula of specific provinces.

67 For a slightly different version of her recollections of the various volumes in the Royal Reader series, see Montgomery, 7 January 1910, in *CJLMM*, 2: 252–53.

68 For more on this memory, including commentary on Aunt Emily's wedding dress, see Montgomery, 7 January 1910, in *CJLMM*, 2: 255. Compare this to Montgomery's remarks in a journal entry dated two years earlier, during which she mentioned, concerning Aunt Emily leaving home after her marriage, "I don't recall having missed her at all" (Montgomery, 3 May 1908, in *CJLMM*, 2: 185).

69 An allusion to Acts 3:2 (*KJV*): "the gate of the temple which is called beautiful."

70 "Live-forevers" are robust perennial plants known for their green, coarsely toothed leaves and pithy stalks and for clusters of purplish-pink flowers shaped like stars.

71 Here and below, Montgomery's recollections of Well and Dave Nelson appear with only minor variations in Montgomery, 1 August 1892, in *CJLMM*, 1: 130–35.

72 See chapter 20, "A Good Imagination Gone Wrong," in *Anne of Green Gables*.

73 Properly, "There are more things in heaven and earth, Horatio, / Than are dreamt of in your philosophy." From *Hamlet* (ca. 1599–1602), a tragic play by Shakespeare. These lines are spoken by Hamlet immediately after he is visited by the ghost of his late father.

74 A wraith is "an apparition or spectre of a dead person; a phantom or ghost" (*OED*).

75 Montgomery published a poem with this title in *The Ladies' Journal*, a Toronto magazine, in May 1898.

76 Properly, "in their death they were not divided," referring to the strong bond between Saul and Jonathan, in 2 Samuel 1:23 (*KJV*). In chapter 26 of *Anne of Green Gables*, Anne narrates to Diana an unintentionally comic story entitled "The Jealous Rival; or, in Death Not Divided" (see *AGG*, 290–92).

77 These paragraphs about trees appear with only minor variations as part of a longer journal entry in Montgomery, 22 January 1911, in *CJLMM*, 2: 341–46.

78 "To ween" is an archaic transitive verb meaning "to think, surmise, suppose, conceive, believe, consider ... in regard to what is present or past" (*OED*).

79 From "The Deacon's Masterpiece; or, the Wonderful 'One-Hoss Shay': A Logical Story" (1858), a poem by Holmes.

80 Properly, "The lands of Dream among." From "Lost Love," a poem in *Ban and Arrière Ban: A Rally of Fugitive Rhymes* (1894), by Andrew Lang (1844–1912), Scottish poet. Chapter 3 of *Anne's House of Dreams*, published the same year as "The Alpine Path," is entitled "The Land of Dreams Among."

81 Chapter 3 of the 1974 book version of "The Alpine Path" ends here.

82 Montgomery's account of the wreck of the *Marco Polo* appears in slightly different form in Montgomery, 3 June 1909, in *CJLMM*, 2: 229–32. Her early essay on this event, published in 1891 and appearing earlier in this volume, was followed by a poem of the same name in 1892. Although Montgomery's account here of the *Marco Polo* mentions that the ship was grounded on the Cavendish shore, she omits here the second half of this historical event, during which the ship was wrecked during a second bad storm.

83 Samuel Plimsoll (1824–1898), a member of the British Parliament and author of *Our Seamen* (1872), led an investigation of the overloading of cargo ships, which created unsafe conditions for crew members. The Unseaworthy Ships Bill went into law in 1876.

84 For the definition of deal planks, see "The Wreck of the 'Marco Polo,'" note 12, above.

85 For Montgomery's clarifying comments on the crash as reported in her journal, see "The Wreck of the 'Marco Polo,'" note 16, above. In her journal, she specified the date of the crash (25 July 1883), omitted here, possibly to camouflage her age (Montgomery, 3 June 1909, in *CJLMM*, 2: 230).

86 See "The Wreck of the 'Marco Polo,'" note 17, above.

87 In her essay "The Wreck of the 'Marco Polo,'" Montgomery identifies this captain as P.A. Bull.

88 These paragraphs about the seashore and about Alexander Macneill's dramatic stories appear with minor variations in Montgomery, 3 June 1909, in *CJLMM*, 2: 226–28. A passing reference to Montgomery's Uncle John F. Macneill is omitted here, possibly due to the animosity between them but more likely to avoid confusion with Montgomery's Uncle John Campbell, whereas the

reference here to Oliver Wendell Holmes's poetry is absent from that version.

89 See "The Wreck of the 'Marco Polo,'" note 14, above.

90 Properly, "Leaving thine outgrown shell by life's unresting sea!" Also from "The Chambered Nautilus," by Holmes.

91 In her journal, Montgomery identifies this "chum" as Penzie Macneill (Montgomery, 3 June 1909, in *CJLMM*, 2: 227).

92 In her journal, Montgomery added here: "It is a spot I have always loved" (Montgomery, 3 June 1909, in *CJLMM*, 2: 227).

93 This "Yankee storm" occurred in October 1851. See Montgomery, 3 June 1909, in *CJLMM*, 2: 227–28.

94 Montgomery offered far more detail about this story in her journal. After the *Franklin Dexter* went ashore and all on board drowned, the bodies of four brothers were among the many that were buried in Cavendish churchyard. When their father insisted that they be disinterred so that they could be buried at home, "The coffins were put on board a trading vessel at New London, while the father returned home in a passenger vessel. The trading vessel was called the *Seth Hall*. She left New London harbour with the four bodies on board – *and was never heard of again*" (Montgomery, 3 June 1909, in *CJLMM*, 2: 228). This story appears in nearly identical form in a letter to MacMillan, in which she stated that the parents of the four sons had lived in Massachusetts (Montgomery to MacMillan, 21 May 1909, in *MDMM*, 44). Chapter 22 of *The Golden Road*, entitled "The Yankee Storm," retells both stories.

95 The story of Captain Leforce is told with only minor variations in Montgomery, 3 June 1909, in *CJLMM*, 2: 228. Montgomery also narrates this story in her first published poem, "On Cape Le Force," which appeared in November 1890 and which followed her 1889 entry on the subject for the essay writing contest hosted by the *Montreal Daily Witness* (see Montgomery, 19 February 1890, in *CJLMM*, 1: 21).

96 This paragraph appears with only minor variations in Montgomery to MacMillan, 21 May 1909, in *MDMM*, 45–46, and in Montgomery, 3 June 1909, in *CJLMM*, 2: 229 (in which she referred to "New London Point"). New London Point is now Cape Tryon. In a journal entry dated 1917, Montgomery revealed that Four Winds Harbour, the setting of *Anne's House of Dreams*, had been based loosely on the harbour at New London, less than

10 kilometres northwest of Cavendish. See Montgomery, 21 July 1917, in *LMMCJ*, 1: 306.

97 In her journal, in place of this reference to "fairyland," Montgomery quotes two lines from "Ode to a Nightingale," a poem by Keats (Montgomery, 3 June 1909, in *CJLMM*, 2: 229; Rubio and Waterston, in *CJLMM*, 2: 229n1).

98 Capital city of Prince Edward Island, 40 kilometres southeast of Cavendish.

99 Built in 1872, the home of Annie Macneill Campbell (1848–1924), older sister of Montgomery's mother, and her husband, John Campbell (1833–1917), 20 kilometres from Cavendish, was a second home to Montgomery. It remains open today as "Anne of Green Gables Museum," a popular tourist site operated by descendants of the Campbell family. This paragraph and the anecdote about Montgomery's first trip to Charlottetown appear with only minor variations in Montgomery, 16 March 1909, in *CJLMM*, 2: 217. The phrase "or before the war" later in the paragraph does not appear in this 1909 journal entry.

100 A reference to the alternate world depicted in *Alice's Adventures in Wonderland* (1865), by Carroll.

101 These two sentences first appear with slight variations in Montgomery, 31 December 1898, in *CJLMM*, 1: 427–28. Some of the later details about the Campbell home, including the pantry and the "certain old screw" in the wall, appear with minor variations in Montgomery, 2 March 1901, in *CJLMM*, 2: 7–8.

102 In *Anne of Green Gables*, eleven-year-old Anne expresses a similar fear: "I'm always afraid going over bridges. I can't help imagining that perhaps, just as we get to the middle, they'll crumple up like a jack-knife and nip us" (*AGG*, 29).

103 In her journal, it was Fred Macneill who witnessed her catch of "quite a large trout," and "I felt that I went up ten percent in his estimation" (Montgomery, 7 January 1910, in *CJLMM*, 2: 268). See also Montgomery, "The Gay Days of Old," 164.

104 Parts of this paragraph appear in slightly different form in Montgomery, 7 January 1910, in *CJLMM*, 2: 268.

105 This recollection of Montgomery's fear of walking through the woods alone appears in slightly different form in Montgomery, 14 December 1907, in *CJLMM*, 2: 178.

106 The second instalment of the 1917 version of "The Alpine Path" ends here, as does chapter 4 of the 1974 book version.

107 This phrase likely refers to "death entered the world," a common paraphrase of Romans 5:12 (*KJV*) pertaining to the Christian doctrine of Original Sin. The phrase is used in "God's Love to Fallen Man," an essay by John Wesley (1703–1791), English theologian and one of the founders of the Methodist church.

108 This memory appears in slightly different form as part of a recollection of Montgomery's childhood pets in Montgomery, 7 January 1910, in *CJLMM*, 2: 263–65. A substantially different version of this anecdote appears in Montgomery, 2 January 1905, in *CJLMM*, 2: 120.

109 The Cavendish Presbyterian Church was torn down in 1899; it was rebuilt at its current location in 1901 and became the Cavendish United Church in 1925. Montgomery's funeral was held at this church on 29 April 1942 (see "Island Writer").

110 In her journal, Montgomery referred to Sacrament Sunday as "the annual Communion Sunday," a reference to the congregation partaking in the sacrament of Holy Communion, which historically happened infrequently in the Presbyterian Church; Montgomery's comments dovetail with suggestions that, at some churches, Sacrament Sunday could be more a carnival than a church service. See Montgomery, 24 July 1899, in *CJLMM*, 1: 439–40.

111 Hymn with lyrics by John Morrison (1746–1798), Scottish poet and minister.

112 I have corrected the original, which reads "were made learn our catechism."

113 This recollection appears in slightly different form in Montgomery, 29 January 1911, in *CJLMM*, 2: 352. The quotation is from "The Race That Long in Darkness Pined," an eighteenth-century hymn with words adapted from Isaiah 9:2 by John Morrison. The *Spectator* review of *Anne of Green Gables*, first published on 13 March 1909, appears as "[An Alternative Entertainment]" in Volume 3 of *The L.M. Montgomery Reader* ("*Anne of Green Gables*," 65–66).

114 From "Ode: Intimations of Immortality from Recollections of Early Childhood," a poem by Wordsworth. Montgomery also used this quotation as the title of chapter 36 of *Anne of Green Gables*. This paragraph appears in earlier form in Montgomery, 29 September 1894, in *CJLMM*, 1: 241.

115 Also from "Ode: Intimations of Immortality from Recollections of Early Childhood," by Wordsworth.

116 This paragraph first appears in slightly different form in Montgomery, 2 January 1905, in *CJLMM*, 2: 119, as part of a journal entry in which Montgomery reflected on the "starved childhood mine was *emotionally*" (Montgomery, 2 January 1905, in *CJLMM*, 2: 118). This paragraph appears with only minor variations in *Emily of New Moon* (see *ENM*, 7).

117 For alternative accounts of Montgomery's childhood reading, see Montgomery, 7 January 1910, in *CJLMM*, 2: 258; Montgomery, "The Gay Days of Old," 166–67.

118 See "Around the Table," note 281, above. For an earlier mention of *Godey's Lady's Book* in her journals, see Montgomery, 7 January 1910, in *CJLMM*, 2: 258.

119 Likely an allusion to *The History of the World* (1614), by Sir Walter Raleigh (1552?–1618), English author and adventurer, a massive project that was continued after Raleigh's death and reissued in multiple forms. *The General History of the World, Being an Abridgment of Sir Walter Raleigh with a Continuation from the Best Historians to the Present Times*, had appeared in four volumes in 1708. An unrelated volume entitled *A General History of the World, Briefly Sketched, Upon Scriptural Principles*, by Christian Gottlob Barth (1799–1862), German minister and author, and revised by D.P. Kidder, had appeared in 1847.

120 From the 1845 revised version of "To Helen," a poem by Edgar Allan Poe (1809–1849), American author.

121 Queen Victoria (1819–1901) reigned as Queen of the United Kingdom from 1837 to her death.

122 See "Around the Table," note 212, above.

123 See "Around the Table," note 9, above.

124 *Rob Roy* (1817), a historical novel by Scott set before the Jacobite rising of 1715; *The Pickwick Papers* (1837), by Dickens; *Zanoni* (1842), by Bulwer-Lytton. As I note in the afterword to this volume, *Rob Roy* and *The Pickwick Papers* had been among Montgomery's answers to the question "What Are the Greatest Books in the English Language?" in a article published in 1916.

125 John Greenleaf Whittier (1807–1892), American poet; John Milton (1608–1674), English poet. In a journal entry dated 1914, Montgomery listed Byron and Scott as her favourite poets (Montgomery, 15 April 1914, in *LMMCJ*, 1: 154). Montgomery selected excerpts from the work of some of these poets as epigraphs to some of her novels: Whittier for *Anne of Avonlea* and

Chronicles of Avonlea, Byron for *The Story Girl*, Tennyson for *Anne of the Island*, and Longfellow for *Rainbow Valley*.

126 The source of this allusion is unknown. The phrase "the music of the immortals" also appears in *Rainbow Valley* (see *RV*, 26), and in Montgomery, "An Autobiographical Sketch," 255. These comments on poets read in childhood also appear in Montgomery, 3 March 1909, in *CJLMM*, 2: 216, in which only "the music of the immortals" is within quotation marks.

127 *The Pilgrim's Progress* (1678), a religious allegory by Bunyan; *New Tabernacle Sermons* (1886), by Thomas De Witt Talmage (1832–1902), American preacher. This recollection of her childhood reading of these texts also appears in Montgomery, 7 January 1910, in *CJLMM*, 2: 260.

128 *The Young Disciple; or, A Memoir of Anzonetta R. Peters*, signed Rev. John A. Clark, had been published in Philadelphia in 1837. Although Montgomery refers to it here as "a thin little volume," it runs over three hundred pages.

129 See Clark, *The Young Disciple*, 294.

130 George Whitefield (1714–1770), an English preacher who helped found the evangelical Methodist movement. In her journals, in which this description appears with minor variations, Montgomery quotes a line from a hymn by Whitefield referring to the afterlife, "But what must it be to be there?" (Montgomery, 7 January 1910, in *CJLMM*, 2: 260). She destroyed her childhood journal when she was fourteen (see Montgomery, 21 September 1889, in *CJLMM*, 1: 3) but later regretted doing so.

131 The phrase "cabbages and kings" is from a poem appearing in *Through the Looking-Glass and What Alice Found There* (1872), by Carroll. Chapter 5 of the 1974 book version of "The Alpine Path" ends here.

132 This section and the "Evening Dreams" anecdote appeared in print first in Montgomery, "How I Began to Write," 67–70. The section from the anecdote about "Evening Dreams" to the acceptance of her first short story also appeared with only minor variations in Montgomery, 21 March 1901, in *CJLMM*, 2: 10–15.

133 *The Seasons* (1730), by Thomson. Here and below, I have left intact Montgomery's misspelling of his name as "Thompson."

134 This sentence does not appear in past iterations of this anecdote; it refers presumably to a shortage of paper during the First World War.

135 Montgomery told this anecdote about her father's lukewarm reaction to her first poem several times, including in a 1921 essay in the *Winnipeg Evening Tribune* entitled "Blank Verse? 'Very Blank,' Said Father," included in Volume 1 of *The L.M. Montgomery Reader*.

136 I have corrected the original, which reads "'Lives' to my friends."

137 Alma Macneill, Montgomery's third cousin. Montgomery's recollection of Alma appears in earlier and more detailed form in Montgomery, 1 July 1894, in *CJLMM*, 1: 223–24.

138 An acrostic is "a (usually short) poem (or other composition) in which the initial letters of the lines, taken in order, spell a word, phrase, or sentence" (*OED*).

139 Here and in her 1911 essay "How I Began to Write," Montgomery does not identify the visitor in question – Izzie Robinson, Montgomery's schoolteacher, who was not visiting but boarding with Montgomery and her grandparents – and omits any mention of the animosity between them. See Montgomery, 21 March 1901, in *CJLMM*, 2: 10–12; Montgomery, 7 January 1910, in *CJLMM*, 2: 270–71; Montgomery, "How I Began to Write," 69; Montgomery, 15 July 1923, in *LMMCJ*, 3: 153–54.

140 Montgomery would publish the short story "Miss Marietta's Jersey" in the July 1899 issue of this Boston periodical; she would then rework the story into part of *Anne of Avonlea*.

141 The Charlottetown *Examiner*, a Liberal weekly newspaper, had been founded in 1847 and would later merge with the *Guardian*. In her essay "How I Began to Write," she anonymizes the name of the newspaper: "It was not called *The Standard*, but that name will do" (Montgomery, "How I Began to Write," 70).

142 In her journal entry describing this anecdote, Montgomery identifies these friends as Jamie Simpson and Amanda Macneill. In a later entry, Montgomery names a "Janie" Simpson as one of the children of her neighbour William Simpson who were classmates of hers. See Montgomery, 27 January 1911, in *CJLMM*, 2: 355–56; Montgomery, 28 January 1912, in *CJLMM*, 2: 393.

143 In chapter 35 of *Anne of the Island*, twenty-one-year-old Anne reminisces about her own Story Club experience and likewise calls this story her "masterpiece" (*AIs*, 278).

144 Although several reviews of Montgomery's books commented on the element of humour, the closest equivalent to this extract is a journal entry dated 1913 in which she stated that "my forte is in

writing humor" (Montgomery, 27 September 1913, in *LMMCJ*, 1: 130).

145 Montgomery describes this cross-Canada train trip in a series of journal entries dated 9 to 20 August 1890, in *CJLMM*, 1: 35–41.

146 When describing this anecdote in her 1911 article "How I Began to Write," she referred to this newspaper as "let us say – *The Charlottetown Enterprise*" (70) – a fictional newspaper mentioned in several of her books.

147 Montgomery would revisit this experience of her first publication in her essay "Blank Verse? 'Very Blank,' Said Father."

148 These items, "The Wreck of the Marco-Polo" and "A Western Eden," appear earlier in this volume. Omitted in this list of early publications are the several school publications also included in this volume.

149 These poems published in the Charlottetown *Daily Patriot* include "On Cape Le Force" (November 1890), "June!" (June 1891), and "The Wreck of the 'Marcopolo,' 1883" (August 1892).

150 A near identical version of this sentence appears in *Emily Climbs*: "She ... was beginning to plume herself on being quite a literary person" (*EC*, 275).

151 The term "filthy lucre," meaning money (especially when gained dishonestly), originates in Titus 1:11 (*KJV*).

152 I have corrected the original, which reads "I kept one to myself." The poem, entitled "The Violet's Spell" and beginning with the line "Only a violet in the trodden street," was published in *The Ladies' World* (New York) in July 1894. In a journal entry dated seven years later, she admitted that "the price" she had received for that poem "was as good as the verses. They were trash" (Montgomery, 21 March 1901, in *CJLMM*, 2: 13). She nonetheless transcribed the entire text of the poem in her journal (Montgomery, 21 March 1901, in *CJLMM*, 2: 14).

153 This journal entry, written upon the acceptance of "The Violet's Spell" by *The Ladies' World*, appears without variation in Montgomery, 28 September 1893, in *CJLMM*, 1: 170.

154 The short story in question, "Our Charivari," was actually her second published short story, appearing in *Golden Days for Boys and Girls* in May 1896. Her first published short story, "A Baking of Gingersnaps," had appeared in *The Ladies' Journal* (Toronto) in July 1895. Both stories were signed "Maud Cavendish."

155 See Luke 15:13 (*KJV*): "And not many days after the younger son gathered all together, and took his journey into a far country, and there wasted his substance with riotous living."

156 According to her journal, Montgomery bought bound volumes of "Tennyson, Longfellow, Whittier and Byron" not with the payment she received for "Our Charivari" but with the money she received for first prize in the 1896 contest hosted by the *Evening Mail* (Halifax) earlier that month, for the best response to the question "Which has the more patience under the ordinary cares and trials of life – man or woman?" Her responses appear earlier in this volume. See Montgomery, 15 February 1896, in *CJLMM*, 1: 311; Montgomery, 20 February 1896, in *CJLMM*, 1: 314.

157 *The Lucy Maud Montgomery Album* (1999) defines the term "wee sma'" as referring to "early morning hours" ("Lucy Maud Words," 415).

158 The poem "Fisher Lassies," signed M.L. Cavendish and appearing in the 30 July 1896 issue of *The Youth's Companion*, was subsequently reprinted numerous times in American newspapers. See Montgomery, 21 March 1896, in *CJLMM*, 1: 316.

159 "Art for art's sake" is the English version of the French expression "l'art pour l'art," an early nineteenth-century slogan. This entry appears with minor variations in Montgomery, 23 August 1901, in *CJLMM*, 2: 19. In her journal, she then added, "But the editors who cater to the 'young person' take themselves too seriously for that and so in the moral must go, broad or narrow, as suits the fibre of the particular journal in view" (Montgomery, 23 August 1901, in *CJLMM*, 2: 19–20).

160 See Montgomery, 1 March 1897, in *CJLMM*, 1: 356. I have corrected the original, which reads "'stunt.'"

161 The third instalment of the 1917 text of "The Alpine Path" ends here, as does chapter 6 of the 1974 book version.

162 This poem appears in the April 1901 issue of *Munsey's Magazine*, a popular New York periodical.

163 This journal entry appears with minor variations in Montgomery, 21 March 1901, in *CJLMM*, 2: 10. After the sentence "I never expect to be famous," the entry continues: "I don't want to be, really, often as I've dreamed of it." It is in this entry that Montgomery first reminisced about her early literary work.

164 For the etymology of "presto-change," see "Around the Table," note 96, above.

165 The phrase "beer and skittles" is "used to denote that something is (not) unmixed enjoyment" (*OED*). It originated in *Tom Brown's Schooldays* (1857), a novel by Thomas Hughes (1822–1896), English lawyer and author.

166 The parts of this journal entry up till this point appear with minor variations in Montgomery, 13 November 1901, in *CJLMM*, 2: 22–23; the parts that follow appear with minor variations in Montgomery, 14 November 1901, in *CJLMM*, 2: 25.

167 The phrase "thorns in the flesh" originates in 2 Corinthians 12:7 (*KJV*).

168 "Nom de plume" is French for "pen name." Such society letters were unsigned, and since Montgomery did not include any of hers in her scrapbooks, they cannot be identified.

169 Omitted in this memoir is the modest self-congratulation that Montgomery permitted in her journal: "I think it rather goes" (Montgomery, 14 November 1901, in *CJLMM*, 2: 26).

170 In her journal, Montgomery identified the cat from home as "Bobs" (Montgomery, 14 November 1901, in *CJLMM*, 2: 26). She later had three cats named Daffy, including one who lived with her in Leaskdale when she wrote "The Alpine Path."

171 This journal entry appears with minor variations and with lukewarm descriptions of her landlady in Montgomery, 18 November 1901, in *CJLMM*, 2: 30–32.

172 For the origins of this Wellerism, see "Around the Table," note 128, above.

173 In a journal entry dated 23 November 1901 and not included in "The Alpine Path," Montgomery mentioned receiving from *The Delineator* a cheque for $25 for a short story, but her earliest known story in this magazine, "The Promise of Lucy Ellen," was not published until February 1904, and her earliest known contribution to this magazine, the poem "In Lovers' Lane," did not appear until July 1903. Montgomery published the poem "To My Enemy" in *The Smart Set: A Magazine of Cleverness* and the poem "Harbor Sunset" in *Ainslee's Magazine* (which she spells *Ainslie's*), both in January 1902; as I note in the preface to this volume, the latter poem was republished as "Sunset on Halifax Harbor" in the *Halifax Daily Echo* in March 1902. See Montgomery, 23 November 1901, in *CJLMM*, 2: 33.

174 This entry appears with only minor variations in Montgomery, 8 December 1901, in *CJLMM*, 2: 37.

175 Samples from this assignment appear as "Christmas Shopping in Halifax Stores" earlier in this volume.

176 This entry appears with only minor variations in Montgomery, 12 December 1901, in *CJLMM*, 2: 37.

177 Bon Marche Milliners was located in what is now the Colwell Building, built in 1871, at 1673 Barrington Street.

178 An allusion to Galatians 6:9 (*KJV*): "And let us not be weary in well doing."

179 This entry appears with minor variations in Montgomery, 20 December 1901, in *CJLMM*, 2: 38.

180 The full text of "A Royal Betrothal" appeared in the *Morning Chronicle*, the counterpart of the *Halifax Daily Echo*, on 21 December 1901 (a day after the date of this entry). Montgomery would reuse this experience in *Emily's Quest*, except that later the author of the story tracks Emily down and promptly falls in love with her (*EQ*, 179–87).

181 The phrase "stranger in a strange land" alludes to Exodus 2:22 (*KJV*).

182 In her journal, where this entry appears with only minor variations, "B." is identified as Bertha Clark, who had been the housekeeper at the Halifax Ladies' College, where Montgomery had lived during her year at Dalhousie University in 1895–1896. It is with Bertha's brother, Worth, however, that Montgomery went to see *The Little Minister*, a play based on the novel of the same title by Barrie, and there is no mention in the journal entry of her having to write a review of the play for the *Morning Chronicle*. Searches for this review in both newspapers in the days following the date of this journal entry were unsuccessful. See Montgomery, 27 December 1901, in *CJLMM*, 2: 39–40.

183 Most of this entry appears with only minor variations in Montgomery, 29 March 1902, in *CJLMM*, 2: 50–51, except for the last two sentences, which appear in Montgomery, 12 April 1902, in *CJLMM*, 2: 52. In her journal, however, the phrase "blameless rhymes" is replaced with "Sunday schooly rhymes" (Montgomery, 29 March 1902, in *CJLMM*, 2: 50). For the origins of the term "filthy lucre," see "The Alpine Path," note 151, above.

184 The Anglo-Irish expression "bad 'cess to him" means "bad luck to, evil befall" (*OED*).

185 My searches for this item in the microfilm copies of the *Halifax Daily Echo* and the *Morning Chronicle* as well as in Montgomery's scrapbooks were unsuccessful.

186 Otherwise known as Palm Sunday, Palmday refers to the Sunday preceding Easter in the Christian calendar. As implied in the preceding journal extract, however, Easter in 1902 fell on 30 March, whereas this entry appears with minor variations in Montgomery, 4 May 1902, in *CJLMM*, 2: 53. Missing from this excerpt are two sentences in which Montgomery announced her plans to return to Cavendish at the end of the month.

187 This unsigned work of fiction ran in the *Halifax Daily Echo* from 18 March to 29 May 1902.

188 Founded in Chicago in 1882, the American Press Association provides ready-to-print journalistic materials to smaller newspapers across North America.

189 This journal entry and the one that follows appear with only minor variations in *Emily Climbs*, in which Emily likewise is asked to cut ruthlessly the text of "a sensational and sentimental English novel" entitled *A Bleeding Heart*, with the same amusing result (see *EC*, 249, 252).

190 In Montgomery's journal entry, dated 20 May instead of 31 May 1902, it was a new member of staff who said this to her; it was not a conversation between two people that she overheard. Her journal entry dated 31 May 1902 concerns her final day at the office. See Montgomery, 20 May 1902, in *CJLMM*, 2: 54; Montgomery, 31 May 1902, in *CJLMM*, 2: 55. Chapter 7 of the 1974 book version of "The Alpine Path" ends here.

191 Montgomery's description of the writing process of *Anne of Green Gables* appeared elsewhere in similar form. See, for instance, Montgomery, 16 August 1907, in *CJLMM*, 2: 171–72; Montgomery, "An Autobiographical Sketch," 257.

192 In her journal, in which this description of the genesis of *Anne of Green Gables* is narrated in almost identical form, Montgomery recorded her recollection that she had found the kernel of the story in her notebook of ideas "two years ago in the spring of 1905" (Montgomery, 16 August 1907, in *CJLMM*, 2: 171; see also Montgomery, 18 April 1914, in *LMMCJ*, 1: 156).

193 This is evidently an allusion to Montgomery's own 1915 essay "The Way to Make a Book" (139), where an earlier version of

this paragraph appears. She returns to this notion in "'I Dwell among My Own People,'" an essay published around 1921; both essays appear in Volume 1 of *The L.M. Montgomery Reader*.

194 The model for Peg Bowen, Mag Laird, was mentioned earlier in this memoir. The expression "to paint the lily," meaning "to embellish excessively, to add ornament where none is necessary" (*OED*), can be traced to Shakespeare's *King John* (1623).

195 Montgomery's details about characters and settings in her books appear in more elaborate form, in a different order, and with minor variations in Montgomery, 27 January 1911, in *CJLMM*, 2: 348–54. In her journals, it was certain details about the Cuthbert yard that were "transplanted from the estates of my castle in Spain," whereas the White Way of Delight, Willowmere (not "Wiltonmere" as stated here), and Violet Vale were deemed products of her imagination (see Montgomery, 27 January 1911, in *CJLMM*, 2: 349, 350, 354). For more on the "castle in Spain," see "Around the Table," note 225, above.

196 "Lovers' Lane," also known as "Lover's Lane," a stretch of woods near the farm on which Montgomery drew to an extent for the original of Green Gables; she referred to it as "my favourite object in Nature" (Montgomery, 15 April 1914, in *LMMCJ*, 1: 153). Montgomery's poem "In Lovers' Lane" had appeared in *The Delineator* in 1903, and this place is also referenced in *Anne of Green Gables* and its sequels as well as in *The Blue Castle*. They also inspired four nature essays that Montgomery had published in 1911 and that appear in Volume 1 of *The L.M. Montgomery Reader* as "[Seasons in the Woods]."

197 These descriptions of Katie Maurice and Lucy Gray appear with only minor variations in Montgomery, 26 March 1905, in *CJLMM*, 2: 127.

198 "Lucy Gray, or Solitude" (1799), a poem by Wordsworth.

199 The fourth instalment of the 1917 version of "The Alpine Path" ends here.

200 For the origins of the "new-fangled flavouring" story, see "Around the Table," note 260, above.

201 Montgomery's account of finding a publisher for *Anne of Green Gables* appears with minor variations in Montgomery, 16 August 1907, in *CJLMM*, 2: 172–73.

202 In her journal, Montgomery identified this publisher as the Bobbs-Merrill Company of Indianapolis, which, although

founded in 1850, had been rebranded as Bobbs-Merrill in 1903 (see Montgomery, 16 August 1907, in *CJLMM*, 2: 172).

203 According to her journal, the established firm was the Macmillan Company of New York, founded in 1843.

204 The idiomatic expression "damn with faint praise," referring to praise that is so lukewarm that it comes across as insincere, originates in "Epistle to Dr. Arbuthnot," a satirical poem by Alexander Pope (1688–1744), English poet.

205 Here, this record departs from the version in Montgomery's journals, in which she mentioned only one "betwixt and between firm" (Lothrop, Lee and Shephard of Boston) and then a fourth firm, Henry Holt Company of New York, which sent the "damned with faint praise" note (see Montgomery, 16 August 1907, in *CJLMM*, 2: 172).

206 Compare this with the version in Montgomery's journal: "The book may or may not sell well. I wrote it for love, not money – but very often such books are the most successful – just as everything in life that is born of true love is better than something constructed for mercenary ends" (Montgomery, 16 August 1907, in *CJLMM*, 2: 173). This paragraph is followed by one in which Montgomery writes dubiously about her publisher, L.C. Page and Company, and her displeasure at her royalty rate, which was far below industry standards.

207 Montgomery's stated surprise that her book appealed to such a diverse readership was one of her set phrases for the conclusion to her "how I began" narratives; see, for instance, Montgomery, "An Autobiographical Sketch," 257–58.

208 Likely a reference to Kenneth Cruit, a young English soldier whom Montgomery mentioned in Montgomery, 3 February 1917, in *LMMCJ*, 1: 280.

209 This entry appears in slightly different form – minus the Scottish phrase "spleet-new" – in Montgomery, 20 June 1908, in *CJLMM*, 2: 192. The term "spleet-new" also appears in a similar description of Emily Starr's receipt of her first published book in *Emily's Quest* (see *EQ*, 232).

210 These anecdotes appear in similar form in Montgomery to Weber, 2 September 1909, in *GGL*, 93, and in Montgomery, "Bits from My Mailbag," 186–87.

211 *Anne på Grönkulla*, translated by Karin Lidforss Jensen, was published in Swedish in 1909; *In Veilige Haven*, translated by

Betsy de Vries, was published in Dutch in 1910. Montgomery's comments on the cover art for the Swedish edition of *Anne of Green Gables* appear in different form in Montgomery, 19 March 1910, in *CJLMM*, 2: 290.

212 "Una of the Garden" appeared in five instalments in the Minneapolis magazine *The Housekeeper* between December 1908 and April 1909; its date of composition is unknown. See also "A Canadian Novelist," 106.

213 These details about *The Story Girl* appear in longer form and with only minor variations in Montgomery, 23 May 1911, in *CJLMM*, 2: 404–6.

214 Montgomery appears to have overlooked that she already identified the origin of Peg Bowen as Mag Laird earlier in this autobiography. Parts of this description of Peg appear with minor variations in *The Golden Road* (see *GR*, 245). This account of the origins of Peg Bowen appears with only minor variations as part of a journal entry detailing many of the sources of *The Story Girl*, including the courtship of her Penman ancestors and "the story of the captain of the *Fanny*," which she narrates near the beginning of this autobiography. See Montgomery, 23 May 1911, in *CJLMM*, 2: 404–5.

215 See her similar telling of this story in Montgomery's journals, in which she identified the source of this story as a "Mrs. Boswell" of Hampton immediately after narrating the courtship of her Penman ancestors (Montgomery, 23 May 1911, in *CJLMM*, 2: 405).

216 Scotch expression referring to a narrative that is completely true, as opposed to most tales, which are presumed to be fictitious.

217 In *The Story Girl*, Sara Stanley tells the story of Rachel Ward, who packed up all her wedding trousseau and gifts into a trunk after her fiancé had run away the morning of the wedding ceremony and who then left the island and took the key with her; at the end of the book, her trunk is opened after her death (*SG*, 127–31, 354–63).

218 Chapter 8 of the 1974 book version of "The Alpine Path" ends here.

219 I have amended the dates of the seven journal entries included here, all of which read "1912" instead of "1911"; the 1974 book version of "The Alpine Path" retains the erroneous dates but notes the error in its unsigned preface. The version of this entry in

Montgomery's journal begins with the header "St. Enoch's Hotel, Glasgow" (Montgomery, 20 July 1911, in *LMMCJ*, 1: 3), and this entry is preceded by entries describing their time in Chester (near the Welsh border), Glasgow, and Liverpool.

220 This first paragraph appears in slightly different form in Montgomery, 22 July 1911, in *SJLMM*, 2: 70; the rest of this entry was cut by editors Rubio and Waterston, who refer to Oban, Staffa, and Iona as "a village, and islands, in the west of Scotland described in Walter Scott's *Lord of the Isles* (1804)" (Rubio and Waterston, in *SJLMM*, 2: 411).

221 Loch Awe is a large body of water in the Argyll and Bute area of southwestern Scotland. Kilchurn Castle, which was built in the fifteenth century and which remains a popular site for tourists, is located on the northeastern part of the loch.

222 For more on New London Harbour, see "The Alpine Path," note 96, above.

223 The travel company Thomas Cook and Son (as it was known during the period described here) was founded in 1841 and remains operational to this day.

224 Fingal's Cave is a sea cave on the island of Staffa, renowned for its natural acoustics. A photograph captioned "Climbing over the Staffa rocks to Fingal's Cave" appears in *LMMCJ*, 1: 4.

225 I have corrected the original, which reads "dour guide."

226 Possibly a reference to Isaiah 57:15 (*KJV*): "For thus saith the high and lofty One that inhabiteth eternity, whose name is Holy."

227 Irish-born St. Columba (521–597 CE) established a monastery on the island of Iona in Scotland.

228 King Duncan, a fictional character in Shakespeare's tragic play *Macbeth*.

229 Properly, "storied urn or animated bust." From "Elegy Written in a Country Churchyard," by Gray.

230 In her journal, Montgomery used the phrase "one or two congenial spirits" instead of "a few 'kindred souls'" (Montgomery, 20 July 1911, in *LMMCJ*, 1: 6).

231 In her journals, Montgomery mentioned that the letters from home were from her cousins Frede and Stella, daughters of John and Annie Campbell of Park Corner (Montgomery, 20 July 1911, in *LMMCJ*, 1: 6).

232 Ayr, home of the Robert Burns Birthplace Museum, is a popular resort town 60 kilometres southwest of Glasgow.

233 In her journal, in which this entry appears in slightly different form, Montgomery identified this couple as "Mr. and Mrs. Thorpe from Guelph, Ontario" (Montgomery, 30 July 1911, in *LMMCJ*, 1: 7).

234 Properly, "Where'er we tread, 'tis haunted, holy ground." From *Childe Harold's Pilgrimage*, a narrative poem by Byron.

235 From "Locksley Hall Sixty Years After," a poem by Tennyson. Possibly a reference to the birthplace of Burns in Alloway, just outside Ayr.

236 Alloway Auld Kirk, a sixteenth-century church that is the location of "Tam O'Shanter," a narrative poem by Burns.

237 The Burns Monument at the Burns Birthplace Museum was designed by Thomas Hamilton (1784–1854), Scottish architect.

238 Mary Campbell (1763–1786) died young but was immortalized in several of Burns's songs, including "The Highland Lassie."

239 Properly, "unwept, unhonoured, and unsung." From "The Lay of the Last Minstrel," a poem by Scott.

240 "Laura," the muse of Petrarch's poetry; Beatrice, portrayed as the "ideal woman" in Dante's *Divine Comedy*; Stella, likely a reference to the title character in *Astrophil and Stella* (1591), a sonnet sequence by Sir Philip Sidney (1554–1586), English poet; Lucasta, the addressee of "To Lucasta, Going to the Wars," a poem by Richard Lovelace (1618–1657), English poet; Julia, the addressee of several poems by Robert Herrick (1591–1674), English poet; "Un secret," a poem by Félix Arvers (1806–1850), French poet, which was translated into English by Longfellow.

241 A scenic region 51 kilometres northwest of Glasgow, now known more commonly as "Trossachs" (the 1974 book version of this text updates the spelling accordingly). Similar to Cavendish in Montgomery's novels, this region was popularized in large part due to Scott's epic poem *The Lady of the Lake*; in addition, Robert Browning had published a poem entitled "The Trosachs."

242 *The Lady of the Lake* (1810), an epic poem by Scott, part of which focuses on Ellen Douglas and her three suitors, Roderick Dhu, James Fitz-James, and Malcolm Graeme. For an earlier account of her girlhood fascination with this work of literature, see Montgomery, 14 January 1900, in *CJLMM*, 1: 448.

243 Loch Lomond and Loch Katrine are freshwater lochs in the Trossachs region of Scotland, as is Loch Achray, mentioned later

in this entry; the rural community of Inversnaid is located on the banks of Loch Lomond. Loch Katrine is the setting of Scott's *The Lady of the Lake*, hence Montgomery's disappointment.

244 Stronachlachar, a settlement on Loch Katrine.

245 "Château en Espagne" is French for "castle in Spain." See "Around the Table," note 225, above.

246 Properly, "The beach of pebbles bright as snow." From *The Lady of the Lake*, by Scott.

247 The fifth instalment of the 1917 version of "The Alpine Path" ends here, along with the following note, signed "The Editors": "In the concluding instalment of this fascinating story of the career of L.M. Montgomery, which will appear in 'Everywoman's World' for November, will be four more letters from her Journal giving you a further treat by way of realistic description of noted places in Scotland and in England. The story ends with her leaving Prince Edward Island to move to Ontario as her husband was pastor of an Ontario congregation."

248 In the 1974 book version of the text, the term "Highland plunderers" is within quotation marks (see *AP*, 85).

249 Properly, "Where shall he find, in foreign land, / So lone a lake, so sweet a strand?" From *The Lady of the Lake*, by Scott.

250 A rural community in the Trossachs.

251 One of several islets on Loch Katrine and a central setting of Scott's *The Lady of the Lake*. A photograph of Ellen's Isle by Thomas Ogle had been included in an 1863 edition of Scott's poem.

252 A mountain in the Trossachs, sometimes spelled as "Ben Venue."

253 The phrase "summit hoar" is from *The Lady of the Lake*, by Scott.

254 Abbotsford, Scott's ancestral home, is located in Melrose, a town in the southeastern region of Scotland.

255 The Eildon Hills consist of a three-peaked hill south of Melrose.

256 Here, Montgomery's journal entry continues, "I am sure I would not" – a comment that reveals her self-awareness as a famous author (Montgomery, 6 August 1911, in *LMMCJ*, 1: 13).

257 Scott is interred in the north transept of Dryburgh Abbey in St. Boswells, approximately 7 kilometres southeast of Melrose.

258 "If thou wouldst view fair Melrose aright, / Go visit it by the pale moonlight." From canto 2 of "The Lay of the Last Minstrel,"

a poem by Scott. The partly ruined Melrose Abbey had been founded in 1136.

259 Properly, Michael Scot (1175–c. 1232), Scottish scholar and mathematician.

260 Robert I, the Bruce (1274–1329) ruled as King of Scots from 1306 until his death.

261 A city in the Scottish Highlands, more than 300 kilometres northwest of Melrose.

262 Kirriemuir, almost 200 kilometres north of Melrose, famed as the original setting of *Sentimental Tommy* (1896), a novel by Barrie, who was born and raised in Kirriemuir.

263 "Through the Den runs a tiny burn, and by its side is a pink path, dyed this pretty color, perhaps, by the blushes the ladies leave behind them." From *Sentimental Tommy*, by Barrie. See also Epperly, *Through Lover's Lane*, 50–51.

264 For the etymology of the phrase "Lover's Lane"/"Lovers' Lane," see "The Alpine Path," note 196, above. Chapter 9 of the 1974 book version of "The Alpine Path" ends here.

265 Culloden, a village east of Inverness.

266 Titania, Queen of the Fairies, a character in Shakespeare's *A Midsummer Night's Dream*.

267 Fort William, a large settlement more than 200 kilometres northwest of Edinburgh, is connected to Inverness by the Caledonian Canal.

268 Properly, the Rosslyn Chapel, a fifteenth-century building in the village of Roslin, 12 kilometres south of Edinburgh.

269 Section 23 of canto 6 of "The Lay of the Last Minstrel," by Scott.

270 Alloa, a village 60 kilometres northwest of Edinburgh.

271 Natural area near the town of Dollar (55 kilometres northwest of Edinburgh and 10 kilometres northeast of Alloa) that has been a popular destination for tourists since the mid-nineteenth century.

272 George Boyd MacMillan (1881–1953), with whom Montgomery had been corresponding since 1903 and to whom she would dedicate *Emily of New Moon*. A selection of Montgomery's letters to MacMillan appears in Francis W.P. Bolger and Elizabeth R. Epperly's volume *My Dear Mr. M: Letters to G.B. MacMillan from L.M. Montgomery* (1980). Montgomery's complete correspondence to MacMillan is held at Library and Archives Canada.

273 Stirling, a city almost 60 kilometres northwest of Edinburgh and 10 kilometres west of Alloa. Abbey Craig, a hilltop just north of Stirling.

274 Berwick-upon-Tweed, a town 90 kilometres southeast of Edinburgh, in the northernmost part of England; *Marmion: A Tale of Flodden Field* (1808), an epic poem by Scott.

275 In her journal, Montgomery identifies the "Miss A." in question as Miss Jean Allan, MacMillan's much younger fiancée, who, according to her, had a "dazzling" complexion but "no intellect" and "no conversational powers" (Montgomery, 13 August 1911, in *LMMCJ*, 1: 18, 19). In a letter dated 1917, MacMillan reportedly mentioned to Montgomery that Allan had married someone else (Montgomery to MacMillan, 15 March 1931, in *MDMM*, 160–61).

276 Spittal, just south of Berwick-upon-Tweed, across the Tweed River.

277 Carlisle, a city in the county of Cumbria, in northwest England, 16 kilometres south of the border between England and Scotland and 85 kilometres southwest of Berwick-upon-Tweed.

278 "Shank's mare" refers to using "one's own legs as a means of conveyance" (*OED*) – in other words, travel by foot.

279 Holy Island, 20 kilometres down the coast from Berwick-upon-Tweed and 115 kilometres southwest of Edinburgh, is the location of Lindisfarne Abbey.

280 Norham Castle, near the border between England and Scotland, was built in the twelfth century on the River Tweed.

281 Ladykirk, a village just north of the border between England and Scotland.

282 "Meeter" as an adjective is an archaic term referring to something that is fitting or proper.

283 In Northumberland in England, Flodden Field was the site of the Battle of Flodden, fought on 9 September 1513 between the Kingdom of England and the Kingdom of Scotland, that ended in a victory for England and the death of James IV (1473–1513), King of Scots.

284 Properly, Horncliffe Glen, Horncliffe being a village in Northumberland, south of the River Tweed.

285 York, a city in North Yorkshire, in northeast England, 185 kilometres southeast of Carlisle.

286 Keswick, a market town more than 200 kilometres south of Edinburgh, in the Lake District, a mountainous region in northwestern England.

287 Properly, "The haughtiest breast its wish might bound / Through life to dwell delighted here." From "Childe Harold's Pilgrimage," a poem by Byron.

288 Scott's *The Bridal of Triermain, or The Vale of St. John*, a narrative poem in three cantos, had been published in 1813.

289 Buttermere and Windermere are both in the Lake District in northwestern England.

290 The china dogs mentioned here would figure in *Anne of the Island* and *Anne's House of Dreams*.

291 Westminster Abbey, "Minster" referring to a major church.

292 The phrase "lares and penates" refers to "household gods" in the sense of "household belongings regarded as defining or embodying one's home" (*OED*). The phrase "dignity and aplomb" is used to describe these dogs in *Anne's House of Dreams* (see *AHD*, 78).

293 Properly, Hotel Russell, a four-star hotel built in 1898.

294 The British Museum, the first national museum available to the public, on Russell Street in London, had opened in 1753. The Tower of London, a castle in central London. Westminster Abbey, an abbey church in London. The Crystal Palace, an exhibition hall made of iron and glass, built to house the Great Exhibition of 1851 and subsequently moved to Sydenham Hill, where it was destroyed by fire on the night of 30 November 1936, coincidentally Montgomery's sixty-second birthday. Kenilworth Castle, in Warwickshire, the site of a lavish reception given by Robert Dudley, first Earl of Leicester (1532–1588), English nobleman, for Elizabeth I (1533–1603), Queen of England and Ireland, in 1575. Shakespeare Land, referring to Stratford-upon-Avon, a market town in the West Midlands; Montgomery and Macdonald visited both his birthplace and the site of his burial. Hampton Court Palace, a royal palace southwest of central London. Salisbury, home of the medieval Salisbury Cathedral, 12 kilometres south of Stonehenge, a prehistoric monument. Windsor Castle, an eleventh-century royal residence just west of London.

295 Russell Square, a garden square located in the west end of central London. Amelia Sedley, George Osborne, Becky Sharp, and Joseph Sedley are among the large cast of characters in Thackeray's satirical novel *Vanity Fair*.

296 In July 1575, Robert Dudley, Earl of Leicester, welcomed Elizabeth I, Queen of England and Ireland, as a guest in his home.

297 Amy Robsart (1532–1560), wife of Robert Dudley, whose death as a result of a fall down a flight of stairs was seen as suspicious. Their marriage formed the basis for *Kenilworth* (1821), a novel by Scott.

298 Oliver Goldsmith (1728–1774), Irish author whose works include the novel *The Vicar of Wakefield* (1766).

299 Fleet Street, a major London street that, at the time Montgomery wrote "The Alpine Path," was a major centre for London newspapers. The Pickwick Club in Dickens's *The Pickwick Papers*, one of Montgomery's favourite novels, is also set there.

300 "Poor Noll" refers to an epigraph to Goldsmith attributed to David Garrick (1717–1779), English actor and playwright: "Here lies Nolly Goldsmith, for shortness called Noll, / Who wrote like an angel, and talked like poor Poll." See Roberts, *Hoyt's New Cyclopedia of Practical Quotations*, 231.

301 A reference to "Lady Clara Vere de Vere," a poem by Tennyson about an aristocratic lady.

302 The Marquis of Carabas, a bogus character in "Puss and Boots," a European folk tale about a cat that tricks people in order to gain power.

303 The RMS *Adriatic* had been launched in 1906.

304 Montgomery's account in her journal was even more blunt about her fatigue: "I am beginning to feel that I have had enough of sight seeing and knocking about, for one time. I am tired of living in a trunk – and I am tired of hotel cookery. And I want a *home* again" (Montgomery, 18 September 1911, in *LMMCJ*, 1: 38). Omitted here is an account of her last days in England, which included the discovery of the childhood home of her recently deceased grandmother. See Montgomery, 18 September 1911, in *LMMCJ*, 1: 39–42.

305 Ewan Macdonald (1870–1943) had been the minister at Montgomery's church in Cavendish, where they met in September 1903 and became secretly engaged in October 1906; he had become the pastor of the Presbyterian church in Leaskdale, Ontario, in 1910. See Montgomery, 12 October 1906, in *CJLMM*, 2: 154–58; Rubio and Waterston, in *CJLMM*, 2: 335n2.

306 From *Endymion: A Poetic Romance* (1818), a book-length poem by Keats. Montgomery quoted these lines in a 1909 letter to

MacMillan, in which she mentioned that she had been reading Keats for the first time. See Montgomery to MacMillan, 21 May 1909, in *MDMM*, 46.

307 The quotation from Keats and this final paragraph would reappear in slightly different form in chapter 19 of *Emily Climbs*, entitled "'Airy Voices'" (see *EC*, 248). Montgomery also quoted these lines in Montgomery to Weber, 2 September 1909, in *GGL*, 92. The quotation "far-off divine event" is from "In Memoriam," a poem by Tennyson.

Bibliography

Alexander, Christine, and Juliet McMaster, eds. *The Child Writer from Austen to Woolf*. Cambridge: Cambridge University Press, 2005. Cambridge Studies in Nineteenth-Century Literature and Culture.

Anglin, Margaret. "My Career." *Everywoman's World* (Toronto), December 1916, 5, 43–44, 46, 55; January 1917, 10, 47; April 1917, 10, 45–46, 51.

"*Anne of Green Gables*." In Lefebvre, *The L.M. Montgomery Reader*, 3: 51–68.

Anne of Green Gables. Directed by Kevin Sullivan. Screen adaptation by Kevin Sullivan and Joe Wiesenfeld. Sullivan Films, 1985.

Anne of Green Gables: The Sequel. Written and directed by Kevin Sullivan. Sullivan Films, 1987.

Anne with an "E." Created by Moira Walley-Beckett. Northwood Entertainment, 2017–.

Atkinson, Frank. *Dictionary of Literary Pseudonyms: A Selection of Popular Modern Writers in English*. 3rd ed. London: Clive Bingley, 1982.

"The Author of *Anne of Avonlea*." In Lefebvre, *The L.M. Montgomery Reader*, 1: 37–39.

"Author Tells How He Wrote His Story." In Lefebvre, *The L.M. Montgomery Reader*, 1: 33–34.

Beer, Frances. Introduction to *The Juvenilia of Jane Austen and Charlotte Brontë*, edited by Frances Beer, 7–30. Harmondsworth: Penguin Books, 1986.

Bodenheimer, Rosemarie. "A Woman of Many Names." In *The Cambridge Companion to George Eliot*, edited by George Levine, 20–37. Cambridge: Cambridge University Press, 2001.

Bolger, Francis W.P. *The Years Before "Anne."* N.p.: Prince Edward Island Heritage Foundation, 1974.

Boyce, Neith. "The Novelist's Deadliest Friend." *The Bookman* (New York), September 1901, 27–28.

Braybrooke, Neville. Introduction to *Seeds in the Wind: Juvenilia from W.B. Yeats to Ted Hughes*, edited by Neville Braybrooke, 13–24. London: Hutchinson, 1989.

Brontë, Charlotte [Currer Bell]. "Biographical Notice of Ellis and Acton Bell." In Wuthering Heights *and* Agnes Grey, by Emily Brontë [Ellis Bell] and Anne Brontë [Acton Bell], vii–xvi. Cambridge: Cambridge University Press, 2013. Cambridge Literary Collection.

Brown, Vanessa, and Benjamin Lefebvre. "Archival Adventures with L.M. Montgomery; or, 'As Long as the Leaves Hold Together.'" In Lefebvre, *The L.M. Montgomery Reader*, 2: 371–86.

Bruce, Marian. *A Century of Excellence: Prince of Wales College, 1860–1969*. Charlottetown: Island Studies Press, 2005.

Buss, Helen M. *Mapping Our Selves: Canadian Women's Autobiography in English*. Montreal and Kingston: McGill-Queen's University Press, 1993.

Byron, George Gordon. *Byron's Letters and Journals: A New Selection, from Leslie A. Marchand's Twelve-Volume Edition*. Edited by Richard Lansdown. Oxford: Oxford University Press, 2015.

"A Canadian Novelist of Note Interviewed." In Lefebvre, *The L.M. Montgomery Reader*, 1: 105–9.

Church, Ella Rodman, and Augusta De Bubna. "Tam: The Story of a Woman." *Godey's Lady's Book* (Philadelphia), January 1884, 51–57; February 1884, 128–41; March 1884, 233–46; April 1884, 351–66; May 1884, 458–68; June 1884, 558–71.

Clark, John A. *The Young Disciple; or, A Memoir of Anzonetta R. Peters*. Philadelphia: William Marshall and Company, 1837.

Clarke, Joseph F. *Pseudonyms*. London: Hamish Hamilton, 1977.

Collins, Carolyn Strom. *A Guide to L.M. Montgomery's Story and Poem Scrapbooks 1890–1940: Stories and Poems Published in Periodicals and Preserved by L.M. Montgomery in Twelve Scrapbooks*. Charlottetown: L.M. Montgomery Institute, 2016.

———. "The Scrapbooks." In McCabe, *The Lucy Maud Montgomery Album*, 112–17.

Coultrap-McQuin, Susan. "Pseudonyms." In *The Oxford Companion to Women's Writing in the United States*, edited by Cathy N.

Davidson and Linda Wagner-Martin, 716–17. New York: Oxford University Press, 1995.

Courier-News (Bridgewater, NJ). "Your Questions Answered." 29 June 1934, 10.

Daily Examiner (Charlottetown). "Prince of Wales College." 8 June 1894, 2; 9 June 1894, 2.

Daily Pantagraph (Bloomington, IL). "The Daily Pantagraph's Information Service." 28 June 1934, 4; 18 January 1935, 4.

Dillane, Fionnuala. *Before George Eliot: Marian Evans and the Periodical Press*. Cambridge: Cambridge University Press, 2013. Cambridge Studies in Nineteenth-Century Literature and Culture.

Easley, Alexis. "Making a Debut." In *The Cambridge Companion to Victorian Women's Writing*, edited by Linda H. Peterson, 15–28. Cambridge: Cambridge University Press, 2015.

Elmira (NY) Star-Gazette. "Your Questions Answered." 28 June 1934, 6; 18 January 1935, 6.

Epperly, Elizabeth Rollins. *Imagining Anne: The Island Scrapbooks of L.M. Montgomery*. Toronto: Penguin Canada, 2008. 100 Years of Anne.

———. *Through Lover's Lane: L.M. Montgomery's Photography and Visual Imagination*. Toronto: University of Toronto Press, 2007.

———. "Visual Drama: Capturing Life in L.M. Montgomery's Scrapbooks." In Gammel, *The Intimate Life of L.M. Montgomery*, 189–209.

Everywoman's World (Toronto). Editors' note. October 1917, 8.

———. "The Ground Floor." September 1917, 1.

———. "The Summit Is Reached." November 1917, 25.

"Family Tree." In McCabe, *The Lucy Maud Montgomery Album*, 504–5.

Farmer, Arthur B. "Will My Daughter Be an Author?" *Everywoman's World* (Toronto), August 1917, 8, 47.

Fishbane, Melanie J. *Maud: A Novel Inspired by the Life of L.M. Montgomery*. Toronto: Penguin Teen Canada, 2017.

Fredeman, Jane Cowan. "The Land of Lost Content: The Use of Fantasy in L.M. Montgomery's Novels." *Canadian Children's Literature* 1, no. 3 (Autumn 1975): 60–70.

Freeman, Barbara M. *Kit's Kingdom: The Journalism of Kathleen Blake Coleman*. Ottawa: Carleton University Press, 1989. Carleton Women's Experience.

"From *Fiction Writers on Fiction Writing: Advice, Opinions and a Statement of Their Own Working Methods by More Than One Hundred Authors*." In Lefebvre, *The L.M. Montgomery Reader*, 1: 189–96.

Gammel, Irene, ed. *The Intimate Life of L.M. Montgomery*. Toronto: University of Toronto Press, 2005.

———. *Looking for Anne of Green Gables: The Story of L.M. Montgomery and Her Classic*. New York: St. Martin's Press, 2008.

Gaskell, E.C. *The Life of Charlotte Brontë*. 2 vols. London: Smith, Elder and Company, 1857.

Gerson, Carole. *Canadian Women in Print 1750–1918*. Waterloo: Wilfrid Laurier University Press, 2010.

———. "L.M. Montgomery and the Conflictedness of a Woman Writer." In *Storm and Dissonance: L.M. Montgomery and Conflict*, edited by Jean Mitchell, 67–80. Newcastle: Cambridge Scholars Publishing, 2008.

Gilbert, Sandra M., and Susan Gubar. *The Madwoman in the Attic: The Woman Writer and the Nineteenth-Century Imagination*. New Haven: Yale University Press, 1979.

Headnote to "A Girl's Place at Dalhousie College, 1896." *Atlantis: A Women's Studies Journal / Journal d'études sur la femme* 5 (1979): 146–47.

Globe (Toronto). "Canadian Photos in World Contest." 6 October 1931, 14.

———. "'Nancy Durham' Dies." 29 June 1928, 4.

———. "Nancy Durham Memorial Contest." 4 July 1931, 20.

Halifax Daily Echo. "The Beachcomber." 27 March 1902, 4.

———. "A Royal Welcome to the Duke and Duchess." 19 October 1901, 1, 7, 12.

Halifax Herald. "Fossilized Oxford and Cambridge." 29 April 1896, 12.

———. "Names of Students Who Got Through." 29 April 1896, 6.

———. "The Officers of the Various Societies." 29 April 1896, 6.

Hammill, Faye. *Women, Celebrity, and Literary Culture between the Wars*. Austin: University of Texas Press, 2007.

Harrisburg (PA) Telegraph. "Ask the Telegraph." 28 June 1934, 10.

Haynes, John Edward. *Pseudonyms of Authors: Including Antonyms and Initialisms*. 1882. Detroit: Gale Research Company, 1969.

Heritage Minutes: Lucy Maud Montgomery. Directed by Stephen Dunn. Historica Canada, 2018.

Hollenberg, Martin J. *Marco Polo: The Story of the Fastest Clipper.* Halifax: Nimbus Publishing, 2006.

"In Memoriam, Carol Gaboury." *The Shining Scroll*, Summer 1998, 1.

Island Guardian and Christian Chronicle (Charlottetown). "P. of W. Convocation." 14 June 1894, 2.

"Island Writer Laid to Rest at Cavendish." In Lefebvre, *The L.M. Montgomery Reader*, 1: 369–72.

Ithaca Journal. "Answers from Washington." 7 February 1935, 6.

"Julia Arthur's Own Story of Her Career." *Everywoman's World* (Toronto), May 1916, 10, 33–34; September 1916, 7, 29, 35, 37–39.

Kingsport (TN) Times. "Questions and Answers from Washington." 18 January 1935, 4.

Kirk, Connie Ann. *J.K. Rowling: A Biography.* Westport, CT: Greenwood Press, 2003. Greenwood Biographies.

Lang, Marjory. *Women Who Made the News: Female Journalists in Canada, 1880–1945.* Montreal and Kingston: McGill-Queen's University Press, 1999.

Lansfeldt, Laurie. "Her Bid for Love." *Halifax Daily Echo*, 21 September 1901, 10.

Lee, Katja. "Protecting Her Brand: Contextualizing the Production and Publication of L.M. Montgomery's 'The Alpine Path.'" *Studies in Canadian Literature / Revue d'études canadiennes* 38, no. 2 (2013): 184–204.

Lefebvre, Benjamin. "Epilogue: Posthumous Titles, 1960–2013." In Lefebvre, *The L.M. Montgomery Reader*, 3: 353–90.

———. Headnote to "Something about L.M. Montgomery." In Lefebvre, *The L.M. Montgomery Reader*, 1: 209–10.

———. Headnote to "What Are the Greatest Books in the English Language?" In Lefebvre, *The L.M. Montgomery Reader*, 1: 151.

———. "Introduction: A Critical Heritage." In Lefebvre, *The L.M. Montgomery Reader*, 2: 3–49.

———. "Introduction: A Life in Print." In Lefebvre, *The L.M. Montgomery Reader*, 1: 3–28.

———, ed. *The L.M. Montgomery Reader*, Volume 1: *A Life in Print*; Volume 2: *A Critical Heritage*; Volume 3: *A Legacy in Review.* Toronto: University of Toronto Press, 2013, 2014, 2015.

Linton, Henry P. *Select Orations of Marcus Tullius Cicero, for the Hilary Term Examination of the Junior Sophister Year, from the Text of Jo. Case. Trellis, with a Literal Translation and Notes.* Dublin: T.V. Morris, 1845.

Litster, Jennifer H. “The Scotsman, the Scribe, and the Spyglass: Going Back with L.M. Montgomery to Prince Edward Island.” In *L.M. Montgomery and the Matter of Nature(s)*, edited by Rita Bode and Jean Mitchell, 42–57, 221–24. Montreal and Kingston: McGill-Queen’s University Press, 2018.

Little, Jean. “But What about Jane?” *Canadian Children’s Literature* 1, no. 3 (Autumn 1975): 71–81.

“L.M. Montgomery Issue.” *Canadian Children’s Literature* 1, no. 3 (Autumn 1975).

“Lucy Maud Words.” In McCabe, *The Lucy Maud Montgomery Album*, 414–15.

MacMurchy, Marjory. “L.M. Montgomery of the Island.” In Lefebvre, *The L.M. Montgomery Reader*, 1: 129–33.

———. “L.M. Montgomery: Story Writer.” In Lefebvre, *The L.M. Montgomery Reader*, 1: 120–25.

Macneill, Charles, and L.M. Montgomery. *The Diary of Charles Macneill, Farmer, 1892–1896*. N.p.: Rock’s Mills Press, 2018.

Manuel, Lynn. *The Summer of the “Marco Polo.”* Illustrated by Kasia Charko. Victoria: Orca Book Publishers, 2007.

McCabe, Kevin, comp. *The Lucy Maud Montgomery Album*. Edited by Alexandra Heilbron. Toronto: Fitzhenry and Whiteside, 1999.

———. “Lucy Maud Montgomery’s Table Talk.” In McCabe, *The Lucy Maud Montgomery Album*, 160–67.

Meade, L.T. *A Sweet Girl Graduate*. London: Cassell and Company, 1891.

Middletown (NY) Times-Herald. “Questions and Answers.” 18 January 1935, 4.

“Miss L.M. Montgomery, Author of *Anne of Green Gables*.” In Lefebvre, *The L.M. Montgomery Reader*, 1: 62–66.

Montgomery, L.M. *Across the Miles: Tales of Correspondence*. Edited by Rea Wilmshurst. Toronto: McClelland and Stewart, 1995.

———. *After Green Gables: L.M. Montgomery’s Letters to Ephraim Weber, 1916–1941*. Edited by Hildi Froese Tiessen and Paul Gerard Tiessen. Toronto: University of Toronto Press, 2006.

———. *After Many Days: Tales of Time Passed*. Edited by Rea Wilmshurst. Toronto: McClelland and Stewart, 1991.

———. *After Many Years*. Edited by Carolyn Strom Collins and Christy Woster. Halifax: Nimbus Publishing, 2017.

———. *Against the Odds: Tales of Achievement*. Edited by Rea Wilmshurst. Toronto: McClelland and Stewart, 1993.

———. *Akin to Anne: Tales of Other Orphans*. Edited by Rea Wilmshurst. Toronto: McClelland and Stewart, 1988.

———. *Along the Shore: Tales by the Sea*. Edited by Rea Wilmshurst. Toronto: McClelland and Stewart, 1989.

———. *The Alpine Path: The Story of My Career*. 1917. N.p.: Fitzhenry and Whiteside, n.d. [1974].

———. *Among the Shadows: Tales from the Darker Side*. Edited by Rea Wilmshurst. Toronto: McClelland and Stewart, 1990.

———. *Anne of Avonlea*. Boston: L.C. Page and Company, 1909.

———. "Anne of Green Gables." MS. CM 67.5.1, Confederation Centre Art Gallery, Charlottetown.

———. *Anne of Green Gables*. Boston: L.C. Page and Company, 1908.

———. *Anne of Green Gables*. 1908. Edited by Cecily Devereux. Peterborough: Broadview Editions, 2004.

———. *Anne of Green Gables*. 1908. Edited by Mary Henley Rubio and Elizabeth Waterston. New York: W.W. Norton, 2007. A Norton Critical Edition.

———. "Anne of Ingleside." MS. CM 67.5.4, Confederation Centre Art Gallery, Charlottetown.

———. *Anne of Ingleside*. Toronto: McClelland and Stewart, 1939.

———. *Anne of the Island*. Boston: The Page Company, 1915.

———. "Anne of Redmond." MS. CM 78.5.5a, Confederation Centre Art Gallery, Charlottetown.

———. "Anne of Windy Poplars." MS. CM 67.5.7, Confederation Centre Art Gallery, Charlottetown.

———. *Anne of Windy Poplars*. Toronto: McClelland and Stewart, 1936.

———. *Anne på Grönkulla* [Anne of Green Hills]. Translated by Karin Lidforss Jensen. Lund: C.W.K. Gleerups, 1909. Swedish translation of *Anne of Green Gables*.

———. "Anne's House of Dreams." MS. CM 67.5.2, Confederation Centre Art Gallery, Charlottetown.

———. *Anne's House of Dreams*. Toronto: McClelland, Goodchild, and Stewart, 1917.

———. *The Annotated Anne of Green Gables*. Edited by Wendy E. Barry, Margaret Anne Doody, and Mary E. Doody Jones. New York: Oxford University Press, 1997.

———. *At the Altar: Matrimonial Tales*. Edited by Rea Wilmshurst. Toronto: McClelland and Stewart, 1994.

———. "An Autobiographical Sketch." In Lefebvre, *The L.M. Montgomery Reader*, 1: 254–59.
———. "Bits from My Mailbag." In Lefebvre, *The L.M. Montgomery Reader*, 1: 185–88.
———. "The Bitterness in the Cup." *The American Home* (Waterville, ME/New York), December 1903, 3–8; January 1904, 6–8. Also as "Schooled with Briars," illustrated by Estelle M. Kerr, in *Everywoman's World* (Toronto), May 1916, 11, 34–36; June 1916, 10, 25; July 1916, 10, 25; August 1916, 12, 30.
———, comp. Black Scrapbook 1 and 2. In "Scrapbooks of Clippings, Programs and Other Memorabilia, compiled by L.M. Montgomery, ca. 1910–1936." XZ5 MS A002, L.M. Montgomery Collection, Archival and Special Collections, University of Guelph Library.
———. "Blank Verse? 'Very Blank,' Said Father." In Lefebvre, *The L.M. Montgomery Reader*, 1: 180–81.
———. "The Blue Castle." MS. CM 67.5.9, Confederation Centre Art Gallery, Charlottetown.
———. *The Blue Castle*. Toronto: McClelland and Stewart, 1926.
———, comp. Blue Scrapbook. CM 67.5.15, Confederation Centre Art Gallery, Charlottetown.
———. "The Blythes Are Quoted." TS. XZ1 MS A098001, L.M. Montgomery Collection, Archival and Special Collections, University of Guelph Library.
———. "The Blythes Are Quoted." TS. XZ1 MS A098002, L.M. Montgomery Collection, Archival and Special Collections, University of Guelph Library.
———. "The Blythes Are Quoted." TS. XZ1 MS A100000, L.M. Montgomery Collection, Archival and Special Collections, University of Guelph Library.
———. *The Blythes Are Quoted*. Edited by Benjamin Lefebvre. Toronto: Viking Canada, 2009.
———. *Christmas with Anne and Other Holiday Stories*. Edited by Rea Wilmshurst. Toronto: McClelland and Stewart, 1995.
———. *Chronicles of Avonlea*. Boston: L.C. Page and Company, 1912.
———. "Come Back with Me to Prince Edward Island." In Lefebvre, *The L.M. Montgomery Reader*, 1: 330–40.
———. "Comparisons." *Munsey's Magazine* (New York), April 1901, 16.
———. *The Complete Journals of L.M. Montgomery: The PEI Years,*

1889–1900. Edited by Mary Henley Rubio and Elizabeth Hillman Waterston. Toronto: Oxford University Press, 2012.

———. *The Complete Journals of L.M. Montgomery: The PEI Years, 1901–1911*. Edited by Mary Henley Rubio and Elizabeth Hillman Waterston. Toronto: Oxford University Press, 2013.

———. "The Courtship of Josephine." *Springfield (MA) Sunday Republican*, 11 August 1901, 14. Also as "Akin to Love" in *The Canadian Magazine* (Toronto), December 1909, 143–52. Also as "Akin to Love" in *Everywoman's World* (Toronto), May 1915, 7, 30–31.

——— [L.M. Montgomery Macdonald]. "The Day before Yesterday." In Lefebvre, *The L.M. Montgomery Reader*, 1: 230–36.

———. *The Doctor's Sweetheart and Other Stories*. Selected by Catherine McLay. Toronto: McGraw-Hill Ryerson, 1979.

———. "Emily Climbs." MS. CM 67.5.6, Confederation Centre Art Gallery, Charlottetown.

———. *Emily Climbs*. Toronto: McClelland and Stewart, 1925.

———. "Emily of New Moon." MS. CM 67.5.8, Confederation Centre Art Gallery, Charlottetown.

———. *Emily of New Moon*. Toronto: McClelland and Stewart, 1923.

———. "Emily's Quest." MS. CM 78.5.1, Confederation Centre Art Gallery, Charlottetown.

———. *Emily's Quest*. Toronto: McClelland and Stewart, 1927.

——— [Maud Cavendish, pseud.]. "Fisher Lassies." *The Youth's Companion* (Boston), 30 July 1896, 388.

———. "From *Courageous Women*." In Lefebvre, *The L.M. Montgomery Reader*, 1: 298–315.

——— [Lucy Maud Montgomery]. "Four Questions Answered." In Lefebvre, *The L.M. Montgomery Reader*, 1: 59–61.

———. *Further Chronicles of Avonlea*. Boston: The Page Company, 1920.

———. "The Gay Days of Old." In Lefebvre, *The L.M. Montgomery Reader*, 1: 163–68.

———. "The Girls of Silver Bush." MS. CM 78.5.6, Confederation Centre Art Gallery, Charlottetown.

———. "The Golden Road." MS. CM 78.5.5b, Confederation Centre Art Gallery, Charlottetown.

———. *The Golden Road*. Boston: L.C. Page and Company, 1913.

———. *The Green Gables Letters from L.M. Montgomery to Ephraim*

Weber, 1905–1909. Edited by Wilfrid Eggleston. Toronto: The Ryerson Press, 1960.

———. "Harbor Sunset." *Ainslee's Magazine* (New York), January 1902, 490. Also as "Sunset on Halifax Harbor" in *Halifax Daily Echo*, 27 March 1902, 4.

———. "How I Began." In Lefebvre, *The L.M. Montgomery Reader*, 1: 144–47.

———. "How I Began to Write." In Lefebvre, *The L.M. Montgomery Reader*, 1: 67–72.

———. "'I Dwell among My Own People.'" In Lefebvre, *The L.M. Montgomery Reader*, 1: 182–84.

———. "If I Were King." *Everywoman's World* (Toronto), January 1917, 15.

———. "The Importance of Beauty in Everything." In Lefebvre, *The L.M. Montgomery Reader*, 1: 295–97.

———. "In Lovers' Lane." *The Delineator* (New York), July 1903, 16.

———. "In the Sweet o' the Year." *The Housekeeper* (Minneapolis), June 1907, 5–6.

———. *In Veilige Haven*. Translated by Betsy de Vries. Haarlem: H.D. Tjeenk Willink & Zoon, 1910. Dutch translation of *Anne of Green Gables*.

———. "Jane of Lantern Hill." MS. CM 67.5.3, Confederation Centre Art Gallery, Charlottetown.

———. *Jane of Lantern Hill*. Toronto: McClelland and Stewart, 1937.

——— [Lucy Maud Montgomery]. "June!" *Daily Patriot* (Charlottetown), 12 June 1891, 4.

———. *Kilmeny of the Orchard*. Boston: L.C. Page and Company, 1910.

———. "Kindly Criticisms." *Globe* (Toronto), 17 October 1931, 20.

——— [Lucy Maud Montgomery]. "The Last Prayer." *The College Record* (Charlottetown), [1894].

———. "Letters from the Literati." *The Editor: The Journal of Information for Literary Workers* (Fort Montgomery, NY), July 1912, 4–5.

——— [Mrs. L.M. Macdonald (L.M. Montgomery)]. "Life Has Been Interesting." In Lefebvre, *The L.M. Montgomery Reader*, 1: 293–94.

———. "Live So That You Beautify Your Name." *Baylor County Banner* (Seymour, TX), 11 May 1906, 18. Also as "A Happy Thought" in *Decatur (IN) Daily Democrat*, 6 October 1910, 2.

Also, untitled and unsigned, in *Iowa State Register and Farmer* (Des Moines), 1 May 1911, 21. Also in *Master Mind Magazine* (Los Angeles), October 1918, 34.

———. *L.M. Montgomery's Complete Journals: The Ontario Years, 1911–1917*. Edited by Jen Rubio. N.p.: Rock's Mills Press, 2016.

———. *L.M. Montgomery's Complete Journals: The Ontario Years, 1918–1921*. Edited by Jen Rubio. N.p.: Rock's Mills Press, 2017.

———. *L.M. Montgomery's Complete Journals: The Ontario Years, 1922–1925*. N.p.: Rock's Mills Press, 2018.

———. *L.M. Montgomery's Complete Journals: The Ontario Years, 1926–1929*. Edited by Jen Rubio. N.p.: Rock's Mills Press, 2017.

———. "Magic for Marigold." MS. CM 78.5.3, Confederation Centre Art Gallery, Charlottetown.

———. *Magic for Marigold*. Toronto: McClelland and Stewart, 1929.

———. Miscellaneous Needlework: 1 Embroidered Doily, n.d. XZ5 MS A029, L.M. Montgomery Artifact Collection, Archival and Special Collections, University of Guelph Library.

———. Miscellaneous Needlework: 1 Hairpin Lace Doily, n.d. XZ5 MS A037, L.M. Montgomery Artifact Collection, Archival and Special Collections, University of Guelph Library.

———. Miscellaneous Needlework: 3 Miscellaneous Doilies, n.d. XZ5 MS A040, L.M. Montgomery Artifact Collection, Archival and Special Collections, University of Guelph Library.

———. Miscellaneous Needlework: 7 Crocheted Doilies, n.d. XZ5 MS A031, L.M. Montgomery Artifact Collection, Archival and Special Collections, University of Guelph Library.

———. Miscellaneous Needlework: 7 Lace Doilies, n.d. XZ5 MS A034, L.M. Montgomery Artifact Collection, Archival and Special Collections, University of Guelph Library.

———. "Miss Marietta's Jersey." *The Household* (Boston), July 1899, 5–6.

———. *Mistress Pat: A Novel of Silver Bush*. Toronto: McClelland and Stewart, 1935.

———. "Mother's Mending Basket." *The Ram's Horn* (Chicago), 15 September 1909, 11.

——— (unsigned). "Mother, Teach Your Son." *Kansas City (KS) Gazette*, 23 May 1906, 1. Also in *Kansas City (KS) Gazette*, 26 May 1906, 3. Also in *Owosso (MI) Times*, 6 July 1906, 2. Also in *Wilkes-Barre (PA) Semi-Weekly Record*, 7 September 1906, 4. Also in

Danville (PA) Intelligencer, 14 September 1906, 3. Also in *Kansas City (KS) Gazette*, 17 October 1907, 5. Also in *Davenport (IA) Weekly Democrat and Leader*, 5 December 1907, 10.

———. *My Dear Mr. M: Letters to G.B. MacMillan from L.M. Montgomery*. Edited by Francis W.P. Bolger and Elizabeth R. Epperly. Toronto: McGraw-Hill Ryerson, 1980.

———. Needlework: Lady's Handkerchief and Doily, ca. 1915. XZ5 MS A018, L.M. Montgomery Artifact Collection, Archival and Special Collections, University of Guelph Library.

———. "A New-Fashioned Flavoring." *Golden Days for Boys and Girls* (Philadelphia), 27 August 1898, 641–42.

———. "Novel Writing Notes." In Lefebvre, *The L.M. Montgomery Reader*, 1: 197–98.

———. "The Old Mirror." *New England Magazine* (Boston), May 1904, 384. Also in *Everywoman's World* (Toronto), August 1916, 9.

——— [Lucy Maud Montgomery]. "On Cape Le Force." *Daily Patriot* (Charlottetown), 26 November 1890, 1.

———. "One Mother's Opinion." *The Standard* (Chicago), 9 November 1907, 16. Also in *The Pacific* (Berkeley), 30 July 1908, 12–13.

———. "Our Mistakes." *Brainerd (MN) Dispatch*, 26 August 1916, 2. Also in *Lynden (WA) Tribune*, 28 December 1916, 4. Also in *Middletown (NY) Times-Press*, 11 January 1917, 10. Also in *Xenia (OH) Daily Gazette*, 7 February 1917, 4.

———. "Pat of Silver Bush." MS. CM 78.5.4, Confederation Centre Art Gallery, Charlottetown.

———. *Pat of Silver Bush*. Toronto: McClelland and Stewart, 1933.

———. "A Pioneer Wooing." *The Farm and Fireside* (Springfield, OH), 15 September 1903, 14–15. Also in *The Canadian Courier* (Toronto), 20 May 1911, 8, 26–28.

———. *The Poetry of Lucy Maud Montgomery*. Selected by John Ferns and Kevin McCabe. Markham, ON: Fitzhenry and Whiteside, 1987.

———. "Prince Edward Island." In Lefebvre, *The L.M. Montgomery Reader*, 1: 352–55.

———. "The Promise of Lucy Ellen." *The Delineator* (New York), February 1904, 268–71. Also in *The Canadian Courier* (Toronto), 3 May 1913, 8–9, 25.

———. "Rainbow Valley." MS. CM 78.5.2, Confederation Centre Art Gallery, Charlottetown.

———. *Rainbow Valley*. Toronto: McClelland and Stewart, 1919.
———. *Readying Rilla*. Edited by Elizabeth Waterston and Kate Waterston. N.p.: Rock's Mills Press, 2016.
———, comp. Red Scrapbook. CM 67.5.12, Confederation Centre Art Gallery, Charlottetown.
———, comp. Red Scrapbook 1 and 2. In "Scrapbooks of Clippings, Programs and Other Memorabilia, compiled by L.M. Montgomery, ca. 1910–1936." XZ5 MS A002, L.M. Montgomery Collection, Archival and Special Collections, University of Guelph Library.
———. "Rilla of Ingleside." MS. XZ5 MS A004, L.M. Montgomery Collection, Archival and Special Collections, University of Guelph Library.
———. *Rilla of Ingleside*. Toronto: McClelland and Stewart, 1921.
———. *The Road to Yesterday*. Toronto: McGraw-Hill Ryerson, 1974.
———. "The Schoolmaster's Bride." Illustrated by Marcel Olis. *Everywoman's World* (Toronto), July 1917, 5, 43.
———, comp. "Scrapbook of Reviews from Around the World Which L.M. Montgomery's Clipping Service Sent to Her, 1910–1935." XZ5 MS A003, L.M. Montgomery Collection, Archival and Special Collections, University of Guelph Library.
———, comp. Scrapbooks 1–12. PEI.OSZ PS 8525.068 A16 1981, University Archives and Special Collections, University of Prince Edward Island Library.
———. "[Seasons in the Woods]." In Lefebvre, *The L.M. Montgomery Reader*, 1: 73–97.
———. *The Selected Journals of L.M. Montgomery*, Volume 1: *1889–1910*; Volume 2: *1910–1921*; Volume 3: *1921–1929*; Volume 4: *1929–1935*; Volume 5: *1935–1942*. Edited by Mary Rubio and Elizabeth Waterston. Toronto: Oxford University Press, 1985, 1987, 1992, 1998, 2004.
———. *The Story Girl*. Boston: L.C. Page and Company, 1911.
———. "The Sweetest Days." *Minneapolis Tribune*, 31 May 1914, 10. Also in *Daily Pantagraph* (Bloomington, IL), 1 June 1914, 12. Also in *Daily Chronicle* (De Kalb, IL), 15 June 1914, 3. Also in *Lincoln County News* (Lincolnton, NC), 16 June 1914, 2. Also in *Altoona (PA) Times*, 18 June 1914, 5. Also in *Kingston (NY) Daily Freeman*, 24 June 1914, 5. Also in *Daily Chronicle* (De Kalb, IL), 29 June 1914, 3. Also in *Daily Republican* (Monongahela, PA), 2 July 1914, 2. Also in *Herington (KS) Times*, 2 July 1914, 9. Also in *Blocton Enterprise* (West Blocton, AL), 9 July 1914, 1. Also in

Aberdeen (WA) Herald, 10 July 1914, 3. Also in *Mauch Chunk (PA) Daily Times*, 11 July 1914, 3. Also in *Evening Kansan-Republican* (Newton), 13 July 1914, 3. Also in *Gazette* (Stevens Point, WI), 15 July 1914, 6. Also in *Allentown (PA) Leader*, 16 July 1914, 12. Also in *Danville (PA) Morning News*, 16 July 1914, 2. Also in *Beloit (KS) Daily Call*, 17 July 1914, 4. Also in *Gettysburg (PA) Times*, 17 July 1914, 4. Also in *Sheboygan (WI) Press*, 18 July 1914, 4. Also in *Manchester (IA) Democrat-Radio*, 29 July 1914, 8. Also, untitled and unsigned, in *Our Southern Home* (Livingston, AL), 5 August 1914, 4. Also in *Lawrence (KS) Daily Journal-World*, 11 August 1914, 8. Also in *Atchison (KS) Champion* (Atchison, KS), 16 August 1914, 6. Also in *Daily Ardmoreite* (Ardmore, OK), 18 August 1914, 4. Also in *Blocton Enterprise* (West Blocton, AL), 20 August 1914, 2. Also in *Leavenworth (KS) Post*, 21 August 1914, 4. Also in *Chatham (NJ) Press*, 22 August 1914, 4. Also in *Evening Republican* (Meadville, PA), 24 August 1914, 7. Also in *Lawrence (KS) Daily Journal-World*, 14 September 1914, 6. Also in *Jeffersonian Gazette* (Lawrence, KS), 30 September 1914, 2. Also in *Daily Gazette* (Lawrence, KS), 6 October 1914, 4. Also in *Daily Gazette* (Lawrence, KS), 7 October 1914, 5. Also in *Jeffersonian Gazette* (Lawrence, KS), 7 October 1914, 3. Also in *Star-Independent* (Harrisburg, PA), 27 October 1914, 3. Also in *Western North Carolina Times* (Hendersonville), 19 March 1915, 6. Also in *Washington (NC) Progress*, 16 September 1915, 3. Also in *Western North Carolina Times* (Hendersonville), 8 October 1915, 3. Also in *Washington (NC) Progress*, 6 January 1916, 2. Also in *Washington (NC) Progress*, 3 February 1916, 2. Also in *Maui News* (Wailuku, HI), 26 May 1916, 8.

———. "A Tangled Web." MS. CM 67.5.5, Confederation Centre Art Gallery, Charlottetown.

———. *A Tangled Web*. Toronto: McClelland and Stewart, 1931.

——— (unsigned). "Teach the Boy." *Galena (KS) Evening Times*, 7 April 1906, 2. Also in *Wilkes-Barre (PA) Semi-Weekly Record*, 13 July 1906, 4. Also in *Morning Call* (Allentown, PA), 17 July 1906, 8. Also in *Ottawa Journal*, 24 July 1906, 4. Also in *Albany (OR) Democrat*, 27 July 1906, 6. Also in *Evening Journal* (Wilmington, DE), 1 August 1906, 3. Also in *Frankfort (KS) Review*, 24 August 1906, 4. Also in *Adair County News* (Columbia, KY), 12 September 1906, 7. Also in *Crenshaw County News* (Luverne, AL), 24 September 1908, 4. Also in *Racine (WI) Weekly*

Journal, 6 November 1906, 5. Also in *Caucasian* (Clonton, NC), 30 September 1909, 4. Also in *Roanoke Beacon* (Plymouth, NC), 10 December 1909, 3. Also in *Daily Republican* (Monongahela, PA), 18 December 1909, 2. Also in *Newton (MI) Record*, 30 December 1909, 2.

———. "The 'Teen-Age Girl." In Lefebvre, *The L.M. Montgomery Reader*, 1: 161–68.

———. "To My Enemy." *The Smart Set* (New York), January 1902, 92.

———. "The Tree Lovers." *The Ladies' Journal* (Toronto), [May 1898].

———. "A Trip to Mammoth Cave." MS. 933 SI, Ryrie-Campbell Collection, University Archives and Special Collections, University of Prince Edward Island Library.

———. "Una of the Garden." *The Housekeeper* (Minneapolis), December 1908, 7, 18; January 1909, 11–12; February 1909, 8–9, 16; March 1909, 7, 17; April 1909, 8–9, 32.

———. Untitled extract from *Anne of Avonlea*. *Caucasian* (Clinton, NC), 5 September 1912, 7. Also in *Arizona Sentinel and Yuma Weekly Examiner*, 3 December 1914, 2.

——— [Lucy Maud Montgomery]. "The Violet's Spell." *The Ladies' World* (New York), July 1894, 5.

———. *The Watchman and Other Poems*. Toronto: McClelland, Goodchild, and Stewart, 1916.

———. "The Way to Make a Book." In Lefebvre, *The L.M. Montgomery Reader*, 1: 137–43.

——— (unsigned). "What to Teach Boys." *Moulton (AL) Advertiser*, 10 August 1909, 1. Also in *Guntersville (AL) Democrat*, 26 August 1909, 1.

———. "What to Teach the Boy." *East Oregonian* (Pendleton), 23 April 1906, 4.

——— (unsigned). "What to Teach Your Boy." *Goldsboro (NC) Daily Argus*, 2 July 1906, 1.

——— (unsigned). "What to Teach Your Son." *Harrisburg (PA) Telegraph*, 23 March 1906, 10. Also in *New Oxford (PA) Item*, 25 May 1906, 21. Also in *Hondo (TX) Anvil Herald*, 26 May 1906, 8. Also in *Reading (PA) Times*, 29 June 1906, 4. Also in *Goldsboro (NC) Weekly Argus*, 5 July 1906, 4. Also in *Monroe City (MO) Democrat*, 14 October 1909, 7. Also in *Shelbina (MO) Torchlight*, 29 October 1909, 6.

———. "What to Teach Your Son." *Altoona (PA) Tribune*, 27 March

1906, 8. Also in *East Oregonian* (Pendleton), 23 April 1906, 4. Also in *Wilkes-Barre (PA) Times*, 26 April 1906, 4. Also in *Cook County Herald* (Grand Marais, MN), 9 March 1907, 6. Also in *Shelbina (MO) Torchlight*, 17 December 1909, 2. Also in *Shelby County Herald* (Shelbyville, MO), 2 February 1910, 2.

Montgomery, L.M., Marian Keith, and Mabel Burns McKinley. *Courageous Women*. Toronto: McClelland and Stewart, 1934.

Montgomery, L.M., and Nora Lefurgey. "'... Where Has My Yellow Garter Gone?' The Diary of L.M. Montgomery and Nora Lefurgey." Edited by Irene Gammel. In Gammel, *The Intimate Life of L.M. Montgomery*, 19–87.

Montreal Daily Witness. "Canada Prize Competition: The Recognition Medal and Prince Edward Island." 31 May 1890, 3.

———. "Dominion Prize Competition: Report on the Prince Edward Island Stories." 1 June 1889, 3.

Morning Chronicle (Halifax). "Grand Welcome to the King's Son in Nova Scotia's Capital." 21 October 1901, 1.

———. "Nova Scotia Welcomes Their Royal Highnesses." 19 October 1901, 1.

———. "A Royal Betrothal." 21 December 1901, 3.

———. "The Wireless Way: A Chat with Marconi." 30 December 1901, 1.

North Adams (MA) Evening Transcript. "Ask the Transcript." 5 July 1934, 14.

"Noted Author Dies Suddenly at Home Here." In Lefebvre, *The L.M. Montgomery Reader*, 1: 359–62.

Pittsburgh Press. "Questions – Answers." 3 July 1934, 4; 18 January 1935, 14.

Preface to Montgomery, *The Alpine Path*, 5–6.

Richardson, Christian. "'Anne of Green Gables': A Little Talk with the Author on Her Honeymoon." *The Westminster* (Toronto), November 1911, 352–54.

R.M.H. "Dalhousie College Gazette." *Halifax Herald*, 29 April 1896, 12, 6.

———. "Dalhousie College Students' Societies." *Halifax Herald*, 29 April 1896, 6.

Roberts, Kate Louise, comp. *Hoyt's New Cyclopedia of Practical Quotations, Drawn from the Speech and Literature of All Nations, Ancient and Modern, Classic and Popular, in English and Foreign Text; With the Names, Dates, and Nationality of Quoted Authors, and Copious Indexes*. Revised ed. New York: Funk and Wagnalls Company, 1922.

Rubio, Mary Henley. "Introduction: Harvesting Thistles in Montgomery's Textual Garden." In *Harvesting Thistles: The Textual Garden of L.M. Montgomery; Essays on Her Novels and Journals*, edited by Mary Henley Rubio, 1–13. Guelph: Canadian Children's Press, 1994.

———. *Lucy Maud Montgomery: The Gift of Wings*. N.p.: Doubleday Canada, 2008.

———. "Satire, Realism, and Imagination in *Anne of Green Gables*." *Canadian Children's Literature* 1, no. 3 (Autumn 1975): 27–36.

———. "Subverting the Trite: L.M. Montgomery's 'Room of Her Own.'" In Lefebvre, *The L.M. Montgomery Reader*, 2: 109–48.

Rubio, Mary, and Elizabeth Waterston. Introduction to Montgomery, *The Selected Journals of L.M. Montgomery*, 1: xiii–xxiv.

Russell, Ruth Weber, D.W. Russell, and Rea Wilmshurst. *Lucy Maud Montgomery: A Preliminary Bibliography*. Waterloo: University of Waterloo Library, 1986. University of Waterloo Library Bibliography 13.

"Says Woman's Place Is Home." In Lefebvre, *The L.M. Montgomery Reader*, 1: 50–52.

Sharp, Harold S., comp. *Handbook of Pseudonyms and Personal Nicknames*. Metuchen, NJ: The Scarecrow Press, 1972.

Sorfleet, John Robert, ed. *L.M. Montgomery: An Assessment*. Guelph: Canadian Children's Press, 1976.

"[Such a Delightful Little Person]." In Lefebvre, *The L.M. Montgomery Reader*, 1: 31–32.

Thompson, William V. "The Shadow on the House of Dreams: Montgomery's Re-visioning of Anne." In *L.M. Montgomery's Rainbow Valleys: The Ontario Years, 1911–1942*, edited by Rita Bode and Lesley D. Clement, 113–30, 289–90. Montreal and Kingston: McGill-Queen's University Press, 2015.

"What Are the Greatest Books in the English Language?" In Lefebvre, *The L.M. Montgomery Reader*, 1: 151–53.

"What Twelve Canadian Women Hope to See as the Outcome of the War." In Lefebvre, *The L.M. Montgomery Reader*, 1: 134–36.

Wiggins, Genevieve. *L.M. Montgomery*. New York: Twayne Publishers, 1992. Twayne's World Authors Series: Children's Literature.

York, Lorraine. *Literary Celebrity in Canada*. Toronto: University of Toronto Press, 2007.

Index